EAGLE
ANNUAL 1960s

ORION, Covent Garden, London

EAGLE

ANNUAL

THE BEST OF THE 1960S COMIC

EDITED BY DANIEL TATARSKY

INTRODUCTION
DANIEL TATARSKY

The most commonly heard cliché about the 1960s is that if you remember them then you weren't there. Well, whether you were there or not and regardless of how well you remember them this *Annual* will serve as a handy aide-memoire on the 1960s as viewed through the very particular lens that was *Eagle*.

For a comic in which the best known and well loved character was a space pilot, the decade was rather neatly bookended by the first human to orbit the planet, Yuri Gagarin in April 1961, and the first human to set foot on the Moon, Neil Armstrong in July 1969. As far as the *Eagle* was concerned, this rather beautiful symmetry was upset slightly by the sad fact that the final issue of the comic appeared on the 26 April 1969, just twelve weeks before Armstrong's 'small step'. It is not all gloom and doom though because *Eagle* still produced much to be admired during the decade before being consumed by *Lion* (it was called a merger but *Lion* became the main name on the cover).

Dan Dare, still the cover star at the start of the decade, was passed like a baton in a relay race from chief, originating illustrator Frank Hampson to Frank Bellamy, to Don Harley and Keith Watson, then to Bruce Cornwell. Like any relay team some of the exchanges of the baton were smoother than others but so strong was the character that he survives to this day.

The cutaways also stayed the course, although in reduced circumstances. First moving from the double-page spread and then losing colour, but the artistry of the production and accuracy of the minute detail was always of the highest standard and the cutaways remained a core part of the comic's structure.

Historical strips were a predominant feature of the sixties *Eagle* and peaked with the series on Montgomery, drawn by Frank Bellamy. These strips can stand in their own right as works of historical document, with the adventures of some of the country's greatest heroes brought stunningly to life.

Frank Hampson was given a final hurrah in another of these historical series as he took on the life of Jesus Christ in The Road of Courage. All the skill, detail and meticulous research that Hampson poured into his own creation, Dan Dare, was in evidence again here as he signed off from the comic he had helped to create. He did actually return to the pages of *Eagle* some years later and the proof appears in this volume, you just have to look carefully.

The evolution of *Eagle* as one decade became another was initiated by the changes of ownership and editorship. Hulton Press became Longacre Press after being taken over by Odhams, and it was not long afterwards that the *Daily Mirror* Group bought Odhams. The last cover under the Hulton Press banner is shown on page 4. The comic then went through some dizzying times and it is interesting to note that *Eagle*'s creator and first editor Marcus Morris chose to include only selections up to 1962 in his *The Best of Eagle*, which was published in 1977. This does a disservice to issues that appeared after his departure and maybe it is more to do with his absence after that date than any genuine feelings about the output under his replacement and former deputy Clifford Makins.

A very obvious change in tone was the relationship between the Editor and his reader. During Morris' time his personal letters to the reader were a regular feature. It was his opportunity to preach to his nationwide flock. Makins, his immediate replacement Derek Lord and those that followed did not take up this mantel. Whether that is because they did not have the zeal of Morris to pass on their life messages or whether they felt there was no need for this personal touch is not clear, but *Eagle* certainly lost some of what made it special as a result.

One of the reasons the 1960s is so often seen as the decade no one present should remember is the swinging time produced by the explosion of pop music and the lifestyle it encouraged. Whilst read by boys, and girls, a little too young to really become involved in this revolution, *Eagle* still made strenuous efforts to keep up with the times. Features on the pop stars of the day covered everyone from Burt Bacharach to Sandie Shaw via The Beatles and the Rolling Stones. Somewhat quaintly these poptastic tales were able to sit quite happily alongside Scoutsworld and the ever-present tips on what food best to feed your hamster.

Maybe it is this strange juxtaposition that explains why the comic could not survive beyond the decade. With an increasing number of features on sport, especially football, fighting for space alongside comic strips, nature pieces, Scoutsworld and readers' jokes it seems that *Eagle* was trying to please everyone. Whilst you can do that some of the time it is well known that it is not possible to do that all of the time, and so like a star that burns too brightly the black hole that follows was inevitable.

What we have to be thankful for is that unlike an imploded star *Eagle* has left behind its archives. It is these very archives that this *Annual* attempts to bring back to life and introduce to a new generation of fans. It is all here, the colour, the excitement and thrills of the 1960s. If you were there and you can't remember it, don't worry, just start turning the pages

Colin Frewin, CEO of the Dan Dare Corporation, writes, 'I was certainly there and can clearly remember regularly driving down the King's Road on a Saturday afternoon, roof down, of course, even in the rain, with The Stones' "Get off of my Cloud" blaring out from the radio. Mods one side of the road and Rockers glaring on the other side! Twiggy and the latest fashions in mini skirts plastered across the advertising hoardings. This was a time when *The Graduate* and Kubrick's *2001: A Space Odyssey* took the cinema audiences by storm and Cathy McGowan and Ready Steady Go was compulsive viewing, whilst the wonderful Steptoe and Son made British television audiences simply laugh out loud! In sport, Henry Cooper put Cassius Clay flat on his back in the ring and the streets of London were deserted as Bobby Moore stepped up to receive the Jules Rimet Trophy at Wembley.

'Dan Dare and the *Eagle* had already ventured to the stars during the 1950s and who would have thought that at 4 a.m. on 21 July 1969 we would actually see man step on to the Moon followed by exploration probes speeding their way into deep space, to planets such as Venus. The Mekon must have been seriously concerned! And pretty much throughout this exciting period of time we still had

the *Eagle* and Dan Dare to look forward to each week! You could even listen to the repeat adventures of Dan Dare "under the sheets" on "Fabulous 208, Radio Luxemburg".

'What a wonderful, exhilarating period for young people to have been part of and many of these memories will come rushing back as you read this revealing nostalgic volume'

EAGLE

EVERY WEDNESDAY

4½d

COMPANION TO GIRL, SWIFT AND ROBIN

2 JANUARY 1960 Vol. 11 No. 1

DAN DARE
PILOT OF THE FUTURE
TRIP to TROUBLE

THE STORY SO FAR: While searching for Dan's father on the planet *Terra Nova*, Dan Dare and Digby see Lex kidnapped. Calo, leader of a friendly people who are fighting ruthless invaders from *Gaz*, tells Dan that not only is Lex their prisoner, but that Dan's father was killed fighting against them. Dan then asks Calo to lead him to the enemy H.Q. at *Lantor*, where Lex is imprisoned . . .

THERE IS *LANTOR* — THE CITY OF THE FIVE TOWERS. YOUR FRIEND LEX IS IMPRISONED IN THE GOLDEN ONE . . .

FRANK BELLAMY

IT USED TO BE THE TOWER OF TECHNOLOGY — I KNOW IT WELL, FOR THAT WAS WHERE I WORKED . . .

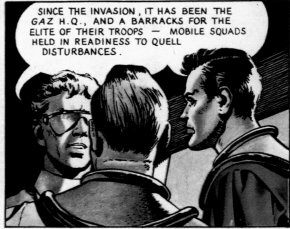

SINCE THE INVASION, IT HAS BEEN THE GAZ H.Q., AND A BARRACKS FOR THE ELITE OF THEIR TROOPS — MOBILE SQUADS HELD IN READINESS TO QUELL DISTURBANCES.

THEN, BY GOLLY, WE'LL DISTURB 'EM! I KNOW THE VERY THING . . .

Hulton Press Ltd., England, 1960

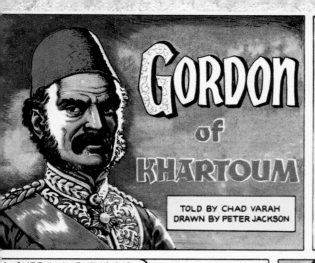

GORDON of KHARTOUM

TOLD BY CHAD VARAH
DRAWN BY PETER JACKSON

Charles George Gordon, born at Woolwich on 28th January, 1833, has a long line of soldiers on his father's side of the family, and whalers and seafaring explorers on his mother's. One of eleven children, he spends part of his boyhood on the island of Corfu, where his father commands the artillery, and then goes to school at Taunton. He has a quick but generous temper, and more energy than actual physical strength . . .

Chad Varah was with *Eagle* pretty much from day one. He sadly passed away in 2007 and is best remembered as the founder of The Samaritans which, as a young vicar, he set up in 1953.

Charles's indifference to the odds against him when he is in the right, induces respect both at Taunton and, later, at the Royal Military Academy in his native town. Not all his superiors, however, think well of his abilities . . .

TWO PASSPORTS TO PALESTINE

BY FRANK HAMPSON

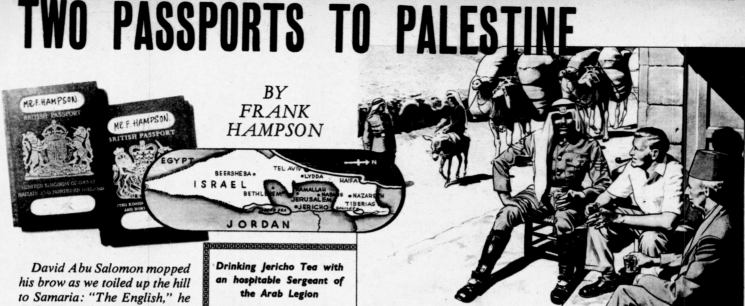

Drinking Jericho Tea with an hospitable Sergeant of the Arab Legion

David Abu Salomon mopped his brow as we toiled up the hill to Samaria: "The English," he said, "always want to see ruins. Show them a ruin and they're happy!" He sighed: "I wish I were back with the Flying Boats again . . ."

David – fiftyish, grey-haired, bird-like – was manager of a B.O.A.C. Flying Boat Base on the Dead Sea, back in the days of the British mandate over Palestine. Now he is a Government-licenced guide in the Hashemite Kingdom of Jordan. But his former home and possessions are in Israel, the new State from which he fled at a moment's notice in 1948. His case epitomizes the unhappy division of Palestine by a smouldering frontier which even splits the Capital City itself. This division dominates the practical arrangements of anyone who, like myself, wants to see the Palestine of the New Testament. It meant that I had to carry two passports, for the Arab Kingdom, which now rules one half of Palestine, will not recognize the visa of the Jewish State which holds the other.

Reminders of the struggle which followed the British withdrawal linger everywhere. Bumping over the desert wastes to the Dead Sea Caves at Khirbet Qhumran, we passed a desolate group of knocked out A.F.Vs, ambushed perhaps on the soil which had once been trodden by the fiery Baptist, St. John, the 'forerunner'.

Across the border and miles to the North, I had suddenly found a derelict Syrian tank, squatting absurdly in the trees around a 'Kibbutz' (communal settlement). "We keep them so that we do not forget," said Blimah Steinberg, my Israeli guide. She, too, like David, left home and possessions at a second's notice; but the home that Mrs Steinberg left behind was in Rumania. Like many Jewish refugees, she came to Israel seeking a secure homeland.

Journeying to Jerusalem, I passed many more wrecked armoured-cars. The road, thrusting up the narrow corridor of Israeli territory, was bitterly fought over in '48, as the Jews forced convoys through to their surrounded garrison in the City.

Towards the end of last year, Frank Hampson — EAGLE's well-known staff artist — flew to Palestine for background material on our new feature, THE ROAD OF COURAGE, which starts on page 20 of next week's edition. Here, he records some impressions of his journey . . .

They call it the 'Road of Courage', this lifeline winding through the red, eroded Judean hills, past the Castell where the Roman X Legion camped long ago, and finally to the ochre and white City crouching on the crest.

However, it was another, greater 'Road of Courage' that I wanted to see – the road trodden by Jesus two thousand years ago, in a country if anything even more tense and explosive than it is today.

"To follow it, I traversed Galilee (with Blimah Steinberg stolidly enduring my puzzled chauffeuring of a left-hand drive Renault Dauphine). At Nazareth, I experienced the uneasy realization that a Bible place-name is a real town, with bus-stops, cafés, and even, while I was there, a general election in progress. The tawdriness which surrounds much in Palestine was best exemplified at Tiberias, where the waterfront café menus feature: "Genuine St. Peter's Fish – with chips".

Otherwise, happily, the Sea of Galilee is unspoilt, perhaps because the trigger-happy frontier runs along the North Eastern shore, and close to the ruined synagogue of Capernaum. This is practically all that is left of the bustling town which was the focal point of Jesus's early ministry. Here, the past came to life under the earnest, eager exposition of Father Coyle of the Franciscans, his brown habit topped by a straw hat, and his ruddy face aglow as he pointed over the water to the brown hills of the 'Country of the Gergesenes'.

Galilee must, I think, have been very dear to Jesus, compared to Jerusalem, whose harsh intolerance is perpetuated today at the 'Mandelbaum Gate', the only place where one can cross the frontier – once only. The beautiful lake seemed already very far behind me as I stood in the middle of this empty sunbaked concrete 'No Man's Land', carefully switching passports before stepping into the Arab check-post, and so into the Moslem World and to David Abu Salomon.

With David, I panted up the Hill to Samaria, and stood on the ancient walls of Jericho and in the Shepherds' Field at Bethlehem. Once he realized my interests, he dropped the 'Holy' voice, which is an irritating feature of many guides, and became what he naturally is, an intelligent, well-informed and humorous companion. "Oh, Mr Frank, my dear," was the prelude to many a sly sally.

Compared to the 'Westernizing' dynamism of the Israelis (who *love* concrete), Jordan is an ancient land clinging tenaciously to ways which give, at least, a glimpse of Biblical life. Caravans of camels sway with ungainly grace along the new roads of the American 'Point Four' programme; sad-eyed, sturdy donkeys trot on dainty feet through appallingly stony fields and dusty lanes; women, bringing water from village wells, walk with that incomparable movement which results from carrying a heavy pitcher (or Jerrican!) on the head.

Everywhere, there are stones, white dust, and olive trees. "If only stones were valuable," lamented David, "what an export trade we'd have!" Jordan, unlike some oil-rich neighbours, is a desperately poor country, but this does not affect the Arab hospitality. Even at Police check-posts, I was often invited to refreshments by the khaki-clad policemen of the famous Arab Legion. At the 'Inn of the Good Samaritan', I sampled mint-flavoured 'Jericho Tea' with an hospitable sergeant, whose detachment stable their horses in a ruined courtyard where, traditionally, stood the famous inn of the parable.

Jesus's story came to life vividly on the spot; I can think of few worse places to be robbed and injured than this desolate road from Jerusalem to Jericho.

Often the past is very elusive, though. "What was it like two thousand years ago?" I constantly asked myself, as the white-painted Dakotas of the U.N. Armistice commission roared overhead to Jerusalem Airport, or the buses and cars hooted angrily at each other and at the shouting merchants under the walls of the old city.

In the narrow lanes of the Old City itself, the many shrines, devotedly tended, are often so cocooned with buildings and decorations that I would despair of gaining any idea of their original state. Then, suddenly, some fragment would emerge – like the flagstones of the 'Lithostrotos' (or pavement where Pilate sat in judgment) uncovered by the Sisters of Notre Dame de Sion. On some of these stones are scratched the games played by off-duty Roman soldiers; others still bear the grooves which prevented horses from slipping as they clattered through the Antonia Fortress, seat of Roman power. Suddenly, you are overwhelmed by the realization that, on these very stones, which your hand is touching, was played one of the last acts in the greatest drama in the history of mankind. Here, Pilate washed his hands of Jesus and sent him forth on the last cruel mile of His Road of Courage, along the Way of Sorrows to Golgotha.

THE ROAD OF COURAGE
The most wonderful story EAGLE has ever told

Starting next week on the back page of EAGLE, Marcus Morris and I will attempt to re-tell the story of the life of Jesus. As readers know, Mr Morris is the clergyman who founded EAGLE and was its Editor for ten years. I can think of no better colleague to write this story. My part, of course, is to draw it and, in unravelling the complexities of dress and custom, I shall be assisted by another EAGLE veteran, Joan Porter, whose interest in Bible research is indefatigable. Probably no man could do full justice to this story – certainly not such an ordinary man as myself – we can only do our best. *That* we shall certainly do.

THE ROAD OF COURAGE

The Road of Courage was Frank Hampson's last major contribution to *Eagle*. Having been relieved of the responsibility for his creation Dan Dare he was free to pursue a topic that had always fascinated him. He documented his trip to the Holy Land, which was part of his research, meticulously as ever. The series itself shows that he had lost none of his talents and these pages illustrate just a small selection of his masterpiece.

THE ROAD OF COURAGE
The story of Jesus

WITH HIS DISCIPLES, JESUS SETS OUT FOR GALILEE —   AND THE ROAD OF COURAGE TO JERUSALEM.

PHILIP — NATHANIEL BAR THOLMAI — THOMAS DIDYMUS — MATTHEW — PETER — ANDREW — JAMES — JOHN — JAMES BARALPHEUS — THADDAEUS — SIMON ZELOTES — JUDAS ISCARIOT

In an upstairs room in Jerusalem, on Thursday evening . . .

THIS IS MY LAST SUPPER WITH YOU.

WHAT DO YOU MEAN?

ONE OF YOU IS GOING TO BETRAY ME . . .

BETRAY YOU? ONE OF US?

Written by MARCUS MORRIS ● Drawn by FRANK HAMPSON

TO BE CONTINUED

YOU HAVE BEEN EYE-WITNESSES OF ALL THIS, AND SO I NOW HAND OVER TO YOU THE MESSAGE OF THE FATHER . . .

SPREAD THE GOOD NEWS TO ALL THE WORLD. TEACH THEM WHAT I HAVE TAUGHT YOU —

AND REMEMBER . . .

I AM WITH YOU ALWAYS – EVEN TO THE END OF THE WORLD.

THE END

L. ASHWELL WOOD

H.M.S. COSSACK
Length, 355 ft. 6 ins.; beam, 36 ft. 6 ins.;
1,870 tons; speed, 36½ knots; 44,000 h.p.
engine capacity; complement, 219.

RD 7

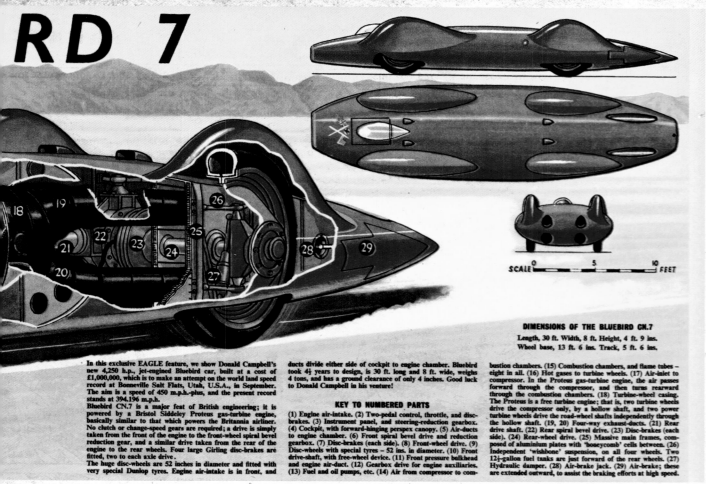

DIMENSIONS OF THE BLUEBIRD CN.7

Length, 30 ft. Width, 8 ft. Height, 4 ft. 9 ins.
Wheel base, 13 ft. 6 ins. Track, 5 ft. 6 ins.

SCALE 0 5 10 FEET

In this exclusive EAGLE feature, we show Donald Campbell's new 4,250 h.p., jet-engined Bluebird car, built at a cost of £1,000,000, which is to make an attempt on the world land speed record at Bonneville Salt Flats, Utah, U.S.A., in September. The aim is a speed of 450 m.p.h.-plus, and the present record stands at 394.196 m.p.h.

Bluebird CN.7 is a major feat of British engineering; it is powered by a Bristol Siddeley Proteus gas-turbine engine, basically similar to that which powers the Britannia airliner. No clutch or change-speed gears are required; a drive is simply taken from the front of the engine to the front-wheel spiral bevel reduction gear, and a similar drive taken from the rear of the engine to the rear wheels. Four large Girling disc-brakes are fitted, two to each axle drive.

The huge disc-wheels are 52 inches in diameter and fitted with very special Dunlop tyres. Engine air-intake is in front, and ducts divide either side of cockpit to engine chamber. Bluebird took 4½ years to design, is 30 ft. long and 8 ft. wide, weighs 4 tons, and has a ground clearance of only 4 inches. Good luck to Donald Campbell in his venture!

KEY TO NUMBERED PARTS

(1) Engine air-intake. (2) Two-pedal control, throttle, and disc-brakes. (3) Instrument panel, and steering-reduction gearbox. (4) Cockpit, with forward-hinging perspex canopy. (5) Air-ducts to engine chamber. (6) Front spiral bevel drive and reduction gearbox. (7) Disc-brakes (each side). (8) Front-wheel drive. (9) Disc-wheels with special tyres – 52 ins. in diameter. (10) Front drive-shaft, with free-wheel device. (11) Front pressure bulkhead and engine air-duct. (12) Gearbox drive for engine auxiliaries. (13) Fuel and oil pumps, etc. (14) Air from compressor to com-bustion chambers. (15) Combustion chambers, and flame tubes – eight in all. (16) Hot gases to turbine wheels. (17) Air-inlet to compressor. In the Proteus gas-turbine engine, the air passes forward through the compressor, and then turns rearward through the combustion chambers. (18) Turbine-wheel casing. The Proteus is a free turbine engine; that is, two turbine wheels drive the compressor only, by a hollow shaft, and two power turbine wheels drive the road-wheel shafts independently through the hollow shaft. (19, 20) Four-way exhaust-ducts. (21) Rear drive shaft. (22) Rear spiral bevel drive. (23) Disc-brakes (each side). (24) Rear-wheel drive. (25) Massive main frames, composed of aluminium plates with 'honeycomb' cells between. (26) Independent 'wishbone' suspension, on all four wheels. Two 12½-gallon fuel tanks are just forward of the rear wheels. (27) Hydraulic damper. (28) Air-brake jack. (29) Air-brake; these are extended outward, to assist the braking efforts at high speed.

THE EPIC OF THE *ALTMARK*

"The Navy's here!" Such was the historic greeting given to 300 British merchant seamen imprisoned in the German supply ship *Altmark*, when a Naval party from the destroyer H.M.S. *Cossack* boarded the *Altmark* in Josing Fjord, Norway, on the night of 16th February, 1940, in World War II.

The *Altmark*, which had on board British seamen captured from ships sunk by the German battleship *Graf Spee*, had tried to get back to Germany, but she was intercepted by the *Cossack* and took shelter in Josing Fjord. The *Cossack* followed her in and, by superb seamanship in the narrow icy waters, her commander – Captain P. L. Vian – ran the *Cossack* alongside and boarded the German ship. After a hand-to-hand fight with fixed bayonets, the British sailors released the imprisoned seamen and brought them home in triumph. It was an adventure that Captain Marryat would have revelled in for one of his robust sea novels.

KEY TO ABOVE DECK

(1) Depth-charge discharger. (2) Depth-charges. (3) After twin 4.7-in. guns. (4) Gun blast-screen. (5) No. 3 twin 4.7-in. guns. (6) Tripod mast. (7) Searchlight. (8) Multiple 2-pounder pom-pom guns. (9) Four 21-in. torpedo-tubes. (10) Multiple machine-guns. (11) Motor launch. (12) Tripod mast. (13) Fire-control tower and range-finder. (14) Multiple machine-guns. (15) Navigating bridge. (16) No. 2 twin 4.7-in. guns. (17) Forward twin 4.7-in. guns. (18) Crew assembled on forecastle, 'prepared to board' the enemy prison-ship *Altmark*.

KEY TO BELOW DECK

(19) Petty Officers' mess; crew's quarters are forward. (20) Radio room. (21) Transmitting room for fire-control. (22) Oil-fuel tanks. (23) Gyro-compass room. (24) No. 1 boiler room. (25) No. 2 boiler room. (26) Engine room control-platform. (27) Port high-pressure steam-turbine. (28) Port low-pressure steam-turbine. (29) Reduction gear-case and propeller-shaft thrust block. (30) Oil-fuel tanks. (31) Stores. (32) Radio room. (33) Officers' quarters. (34) Torpedo war-heads. (35) Ammunition magazine. (36) Wardroom. (37) Twin propellers. (38) Rudder.

CAST YOUR LINE

PART TWO

by GEORGE GOLDSMITH CARTER

FISHING from a boat can often be more exciting than shore-fishing, for bigger fish and bigger catches are usually taken. Almost all the same tackle and baits as for shore-fishing can be used, except for the rod, which should be stiffer and about 6- to 7-ft. long. Heavier leads are also required, as the tides run considerably fiercer further from the shore.

Tides are important when boat-fishing because, if the fierce fortnightly spring tides are running, it is difficult to keep tackle on the sea-bed. Between the spring tides are the gentler neap tides, and this is undoubtedly the best time to go.

Hiring a boat. A largish motor-boat with a boatman costs £4 to £5 a day. A good idea is to make up a party; it is more fun, and cuts the cost if each person pays a share. A rowing-boat without a boatman costs about £1 per day. When fishing this way, don't go more than 400 yards out, watch the weather, and get ashore fast if the wind starts to blow. Also, make sure that there is a spare oar, a baler, and spare rowing crutches in the boat.

Fishing can be done from an anchored boat or moving boat in the following ways:—

General fishing from an anchored boat. A paternoster, nylon trace or 'pat-trace' can be used for this, with medium-sized hooks and any natural bait. This is the most popular kind of boat-fishing, as anything feeding on the bottom can be caught.

Tope fishing from an anchored boat. Tope are small sharks of 30 to 50 pounds, which breed around our

An Angler Fish — the ugliest you're likely to catch

southern and western shores in summer. They are crafty and powerful fighters, and must be fished for on the bottom. A strong rod, a powerful reel, and about 200 yards of 35- to 40-pound line are needed. The bait is usually a whole herring, mackerel or whiting, and must be mounted on a big tope-hook attached to a 6-ft. steel-wire trace. Giant skate and conger-eels are other fish that can be caught in this way.

Float-fishing for mackerel from an anchored or moving boat. This is a sporting method of catching single mackerel by means of a light rod, fine line, float, and a single hook baited with mackerel skin or rag-worm.

FISHING FROM A BOAT

Following last week's article on sea-fishing from the shore, our expert concludes his hints on this great sport—which you can enjoy at the seaside this summer—by taking you out to sea to try your luck from a boat . . .

Drift-lining for black bream from an anchored boat. This attractive silvery-black fish, which is found all round our south and west coasts, rarely exceeds 4 pounds in weight, and gives quite a battle when hooked. It is fished for with a fine line, lightly weighted, and carrying a single hook baited with rag or lug worm. The line must be allowed to drift well away from the boat, as these fish are very wary. Their bite is the merest twitch, so great concentration is needed. When a shoal of these fish has been located, they must be kept interested by 'ground baiting', which consists of throwing pieces of finely chopped mussels, worms or crab overboard.

Trolling from a moving boat. This consists of fishing for bass, mackerel, pollack or coal-fish by dragging an artificial or natural bait behind a moving boat on a weighted line. The depth at which the fish are swimming is found by varying the weight on the line. The *Jigger*, which was mentioned last week, can also be used from a moving or anchored boat, and is called 'feathering'.

Fixing a 'Mark'. When bottom-fishing, it is possible that you may be lucky enough to find a good feeding ground with plenty of fish. This can be marked for future sport in a very simple manner. All you have to do is observe two pairs of prominent objects on the shore, each pair in line — for instance, a tall tree in line with a building, and a factory chimney in line with a lighthouse.

Whiting, such as these fine specimens, are caught in autumn and winter

To find the mark again, one merely has to line the object up. Just as soon as they are in line, or 'on', the anchor must be dropped.

One of the most exciting things about fishing, is the unexpected catch. Here are just a few:—

The John Dory. An odd, flattish, spiny fish found off the south-west coast. Good to eat, in spite of its looks.

Red Mullet. A small, red fish found off Cornwall. It has such a fine flavour that the Roman Emperor Claudius is said to have paid the equivalent of £50 for *one* fish.

The Wrasses. Brightly-coloured fishes found mostly off the south-west coast, the Ballan Wrasse being the most common. Useless as food.

The Gurnards. There are three species, the Grey, Red and Yellow (which grows to two feet, and is the largest). These prickly fishes are found almost everywhere, and should be held in a piece of cloth – their spines are sharp. Good to eat, but must be skinned before cooking.

The Brill. An aristocratic flat-fish, related to the turbot and nearly as good to eat. It is found on sandy bottoms.

The Angler Fish, or 'Fishing Frog'. A real 'Franken-stein' – in fact, the ugliest fish around our shores. It is harmless – apart from its sharp teeth – is caught almost anywhere, and sold in fish shops as 'rock salmon'.

DANGER – DON'T TOUCH! The Lesser Weever (top), Sting Ray (centre) and Greater Weever (bottom), carry poisonous barbs

Fishes to avoid touching

The Lesser and Greater Weevers. Growing to about six inches and one foot respectively, they frequent sand and rocky bottoms and have *very poisonous* spines on back and gills.

The Sting Ray. A skate-like fish whose whip-like tail carries a poisonous barb. Found all around our shores.

The Spur dogfish. Also called the 'Piked dogfish', it carries two poisonous spines on its back. Growing to about three feet in length, this fish swims in vast shoals in the North Sea and off the south-west coast.

'Musts' for boat-fishing. Warm and weather-proof clothing, sandwiches and thermos flask, sweets to suck, preferably fruit- or acid-flavoured, as salt air and excitement make your mouth dry. A sea-sickness tablet, half an hour before you go, if you are afraid of being ill.

Next week, intrepid motor-cyclist Noel Pope takes you riding on a sensational 'Record Attempt'!

MILESTONES IN AVIATION...

AND NOW—

THE REVOLUTIONARY

HOVERCRAFT

MODELLED FOR YOU BY

CORGI

8'6

Also just available—

CHEVROLET NEW YORK TAXI

New York taxis are famous all over the world: here is the Corgi version of the Chevrolet taxi. In the livery of the Yellow Cab Co. of New York, this model has seats, internal trim, steering wheel and the renowned 'Glidamatic' suspension. Model No. 221. Price **4/8d.**

From hot-air balloon to four-jet bomber, from sticks-and-string biplane to supersonic fighter, aviation has made spectacular progress in the space of a comparatively few years. Now the engineers have achieved something entirely new—a machine that supports itself on columns of air. Revolutionary in conception and design, the HDL Hovercraft SR-N1 opens up a new era of long-distance travel.

Authentic in every detail, this Corgi model is an exact replica in miniature of the Hovercraft. Central air intake, propulsion ducts, control cabin and seats, "elevons", rudders—all these are carefully and accurately reproduced. The model is supported on ball bearings, giving the illusion of floating on air. Here's one of the best models ever produced by Corgi—and it's in your local toy or model shop now!   CORGI MAJOR 1119. **8/6d**

Naturally ■ **CORGI TOYS**
TRADE MARK REGISTERED

NOT AS LARGE AS LIFE— BUT JUST AS REAL!

THE REAL WILD WEST

Having removed 4-page supplement from the paper, fold and as indicated to form neat 16-page booklet which you can then keep in the free EAGLE PASSPORT wallet presented with EAGLE issue dated 19th March

On the wide and turbulent Frontier, in the brawling trail towns and lawless mining camps, there developed the legend of the Wild West.

Through this legend stalks the most romanticized figure in history – the American Cowboy – that lean, bronzed rider of the range, with the peculiar high-heeled boots, the jangling spurs and the ever-ready six-gun hanging low in an open holster.

How much of this was fact, and how much was just legend?

Their gear, for example. What was the reason for the huge western saddle, the purpose of the high heels and the heavy leather chaps? Could the gun-fighter really shoot as fast as we see on the films?

This booklet will have helped you to understand some of these points, and to appreciate that, behind the romance and the legend, there is a good deal of hard fact on which they are based.

Written and illustrated by
FRANK HUMPHRIS

FOLD

— CUT ALONG THIS LINE —

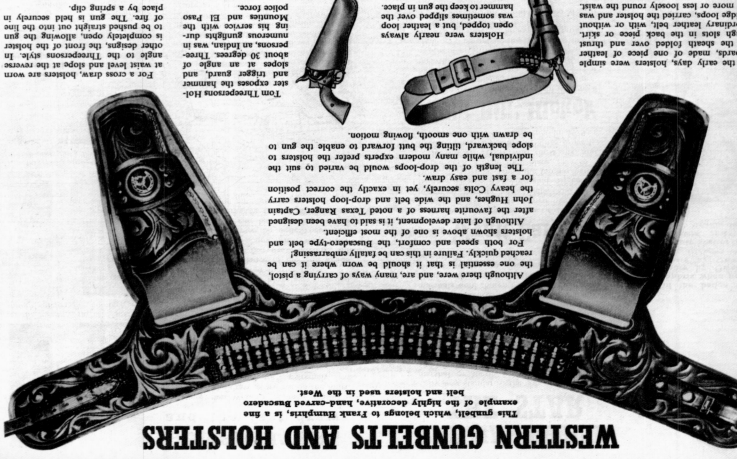

WESTERN GUNBELTS AND HOLSTERS

This gunbelt, which belongs to Frank Humphris, is a fine example of the highly decorative, hand-carved Buscadero belt and holsters used in the West.

Although there were, and are, many ways of carrying a pistol, the one essential is that it should be worn where it can be reached quickly. Failure in this can be fatally embarrassing!

For both speed and comfort, the Buscadero-type belt and holsters shown above is one of the most efficient.

Although of later development, it is said to have been designed after the favourite harness of a noted Texas Ranger, Captain John Hughes, and the wide belt and drop-loop holsters carry the heavy Colts securely, yet in exactly the correct position for a fast and easy draw.

The length of the drop-loops would be varied to suit the individual, while many modern experts prefer the holsters to slope backward, tilting the butt forward to enable the gun to be drawn with one smooth, flowing motion.

In the early days, holsters were simple scabbards, made of one piece of leather with the sheath folded over and thrust through slots in the back piece or skirt.

An ordinary leather belt, with or without cartridge loops, carried the holster and was worn more or less loosely round the waist.

Holsters were nearly always open topped, but a leather loop was sometimes slipped over the hammer to keep the gun in place.

Tom Threepersons Holster exposes the hammer and trigger guard, and slopes at an angle of about 30 degrees. Three-persons, an Indian, was in numerous gunfights during his service with the Mounties and El Paso police force.

For a cross draw, holsters are worn at waist level and slope at the reverse angle to the Threepersons style. In other designs, the front of the holster is completely open, allowing the gun to be pushed straight out into the line of fire. The gun is held securely in place by a spring clip.

WORLD RECORD HOLDERS

LONGEST COACH ROUTE in the world is the *Indiaman* Service from London to Bombay. It was pioneered in 1957 by Mr Paddy Garrow-Fisher, of Kingston-on-Thames, who drove the first A.E.C. coach through nine countries and over some 8,000 miles of roads, byways and desert caravan tracks. The name *Indiaman* was chosen for the service because it was started in the same spirit of adventure that took the old Elizabethan wooden sailing ships trading to the Indies. The enterprise proved popular, so coaches now ply regularly over this difficult and interesting route several times a year.

In 1959, just for a holiday, Mr Garrow-Fisher drove a Standard Vanguard estate car to Calcutta and back. Without a co-driver, he made the outward journey of 7,113 miles in 11 days, 12 hours and 55 minutes, knocking a day off the record set up by a team of two drivers.

THE REAL WILD WEST

One of the quaint things about *Eagle* was the belief that the readers would collect important features. A way in which this was encouraged was the publication of cut-out-and-keep sections. Often these could be folded in ingenious ways to make a small pamphlet for easy reference. Thus the upside down effect seen here.

N E W S

FROM EAGLE

THERE'S a lot of really exciting news to tell you this week! After several months of planning – vividly shown in our cartoon – and sorting your votes in the 'contents election' held recently, we are ready to let you into the big secret and give you details of the surprises that are in store for readers. Next week's EAGLE will not only contain a special FREE gift and the first of four super 4-page supplements, but also 20 pages of first-class fun and adventure. Most of your favourite characters will be setting out on thrilling new missions, and everything that has made EAGLE 'Britain's Foremost National Weekly' will remain. We shall also introduce some new features, and the whole paper will undergo a 'face-lift' to make it 100% bright, attractive and up-to-date. Read on and tell your friends about it.

One final, important point. Last year's dispute in the Printing Industry resulted in substantial increases in the cost of producing EAGLE. We are now obliged to raise the price of EAGLE by one half-penny and, as a result, the next issue will cost 5d. I am sorry about this, but I am sure you will agree that EAGLE is still the best value for money.

Yours sincerely,

Clifford Makins

161/166 FLEET STREET
LONDON, E.C.4.

SPOT THE DIRECTOR!

MR PETER BARKER, Director of the Boys and Girls Exhibition, has issued a challenge to all readers of EAGLE, GIRL and SWIFT visiting the Exhibition, at Olympia, that they will not be able to recognize him among the crowds who come to enjoy this popular Summer Show.

The Director has, therefore, given us his picture to print (and we can say that it is a good likeness of him), so that you can look out for him in the Hall. If you spot Peter Barker, you must issue your challenge in these words: "You are the Exhibition Director and I claim my reward". If you are right, and use the exact words of the challenge, he will present you with a Dan Dare tie, provided that you are the first successful challenger that morning or afternoon; otherwise, he will give you a colourful red and white lapel badge as a memento of the occasion.

Remember the dates – Tuesday 16th to Saturday, 27th August, at Olympia – and keep this announcement for reference when you visit the Boys and Girls Exhibition.

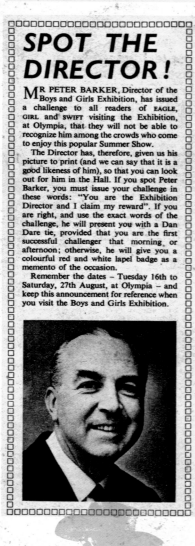

IN YOUR 20-PAGE ISSUE—

THE STORY OF JESUS

Written by Marcus Morris and drawn by Frank Hampson, you can read the artist's introduction to this presentation on page 17.

NEW STRIP SERIAL

Knights of the Road – the gripping adventures of a long-distance lorry driver and his young brother.

EAGLE ROUNDABOUT

A variety feature, providing a regular guide to outstanding films, shows, exhibitions, books, trips and the circus, together with puzzles, jokes and many other items of interest.

MYSTERY and DETECTION

You can join in the thrilling missions of an Interpol agent in his world-wide fight against crime.

VIC VENTURE

Another new EAGLE character, who begins his amusing exploits as an ace fighter pilot in the Royal Flying Corps.

NATURE HAD IT FIRST

George Cansdale's intriguing new series reveals how close many of Man's inventions are to the wonders of Nature.

FOREIGN TRAVEL

Be in at the start of an eventful trip through the continents of Europe, Asia and America on a scooter.

4 NEW ADVENTURES

Dan Dare, Jeff Arnold, Jack o'Lantern and Storm Nelson, all plunge into exciting new adventures which promise weeks of top-line suspense.

HERE'S YOUR CHANCE TO WIN
A WONDERFUL HOLIDAY in
MOSCOW and LENINGRAD

Over 800 other super prizes to be won — and special school awards, too!

HAVE you ever tried to picture the famous Red Square in Moscow, or wondered what it would be like to visit the Kremlin ? EAGLE gives you the opportunity to see all this at first hand — as this year's marvellous top prize is a visit to Moscow and Leningrad ! Even if you don't win the top prize, there's still a good chance to win one of the hundreds of other super prizes we are offering.

The top prize, of a holiday to Russia, will be awarded to the best entry from a girl and boy from either of the two higher age-groups eligible to enter this competition (11 to 13 and 14 to 16 years).

PRIZES INCLUDE

Tape Recorders • Cine-Cameras • Writing Bureaux • Record-Players • Bicycles • Radios • Tool Sets • Artists' Equipment • Wristwatches • Train Sets • Meccano Sets • Cameras

Our 1960 National Painting Competition is open to all readers of EAGLE who are under 17 years of age on 29th February, 1960. The competition is also open to our companion papers, GIRL and SWIFT. Entry is FREE !

Your paintings and drawings will be judged in three age-groups, so that even the youngest competitor has a chance, with special prizes to suit his taste. The judges will be looking not only for painting and drawing ability, but for work which shows imagination and promise.

You may send in as many entries as you like, but a coupon cut from EAGLE must be pasted on the back of each. The closing date for this competition is 29th February, 1960.

SPECIAL SCHOOL AWARDS

We are also giving special prizes of Challenge Cups to the schools which send in the best groups of paintings and drawings. Entries which are submitted in this way will also be included in the individual judging.

School entries will be divided into five different areas :—
LONDON — SOUTH OF ENGLAND — MIDLANDS and WALES — NORTH OF ENGLAND — SCOTLAND.
A challenge cup will be awarded for each of the three age-groups in these areas.

The school entries should, if possible, be sent together in one parcel, but every entry in a school group must have a coupon (cut from EAGLE, GIRL or SWIFT) pasted on the back, plus the words SCHOOL ENTRY in capitals, accompanied by the name and address of the school. Each entry must be signed by a teacher — this is very important.

PLEASE SH THIS TO YE TEACHE

SPORTSMAN IN THE NEWS
GRAHAM HILL
(British motor-racing ace)

FROM Henley boat-crew stroke to Grand Prix ace — that's the story of Graham Hill's life.

Ex-sailor and engineer, Graham threw up his job in 1953 to spend all his time preparing racing-cars for other people. From a job which brought him no pay at all, he struck gold in 1954 when he met Colin Chapman, owner-designer of the Lotus car. Chapman invited Graham to 'pop in any time' to look round his factory.

In 1955, a number of top drivers were invited to Brands Hatch to try out the new Lotus. Graham Hill, still a novice, shocked the assembly by chalking up the second fastest lap.

Driving an unspectacular, but consistent, season in 1959, Graham has now signed up with BRM. If the new, rear-engined model is all it is cracked up to be, we should see Graham Hill taking the chequered flag quite often this year.

Read these rules very carefully, together with your parent

1. Entries may be drawings or paintings, and any colour medium may be used. They may be of any subject, but must be original and not copied from other pictures or paintings. The Post Office regulations restrict the size of your entries, and no entry can be accepted which exceeds 24″ x 20″. On the other hand, the minimum size is 10″ x 8″.

2. The coupon on this page must be filled in by you and signed by a parent, guardian or teacher in the place marked. It must then be glued firmly to the back of your entry.

3. You may send in as many entries as you like, but each one must be accompanied by a coupon cut from EAGLE. These coupons will be appearing every week in this paper.

4. Each parcel must contain stamps for return postage and a self-addressed, gummed label, if you want your painting returned. Paintings chosen for exhibition or reproduction will become the property of EAGLE for the period required for these purposes.

5. Entries must be carefully packed. They shoul sent in flat, unframed and without glass. We ac no responsibility for entries which are lost damaged in transit.

6. All entries should be sent to: EAGLE Art Cou EAGLE Reader Services, Long Lane, Liverpoo Closing date for the Competition is 29th Februa 1960, but we would welcome entries which submitted as soon as possible.

7. The Competition is open to all EAGLE reader will be judged by our panel of art experts in th different age-groups : (a) Ten years and un (b) Eleven, twelve and thirteen years. (c) Fourt fifteen and sixteen years. The age-groups apply on 29th February, 1960, in each case.

8. No overseas entries are eligible.

9. The decision of the Editor in all matters rela to this Competition is final, and we regret tha correspondence can be entered into.

COUPON E1
USE BLOCK LETTERS TO FILL THIS IN, PLEASE

This painting is the original work of :-

SURNAME.....................

CHRISTIAN NAMES.....................

ADDRESS.....................

....

AGE.......... DATE OF BIRTH.....................

SCHOOL.....................

TITLE OF PAINTING.....................

Signature of parent, teacher or guardian

(Maximum size of entry 24 ins. by 20 ins. minimum size of entry 10 ins. by 8 ins.)

PASSPORT TO A RUSSIAN HOLIDAY !

NEWS

FROM EAGLE
161/166 FLEET STREET
LONDON, E.C.4

*A*S you know, boys all over the world – and particularly in the countries which make up the Commonwealth – read EAGLE regularly every week, but you may be interested to learn that many of your favourite characters are also eagerly followed in Italy and the Netherlands.

We have reproduced a cover of IL GIORNO *dei ragazzi* on the left. IL GIORNO (THE DAY) is an Italian national newspaper which has been publishing *dei ragazzi* (boys' supplement), including many items from EAGLE, since April, 1957.

On the right, you can see a cover of AREND – which means EAGLE, and is the Dutch edition of your magazine. The paper is made up of features from GIRL, SWIFT and ROBIN, as well as EAGLE. Published fortnightly, AREND first appeared in July, 1955. You will notice that Dan Dare becomes Daan Durf in Holland.

If you are lucky enough to visit Italy or the Netherlands for a holiday this summer, look out for the latest number of IL GIORNO *dei ragazzi*, or AREND.

Yours sincerely,

Clifford Makins

THE JOURNEY OF A LETTER

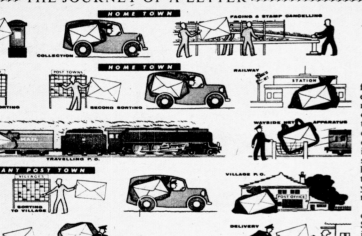

NEWS

FROM EAGLE
161/166 FLEET STREET,
LONDON, E.C.4

The diagram alongside comes from an interesting new booklet entitled 'Our Post Office', and is reproduced by kind permission of the Postmaster General. Written by Mary F. Moore and describing all the different jobs done by the Post Office, this well-illustrated book is first class. You should be able to see it at your local library, and the G.P.O. also tells me that, if you ask at school, your teacher will be able to let you read a copy.

Now that Man is about to set out on the great adventure of Space conquest, there is an added interest in the heavens, so I hope that you will enjoy our new series on Astronomy, which starts to-day on this page and will be appearing from time to time.

EAGLE will soon be celebrating its tenth birthday, and this sets me thinking about anniversaries. A number of people are saying that the world has just begun a new decade with 1960, and that on New Year's Day 2,000, we shall celebrate the start of a fresh century. I'm quite sure that they're wrong, but I would very much like to hear what views EAGLE readers have about this.

Yours sincerely,

Clifford Makins

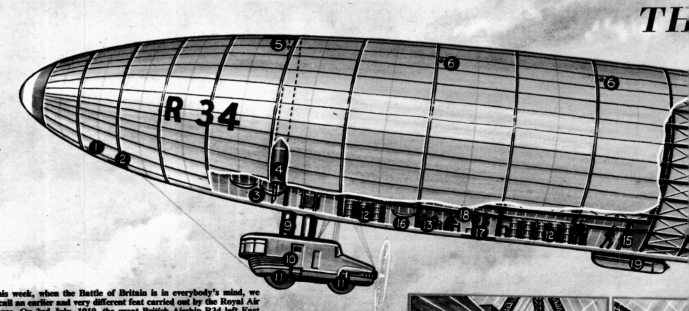

TH

R 34

This week, when the Battle of Britain is in everybody's mind, we recall an earlier and very different feat carried out by the Royal Air Force. On 2nd July, 1919, the great British Airship R34 left East Fortune, in Scotland, on an epoch-making flight across the North Atlantic with a crew of 31, plus one stowaway – a British soldier! The R34 landed at Roosevelt Field, having made the crossing in 108 hours, 12 minutes. Three days later, this famous airship flew back to England and landed at Pulham – a distance of 3,200 miles – in 74 hours, 56 minutes, breaking several records in the process and becoming the first transatlantic liner of the air.

During the following years, a number of countries built airships, but many of these monster dirigibles met with disaster. Probably those considered to be the most reliable were the renowned Zeppelins constructed by Germany during and after the First World War. However, on 6th May, 1937, the Zeppelin *Hindenburg* exploded in flames when landing at Lakehurst, in the U.S.A., with a loss of 36 lives. Since that day, not a single rigid dirigible has carried a paying passenger. These great ships of the sky are now generally regarded as being an unsuccessful type of aircraft, and further construction has ceased in all countries.

The crew space of R34. On the right can be seen two of the 30-gallon drinking-water tanks and, beyond the curtained partition, a glimpse of some of the fuel tanks. Food was cooked by engine exhaust in the engine-cars.

GREEVES 24TCS SCOTTISH TRIALS MODEL

Greeves motor-cycles, small and comparatively recent members of the British motor-cycle industry, have gained a reputation over the past few years as makers of particularly sturdy and successful specialist machines for trials and scrambles. The most important feature of these machines is the replacement of a conventional tubular-steel frame – breakages of which are not uncommon under the strenuous conditions of cross-country competitions – with one employing a light alloy beam for the front frame member. Cast from aluminium alloy, this girder section beam gives greatly improved strength factors with no weight penalty, although greater production costs will probably restrict its general use to competition rather than ordinary road machines. The main Greeves specialist models are: the 250 c.c. Scottish Trials Model illustrated here; the similar 20TC model, with a 200 c.c. engine; and the Hawkstone Special Scrambler models, with 250 c.c. or 200 c.c. engines and close ratio gearboxes. Greeves also make 250 c.c. single-cylinder and two-cylinder two-stroke sports road machines, which also have the light alloy front frame and Greeves bonded rubber-levered front suspension.

The competition mounts have a number of special features, built in as a result of experience gained by factory teams in sporting events. These are included in the key.

KEY TO NUMBERED PARTS (1) Special high-placed tuned silencer gives quieter note, more performance, and is fitted close to frame to avoid obstructions. (2) Rear number-plate is of rubber, to prevent damage in the event of a spill. (3) Bulb horn. (4) Armstrong rear spring and hydraulic damper unit. (5) Security bolts clamp low-pressure tyres to rims. (6) Rear brake adjuster. (7) Speedometer drive take-off. (8) Chain liner guides chain and prevents it coming off the sprocket. (9) Filler for oil reservoir in rear swing arm, which feeds oil via a needle valve on to the rear chain. (10) Toolbox. (11) Petrol tap. (12) Waterproof plug connector. (13) Villiers Mk. 32A single-cylinder 246 c.c. two-stroke engine-gearbox unit. (14) Amal Monobloc down-draught carburettor, with oil-soaked air-filter. (15) Kick-starter, with fold-in head. (16) Lighting system plug-ins. (17) Waterproofed H.T. lead from flywheel magneto. (18) Foot-change gear-lever is reversed because of rear-placed footrest. (19) Footrests are placed well back, to improve balance and increase weight on rear wheels. (20) Ground clearance, 9½ inches. (21) Prop stand tucks well in when retracted. (22) Narrow section 2-gallon fuel-tank. (23) Nearly-flat 31 in.-span handlebars. (24) Speedometer. (25) Ball ends to clutch and brake-levers prevent injury in a spill. (26) Front number-plate. (27) Extra-strong cast alloy front frame member. (28) Rubber-in-torsion spring unit for front wheel. (29) Front-springing hydraulic damper. (30) Heavy-gauge spokes give added wheel strength. (31) Front brake cable and adjuster.

– ROY CROSS –

GREEVES FRONT-SPRINGING SYSTEM

Shown on the right, in diagramatic form, is the Greeves system of front springing by means of Metalastik bonded rubber-in-tension bushes (28), which form the hinge point of the suspension lever arm. The springing action is damped by Girling hydraulic shock-absorbers (29), concealed in the front fork tubes. Main advantage of the system is that maintenance is cut to the absolute minimum.

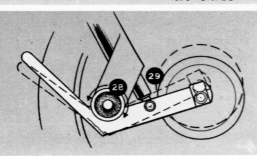

FIRST TRANSATLANTIC AIRLINER
BRITISH AIRSHIP R 34

DIMENSIONS: Length, 643.5ft. Beam, 79ft. Height, 91.8ft.

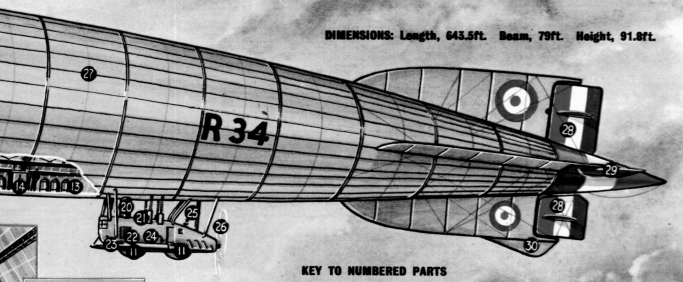

KEY TO NUMBERED PARTS

(1) Mooring-rope tub. (2) Emergency water-ballast discharge. (3) Hammocks. (4) Access tube leading to (5) the forward gun-platform. (6) Openings of corridor ventilating shafts. (7) One of the giant gas-bags. Each of these drum-shaped gas-bags contained several thousand cubic feet of highly inflammable hydrogen. (8) Rigid framework of duralumin girders. (9) Access trunk to (10) the control cabin, which also combined the forward power-car. (11) Compressed-air landing bags. (12) Fuel tanks. (13) Drinking-water tanks, each containing 30 gallons. (14) Larder and stores. (15) Triangular space running the length of the keel. (16) Keel and 'cat-walk'. The latter is a narrow walking-way, running the length of the keel inside the ship. (17) Water-ballast bag. (18) Crew space. (19) The starboard wing power-car; another (not shown) is positioned opposite to this, on the port side. These 'wing' cars were slung a little way up either side of the hull. (20) Access trunk to the aft power-car. Two engines were coupled together in this car, which also housed auxiliary controls, for use in case the steering broke down forward. (21) Adjustable radiators. (22) Oil radiator. (23) Handling rail for ground crews. (24) Engine exhaust silencer. (25) Navigation light – known as the 'steaming' light. (26) Propeller, 19 ft. 6 ins. from tip to tip. (27) Outer envelope of varnished fabric. (28) Rudders. (29) Elevators. (30) Landing skid.

Along each side of the keel and 'cat-walk', hammocks were slung. The 'cat-walk' itself was a girder covered with plywood. In the crew space, and by the hammocks, the whole width of the keel was floored in. Elsewhere, the 'cat-walk' was merely a narrow foot-way, on each side of which was just the fabric outer-cover of the ship!

VILLAGE UNDER THE SEA

THIS underwater 'village' built from a 'kit' should be occupied by 1980. That is the aim of the *General Electric Company of America* who have planned an underwater research station to be assembled on a site somewhere on the mid-Atlantic Ridge – a chain of mountains under the ocean between South America and Africa. The 'kit' consists of a number of spheres or pressure balls which can be 'plugged' together. These will be taken down 12,000 ft. by special submarines to the top of the ridge, where the first sphere will be anchored to a pillar driven by explosives deep into the sea bed, then the second will be joined to the first, and the other spheres connected to form a horizontal string.

The internal diameter of each sphere will be 12 ft. – just sufficient for comfortable living, research laboratories or for storing underwater exploration equipment. New materials are being devised to stand up to pressure of over 5,000 lb. per square inch, which the spheres will be subjected to.

A small atomic reactor will produce electricity for the scientists working beneath the waves. By studying marine life and experimenting with samples, they will, eventually, be able to exploit the sea's minerals. In innumerable other ways they will probe the secrets of the ocean.

Oceanography – the science of the sea – is entering a new and exciting phase.

The mid-Atlantic Ridge between South America and Africa is about 12,000 ft. below the surface (2,000 fathoms). The deepest part of the Atlantic is a chasm off Puerto Rico in the West Indies, 27,962 ft. down (4,660 fathoms).

12,000 FT.

18,000 FT.

ASHWELL WOOD

AN EAGLE cutaway DRAWING

KEY TO NUMBERED PARTS

(1) Anchorage for the first sphere, driven deep into the sea bed. (2) Observation windows. (3) Cine-camera. (4) 1,000-watt floodlight. (5) Camera recorder. (6) Access to sphere above. (7) Watertight connections for future spheres. (8) Higher level sphere joined to the anchorage sphere. (9) Observation windows. (10) Camera recording equipment. (11) Connecting hatch. (12) Pressure hull. (13) Entrance hatch. (14) Each sphere is joined by a watertight connection. (15) Scientists' accommodation. (16) Connecting hatch. (17) Electric galley and eating accommodation. (18) Connecting hatch. (19) Research laboratory. (20) Oxygen cylinders. (21) Pressure hull and atomic radiation shielding. (22) Control rods. (23) Atomic pile reactor. (24) Heat exchanger. Here steam is produced for driving the turbines, which in turn drive the electricity generator. (25) Steam turbines. (26) Electricity generator supplying all the 'village' services. (27) Other spheres containing more living quarters and laboratories. (28) End sphere and watertight connections. (29) Additional sphere about to be connected. (30) Special submarine which brings the spheres down from the surface.

NEWS

FROM EAGLE

161/166 FLEET STREET
LONDON, E.C.4.

PICTURED at the wheel of the motor-tug *Stackgarth*, which will be featured in EAGLE at a later date, is Leslie Ashwell Wood, whose popular drawings have been appearing on our centre pages since the very first issue of the paper.

Our chief contributor of 'land, sea and air' subjects, Leslie has completed nearly 350 special features for us now, and you will find that, this week, he continues his British Railways Modernisation series. One time designer-draughtsman for a famous aircraft company, Ashwell Wood studied Art, Engineering and Science – a rare combination – and has illustrated many books for boys.

He tells me that his hobbies are cricket and scale-model making – when time permits – and that his great ambition for the future is to write and illustrate an absolutely first-class book on 'Inside Knowledge'. There's no doubt that, with all his experience of pictorial cut-away drawings, such a book will be well worth waiting for.

Yours sincerely,

Clifford Makins

EAGLE 10 *December* 1960

EAGLE ROUNDABOUT

FREE seats for PANTOMIMES starring

I'm in Charge

IF you live in or near any of the towns where our pantomimes are taking place, here is your chance to claim a FREE ticket for one of these wonderful Christmas shows. All you have to do is send your application on a postcard to: Panto Visit (insert town required here), EAGLE Reader Services, 5 Dryden Street, London, W.C.99, stating your name, address and age. Then cut out the emblem printed at the top right of this page and stick it firmly on your card, so that we know you are a regular reader of EAGLE.

The senders of the first quota of applications received for each pantomime will be sent an invitation to the show of their choice.

JIMMY JEWEL and BEN WARRISS • RICHARD (MR PASTRY) HEARNE
BERYL REID • NORMAN WISDOM • BRUCE FORSYTH • KEN PLATT
LONNIE DONEGAN • GLADYS MORGAN • CHARLIE CHESTER
ELIZABETH LARNER • NAT JACKLEY • CHARLIE CAIROLI
THE THREE MONARCHS • and a host of others!

PANTO — Cut around dotted line

20 FREE tickets for each of these pantomimes

A WISH FOR JAMIE, *Alhambra Glasgow*	Wed., 28th Dec.
MOTHER GOOSE, *Winter Gardens, Blackpool*	Wed., 28th Dec.
PIED PIPER OF HAMELIN, *Coventry Theatre*	Fri., 30th Dec.
BABES IN THE WOOD, *Empire Theatre, Leeds*	Fri., 30th Dec.
ROBINSON CRUSOE, *Empire Theatre, Liverpool*	Fri., 30th Dec.
CINDERELLA, *Streatham Hill Theatre*	Fri., 30th Dec.
THE SLEEPING BEAUTY, *Hippodrome, Birmingham*	Fri., 30th Dec.
CHRISTMAS CRACKERS, *His Majesty's, Aberdeen*	Fri., 30th Dec.
GOODY TWO SHOES, *Manchester Hippodrome*	Fri., 30th Dec.
CINDERELLA, *Theatre Royal, Nottingham*	Fri., 30th Dec.
ALADDIN, *Grand Opera House, Belfast*	Mon., 2nd Jan.
GOODY TWO SHOES, *King's Theatre, Edinburgh*	Mon., 2nd Jan.
GOLDILOCKS AND THE THREE BEARS, *Empire, Newcastle*	Tues., 3rd Jan.
TURN AGAIN WHITTINGTON, *London Palladium*	Fri., 6th Jan.

15 FREE tickets for each of these pantomimes

MOTHER GOOSE, *Theatre Royal, Hanley*	Thurs., 29th Dec.
PUSS IN BOOTS, *Theatre Royal, Bath*	Fri., 30th Dec.
ALADDIN, *Chester Royalty Theatre*	Fri., 30th Dec.
DICK WHITTINGTON, *New Theatre, Oxford*	Fri., 30th Dec.
MOTHER GOOSE, *New Theatre, Cardiff*	Mon., 2nd Jan.
JACK AND THE BEANSTALK, *Grand Theatre, Swansea*	Mon., 2nd Jan.
DICK WHITTINGTON, *Hippodrome, Brighton*	Tues., 3rd Jan.
BABES IN THE WOOD, *Theatre Royal, Norwich*	Tues., 3rd Jan.

PAINTING COMPETITION

OUR touring exhibition of winning entries for the EAGLE/GIRL 1960 Painting Competition is opening at the Municipal Art Gallery and Museum, Union Street, Oldham on 10th December, and will be on display until 7th January, 1961. Entrance is FREE.

Viewing times: Monday, Wednesday, Thursday and Friday, 10 a.m. to 5 p.m.; Tuesday and Saturday, 10 a.m. to 7 p.m. If you live in or near Oldham, don't miss this opportunity of seeing, with the rest of your family, the talents of your fellow-readers.

Who would have thought on seeing this advert in 1960 that nearly fifty years later Bruce Forsyth would still be a major television star?

WHO'S READING EAGLE?

Why, everybody – including Dr Who!

This is a scene from the exciting new colour film Dr WHO AND THE DALEKS, now on general release and starring Peter Cushing as the eccentric inventor.

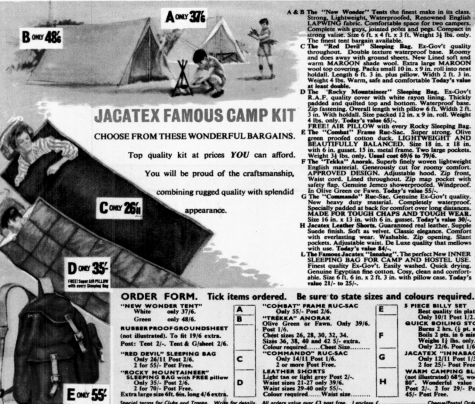

EAGLE ROUNDABOUT brings you
GRAND SEASIDE NEWS

JOIN IN OUR 1960 TREASURE HUNTS!

AYR	Mon.	18 *July*	(3 p.m.)
TROON	Tues.	19 ,,	(3 p.m.)
SALTCOATS	Wed.	20 ,,	(3 p.m.)
ARDROSSAN	Thur.	21 ,,	(3 p.m.)
LARGS	Fri.	22 ,,	(3 p.m.)
REDCAR	Mon.	25 *July*	(3 p.m.)
FLEETWOOD	Mon.	25 ,,	(3 p.m.)
FILEY	Tues.	26 ,,	(3 p.m.)
CLEVELEYS	Tues.	26 ,,	(3 p.m.)
WITHERNSEA	Wed.	27 ,,	(3 p.m.)
LYTHAM ST. ANNES	Wed.	27 ,,	(3 p.m.)
CLEETHORPES	Thur.	28 ,,	(3 p.m.)
SOUTHPORT	Thur.	28 ,,	(11 a.m.)
MABLETHORPE ...	Fri.	29 ,,	(3 p.m.)
NEW BRIGHTON ...	Fri.	29 ,,	(3 p.m.)
HUNSTANTON	Mon.	1 *August*	(3 p.m.)
PRESTATYN	Mon.	1 ,,	(3 p.m.)
CROMER	Tues.	2 ,,	(3 p.m.)
COLWYN BAY	Tues.	2 ,,	(3 p.m.)
GORLESTON	Wed.	3 ,,	(3 p.m.)
PWLLHELI	Wed.	3 ,,	(3 p.m.)
FELIXSTOWE	Thur.	4 ,,	(3 p.m.)
BARMOUTH	Thur.	4 ,,	(3 p.m.)
JAYWICK	Fri.	5 ,,	(3 p.m.)
BORTH	Fri.	5 ,,	(3 p.m.)
HERNE BAY	Mon.	8 *August*	(4 p.m.)
LANGLAND BAY ...	Mon.	8 ,,	(3 p.m.)
DEAL	Tues.	9 ,,	(3 p.m.)
PORT TALBOT	Tues.	9 ,,	(3 p.m.)
HASTINGS	Wed.	10 ,,	(3 p.m.)
WORTHING	Thur.	11 ,,	(3 p.m.)
WOOLACOMBE	Thur.	11 ,,	(3 p.m.)
LITTLEHAMPTON ...	Fri.	12 ,,	(3 p.m.)
WESTWARD HO! ...	Fri.	12 ,,	(3 p.m.)
SANDOWN I.o.W. ...	Mon.	15 *August*	(3 p.m.)
BUDE	Mon.	15 ,,	(3 p.m.)
RYDE I.o.W.	Tues.	16 ,,	(3 p.m.)
PERRANPORTH	Tues.	16 ,,	(3 p.m.)
VENTNOR I.o.W. ...	Wed.	17 ,,	(11 a.m.)
ST. IVES	Wed.	17 ,,	(10.30 a.m.)
SHANKLIN I.o.W. ...	Thur.	18 ,,	(3 p.m.)
FALMOUTH	Thur.	18 ,,	(3 p.m.)
SANDOWN I.o.W. ...	Fri.	19 ,,	(3 p.m.)
PLYMOUTH	Fri.	19 ,,	(3 p.m.)
DAWLISH WARREN	Mon.	22 *August*	(3 p.m.)
DAWLISH	Tues.	23 ,,	(3 p.m.)
LYME REGIS	Wed.	24 ,,	(3 p.m.)
SWANAGE	Thur.	25 ,,	(3 p.m.)
SOUTHSEA	Fri.	26 ,,	(3 p.m.)

An EAGLE organiser

LOOK OUT FOR OUR TREASURE HUNT CARS!

*Y*ES, you can have a wonderful time, and perhaps win a splendid prize, if you are on holiday at one of the towns mentioned here on the date shown. Look out for the gay Treasure Hunt cars — their loudspeakers will tell you where the Treasure Hunt is being held. All you need for entry is the current issue of EAGLE. Treasure Hunt day will be the high point of your holiday — so make a note of the date, place and time now!

EAGLE ROUNDABOUT

YOUR LAST CHANCE!

This week, we are publishing the last entry coupon for our Table Tennis Championship — so, if you would like to enter, and have not yet completed your form, do so NOW. Entry is FREE and open to readers of EAGLE who are under 15 years of age on 1st January, 1960.

There are team as well as individual prizes to be won and, if you think your School or Club would like to organize its own Qualifying Round, in which you could compete and help to win points towards our special team award, ask your school-teacher or club leader to read the following announcement.

INDIVIDUAL ENTRY

TO SCHOOL-TEACHERS AND CLUB LEADERS

We invite you to organize a Qualifying Round in your Club or School for any, or all, of the following events: Boys under 15, Boys under 13, Girls under 15 and Girls under 13, the age qualifications being decided on 1st January, 1960.

A grant will be made to cover each player taking part in your tournament, and every entrant automatically scores a point for your Club or School.

A super Club Table will be awarded to the Club or School scoring the most points in each of the two Regions — Northern and Southern — and a Grand Match Table to the team with the best results.

Winners of events organized by you will win a medal and a place in the next round, where they can continue scoring points for your Club or School, and go on to win the Area Plaque, Regional Cup and Championship Trophy.

If you wish to organize a Qualifying Tournament for your School or Club, simply send a postcard to :—Admin. Secretary, EAGLE/GIRL Table Tennis, 161, Fleet Street, London E.C.4., for full particulars.

Mobile Stamp Album!

A couple of years ago, Frank S. Belville began saving stamps. To-day, he has thousands of stamps and one of the world's most unusual 'albums'. His stamp album is his car!

Frank has pasted from 75,000 to 100,000 postage stamps, sealed with varnish, on to his car. Now, wherever Frank goes, his colourful car stops traffic.

It all started a couple of years ago when Frank, a retired Railroad Express driver, covered a pair of tomtoms and a snare drum with stamps. (Frank is an amateur drummer). The drums attracted such sensational attention, that he decided to give his car the stamp treatment. Six months ago he set to work. The last stamp is now on, and the last square of paint has been covered.

ATOMIC ENERGY FOR ALL

ROBERT CHAPMAN

KEY TO THE FUTURE

A fascinating study of the world of atoms — their composition, and the way in which they are being harnessed to benefit mankind — appears in a book recently published by Odhams Press Ltd. at 18s., 'Atomic Energy for All', by Robert Chapman.

Here, in simple, lucid terms, is an account of the many uses to which atomic energy can be put, not only as a terrible agent of destruction, but as a powerful ally against hunger and disease – two of mankind's most terrible scourges. The author concludes that nuclear energy can lead us to a new and better world – if we use it wisely. His book should give reassurance to many who regard with alarm the rapid changes being wrought today by the mighty atom.

TENTH BIRTHDAY NEWS FROM EAGLE

THIS is our tenth birthday issue, and the staff of EAGLE join me in sending greetings to all readers, the world over. Leslie Ashwell Wood's centre-spread feature this week depicts the progress made on land, sea and air since 1950, and you will find our birthday competition below.

Ten years ago, the paper appeared in the form you see reproduced on the left. It gave me quite a surprise, looking back to the first number, to see how gradual changes, and improvement in our printing process over the years, have altered the appearance of EAGLE.

It set me thinking of all the exciting things that have happened as the years ticked by – of the great developments which your magazine has recorded in strip and illustration, and the various activities which have now become annual events. The family soon grew: first came EAGLE Annual, and then the companion papers – GIRL, ROBIN, SWIFT, and their annuals.

Looking back, our artist has remembered some of the star occasions in his illustration above this letter: Carol Services commence (1951); adoption of H.M.S. *Eagle* (1952); special coverage of the Coronation (1953); Roger Bannister and Chris Chataway tie for EAGLE Sportsman of the Year trophy (1954); Holiday Playtime and EAGLE/Y.H.A. holiday schemes begin (1955); first year of our annual Boys and Girls Exhibition at Olympia, and start of the Painting Competition (1956);

EAGLE presents *The Happy Warrior*, the life-story of Winston Churchill (1957); the colourful ceremony of Trooping the Colour appears on our centre pages (1958).

In 1959, I was proud to take over the editorship of EAGLE, and now here we are in 1960, smartened up and looking forward to the next ten years. It is going to be great fun planning regular, large-size numbers of EAGLE in tune with the thrilling times in which we live.

Yours sincerely,

Clifford Makins

THE YEARS OF PROGRESS

In this special EAGLE composite picture, we show some of the leading features – on land, sea and in the air – that have appeared on the centre pages during the last ten years. The 1950s have been years of progress – momentous years of achievement in the fields of science and engineering. Many records have been broken and, during this period, we have seen the beginning of the great British Railways £1,240,000,000 modernisation scheme.

EAGLE's centre features have always been 'up-to-the-minute', and have included a number of glimpses into the future and glances back at the past. Now we look forward to recording further breathtaking achievements in the years ahead.

1950. Britain's first mail Diesel-electric loco (Nos.

1955. The jet-engined *Bluebird*. Donald Campbell breaks the world's water-speed record at 248 m.p.h.

1954. New bomber look – the first drawing of the crescent-wing *Victor* to appear in any paper.

1956. The Fairey *Delta* gains the world's air-speed record for Britain by attaining 1,132 m.p.h.

1957. The last of the steam locomotives. British Railways will order no more, but many of them will be with us for a long time yet.

ASHWELL WOOD

A FRENCH EXPERIMENTAL AIRCRAFT – THE BAROUDEUR SE-5000

At the outbreak of World War II, the French Air Force was ill-equipped to deal with the might of the German Luftwaffe. Although France had an advanced air-fleet on the drawing-boards, she had an obsolete one in the air, due to an unfortunate lethargy which overcame the French aircraft industry between the two World Wars. Today, however, there is a distinct change, and French ingenuity and inventiveness have developed some revolutionary types – particularly in regard to the considerable amount of experimental work carried out with aircraft suitable for N.A.T.O. One requirement is for an aircraft capable of taking off and landing on unprepared grass fields. The *Baroudeur SE-5000* is a French answer to this problem. The aircraft – a light fighter – is launched from a rocket-propelled trolley and lands on skids. At take-off speed, the pilot cuts the trolley loose and climbs away; meanwhile, the trolley is braked automatically. Our main drawing depicts a *Baroudeur SE-5000* as it is on the point of taking off from its trolley, the actual take-off run being less than 770 yards.

KEY TO NUMBERED PARTS: (1) 30 mm. gun, fitted port and starboard. (2) Gun-sight. (3) Quick-release cockpit canopy. (4) Ejector seat. (5) Oxygen cylinders. (6) Radio equipment. (7) Port wing root air-intake. (8) Skid retracted into fuselage. (9) Air-brakes. (10) Fuel tanks. (11) Rocket-propelled trolley fitted with automatic brakes. (12) Port rocket tubes. Two more tubes are fitted in a similar position on the starboard side of the trolley. The four rockets provide sufficient speed to launch the 'plane. (13) Jet power unit. (14) Strake. (15) Braking parachute, stowed.

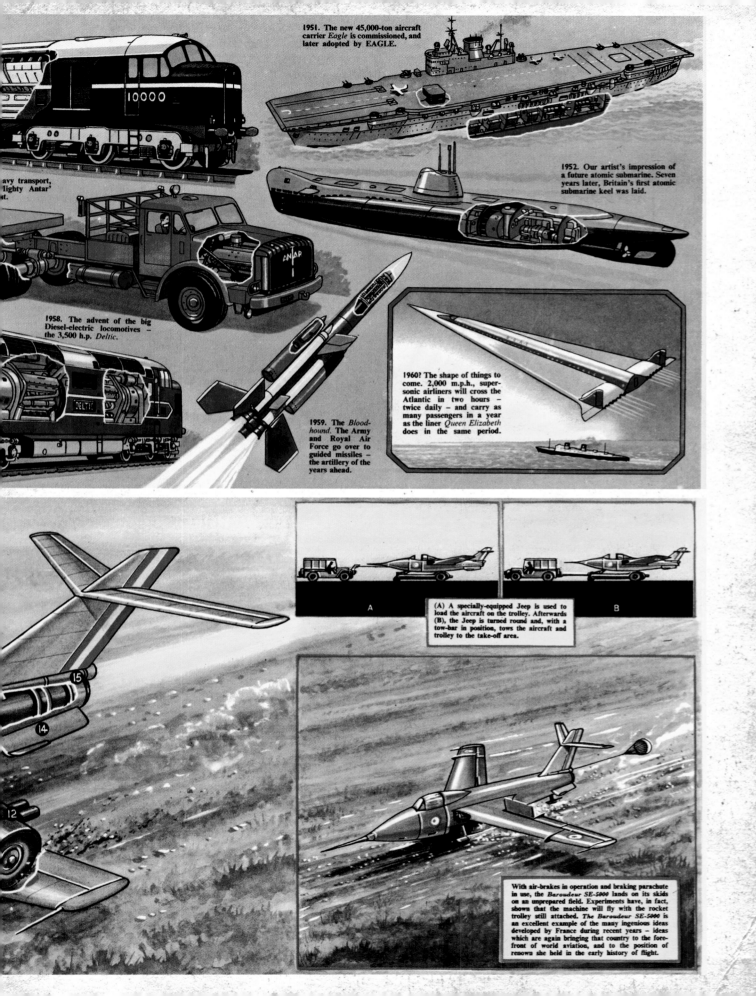

1951. The new 45,000-ton aircraft carrier *Eagle* is commissioned, and later adopted by EAGLE.

1952. Our artist's impression of a future atomic submarine. Seven years later, Britain's first atomic submarine keel was laid.

...avy transport, ...Mighty Antar' ...t.

1958. The advent of the big Diesel-electric locomotives — the 3,500 h.p. *Deltic*.

1959. The *Bloodhound*. The Army and Royal Air Force go over to guided missiles — the artillery of the years ahead.

1960? The shape of things to come. 2,000 m.p.h., supersonic airliners will cross the Atlantic in two hours — twice daily — and carry as many passengers in a year as the liner *Queen Elizabeth* does in the same period.

(A) A specially-equipped Jeep is used to load the aircraft on the trolley. Afterwards (B), the Jeep is turned round and, with a tow-bar in position, tows the aircraft and trolley to the take-off area.

With air-brakes in operation and braking parachute in use, the *Baroudeur SE-5000* lands on its skids on an unprepared field. Experiments have, in fact, shown that the machine will fly with the rocket trolley still attached. The *Baroudeur SE-5000* is an excellent example of the many ingenious ideas developed by France during recent years – ideas which are again bringing that country to the forefront of world aviation, and to the position of renown she held in the early history of flight.

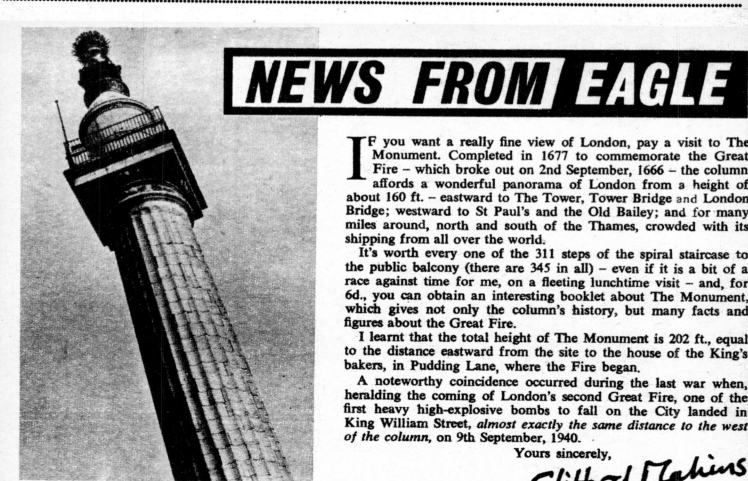

NEWS FROM EAGLE

IF you want a really fine view of London, pay a visit to The Monument. Completed in 1677 to commemorate the Great Fire — which broke out on 2nd September, 1666 — the column affords a wonderful panorama of London from a height of about 160 ft. - eastward to The Tower, Tower Bridge and London Bridge; westward to St Paul's and the Old Bailey; and for many miles around, north and south of the Thames, crowded with its shipping from all over the world.

It's worth every one of the 311 steps of the spiral staircase to the public balcony (there are 345 in all) - even if it is a bit of a race against time for me, on a fleeting lunchtime visit - and, for 6d., you can obtain an interesting booklet about The Monument, which gives not only the column's history, but many facts and figures about the Great Fire.

I learnt that the total height of The Monument is 202 ft., equal to the distance eastward from the site to the house of the King's bakers, in Pudding Lane, where the Fire began.

A noteworthy coincidence occurred during the last war when, heralding the coming of London's second Great Fire, one of the first heavy high-explosive bombs to fall on the City landed in King William Street, *almost exactly the same distance to the west of the column*, on 9th September, 1940.

Yours sincerely,

Clifford Makins

COMPREHENSIVE SCHOOLS

Dear Editor,

I am writing in reply to Alvina Marlowski's letter about Comprehensive Schools (EAGLE, 19th December). I go to a Grammar School and work better without girls in the class. Also, I think it is easier to do high-standard work when you are all as good as one another, because it is more competitive.

Richard Steel, Gravesend, Kent.

Dear Editor,

Alvina Marlowski appears to believe that all Comprehensive Schools are co-educational. This is not so. My previous school, in Coventry, was a boys' Comprehensive. The idea of a Comprehensive School is to provide those who are not so lucky with competition. It also combines the distinct classes to form society.

I now go to a co-educational Grammar School near Derby, but if there was a co-ed Comprehensive I would just as soon have gone there. I most certainly hope the Comprehensive system extends.

Paul V. Summers, Derby.

Dear Editor,

I disagree with Alvina Marlowski. At the school I attend, the boys are generally more intelligent than the girls, and if one has to compete with pupils who are more intelligent than oneself, the standard is higher.

In any case, the schools are being changed to Comprehensive so that Secondary Schools are combined with Grammar Schools, not so that boys are combined with girls. Combining Secondary Schools with Grammar Schools has many advantages. For instance, some children are not sufficiently intelligent at the age of 11 to pass their 11-plus, but by the time they are old enough to take their G.C.E. they are capable of passing. If one of these children goes to a Secondary Modern School, he might never have the opportunity of taking his G.C.E. because of the complications in transferring schools, but if he goes to a Comprehensive School, it is comparatively simple to move from the Secondary Modern stream, to the Grammar stream.

Jolanda Wheeler, Newport, Mon.

Dear Editor,

My opinion is that Comprehensive Schools ought to be banned, partly because in the three or so years you spend there, you might just as well stay in a Primary School, and partly because I don't get on well at any school with *GIRLS*.

John Callen, Edmonton, N.9.

Dear Editor,

I think that Comprehensive Schools are rather silly, for the pupils of Grammar and Technical Schools have to be graded into much higher forms anyway, and so there would be a lot of bother like changing subjects and maybe enlarging schools. I do not mind girls in a school, for when you get a little older they seem to be very important!

Paul Riley, Nr. Maldon, Essex.

Dear Editor,

I went to school in Germany for two years and went to a State school. I found working with boys great fun – much more fun than being only with girls. I now have to go to a private school and I am thoroughly fed up with girls, girls, girls.

Sherida A. Johnson, Romney Marsh, Kent.

Dear Editor,

I think that all Secondary Schools becoming Comprehensive is a jolly good idea. It has already been proved in Comprehensive Schools that mixed classes promote healthy competition between boys and girls in schoolwork. Also, both sides tend to dress smarter and less outlandishly.

J. C. Duddell, Sutton C.F., Warks.

Dear Editor,

I dislike Comprehensive Schools because I think that if a Grammar and Secondary School united, there would always be gangs –one for the Grammar and one for the other – and they would always be fighting. In Australia they have this system, and in our school out there the first-form classes were 1A to 1G! Think of the number of boys in the school!

Barry Charman, Malmesbury, Wilts.

Dear Editor,

I think it would be best if the Grammar Schools and Comprehensive Schools were kept apart. Every child has a certain amount of intelligence. Some are cleverer than others, so if both were joined no one would get on very well. That is why they have been separated into two groups.

I also think work is better without girls in the class. I am afraid to say that hardly any of my friends agree with this.

Richard Brudzynski, Birmingham, 22.

No issue of the comic would be complete without some sort of competition. Often these were pretty straightforward but occasionally they could appear bizarre. Here is a classic example where the young reader has the chance to win a record player. Excellent, very 1960s, except that, in order to get the prize, it is necessary to identify different makes of oven. Rock 'n' Roll.

MOTOR CYCLING ON ICE!

SPEEDWAY on ice! That's the slipping, sliding, slithering sport they practise in Scandinavia. Speedway on circuits created on hard frozen lakes. (They treat the surface with chemicals to make it freeze harder.) And they reach speeds of between 70 and 85 m.p.h.

Speedway on ice differs from ordinary speedway in that no one tries to provoke a slide or broadside. They daren't. A slither and the rider can be straight across the track and up the icy banking that protects the spectators. But should this happen, riders often retain their balance and continue down the banking in wall of death fashion.

They have an uncanny balancing skill, these Norwegian and Swedish stars with names like Carlsson, Pedersen and Knutsson.

Most of them ride with the left leg thrust out as in normal speedway, though some – particularly Finnish riders – bank their bikes so far over that their heavily-padded left knees slide along the ice, and fight the skid.

Special tyres are necessary on their machines, of course. They have steel spikes set in them . . . 150 to 200 to a tyre. The wheels are covered by cage-like mudguards to protect the riders in crashes.

Otherwise the bikes are 500 c.c. mounts like those used in British speedway, except that the engines are placed farther forward.

A FLIP ROUND THE BUOY AT 70 M.P.H....

*T*HEY zoom over the water at speeds approaching the ton, more airborne than waterborne. They are hydroplanes – fast single-seater, flat-bottomed motor boats which skim across the surface with only the stern and propeller submerged.

At 60 m.p.h., in fact, only about 3 square inches of the lightweight craft are in contact with the water.

Hydroplanes – and their big brothers, the Jaguar-engined racing outboards which can carry up to five people but travel lower in the water reaching about 55 m.p.h. – race on many smooth stretches of British water such as Oulton Broad, near Lowestoft.

Willy Ryan, who won this year's European Championships in Berlin, can do about 90 m.p.h. on the straight at Oulton Broad in his hydroplane 'Eggshell' – despite being built like Harry Secombe.

On Lake Windermere, hydroplanes have reached 125 m.p.h.

But in hydroplaning, as in motor cycle racing, it is the way the pilot handles his machine on the bends that is really important. Hydroplane courses are commonly triangular and 2¾ miles long with com-

petitors covering six laps.

Mr Ken Derby, honorary secretary of the British Outboard Racing Club, says: "The skill in hydroplaning is in flipping the craft round a marker buoy at speeds of anything up to 70 m.p.h. It is a simple matter for an inexperienced driver to flip the craft over on to its back, and this is the reason all drivers wear inflatable life jackets and crash helmets.

"Races are won and lost on the turns and this is where experience counts."

Again, as in motor cycling, races are organized in 250 c.c., 350 c.c. and 500 c.c. engine classes. And it is a fact that many of the experts have a motor cycle racing background. Those who have taken part in both sports say: "You go faster on water – or if you don't, it feels as if you do! The same speed seems three times faster when you are lifting into the air from the water."

Cost of hydroplaning? Mr Derby says a boat can be bought new for £250 and "a good second-hand one can be had for as little as £70." But there is little money in hydroplane racing; the drivers do it for the thrills.

—THEN OPEN UP TO 90!

PLAY THE GAME, YOU CHAPS!

My attention has been drawn to the fact that one of the Beatles verses in the Christmas number of EAGLE was actually taken from the October Beatles Book.

Other readers have mentioned that some so-called original contributions to Merry-Go-Round have, in fact, been copied from various books and papers.

Come off it, lads!

I am always glad to hear from you, to read your verse, stories, or cartoon ideas – but I *don't* want second-hand versions.

This is *your* page in which you can express *your* views and news, not someone else's. So keep those letters coming – but make sure they contain your own ideas.

The Editor.

HOW TO BUILD UP YOUR OWN ARMY

This week, EAGLE pays a visit to Denmark, t meet Erling Schatter, a 15-year-old boy who live in the outskirts of Copenhagen . . .

Erling Schatter with some of the things he has made. Apart from soldiers, he also makes weapons in miniature and a variety of military cars. The latter, Erling makes out of pieces of cardboard.

ERLING, who has been building up his own model army since he was ten, has read many books about armies all over the world, and has thus been able to produce a large variety of authentic soldiers and equipment. He does his own casting, and paints the models carefully so that the completed soldier looks just like his real-life counterpart in America, Britain, German India or Russia, to quote just few examples of the countri represented in Erling's larg international force.

As Erling says, there is no en to the possibilities, because it on needs a little imagination to mak models clothed in uniforms of you own design.

This is how Erling Schatter sets about his interesting hobby:—

'To begin with, you must have a mould. Various materials can be used to make this, but I prefer gypsum plaster, because it is the cheapest. To mass-produce my soldiers, I take a pudding-basin which will allow about half an inch all round a ready-made soldier. Mix some plaster and pour it into the basin until it is about one and a half inches deep, and then press the soldier into the plaster, face upwards, until it is half submerged. When the mixture has set hard, remove the plaster from the basin and the model from the plaster. You now have half your mould. File the face of it down until it is almost flat, replace it in the basin, and carefully reposition the toy soldier in its bed. Lightly smear the surface of the plaster with Vaseline, and pour some freshly-mixed plaster over the top to further depth of one and a half inches. When the second lot of plaster has set, remove the casts from the basin; the two halves should part fairly easily, due to the smear of Vaseline.

Now carve a small channel in one half, to allow you to pour lead into the mould. Melt your lead over the gas (I use an old soup-ladle – but be careful, because spilling molten lead over yourself can be very painful!) and pour it into the opening; allow a few seconds, and then pour it out again – that is unless you want your models to be of solid lead. You can make many more if they are hollow.

Melted lead is poured into the mould and, shortly after, the mould can be parted. The hardened lead, which is the beginning of a soldier, can then be carefully removed.

A lead soldier has been taken out the mould, and now Erling is bu removing all the irregularities fro the figure with a file.

When you have cast as many as you want, take a file and remove the rough 'casting' marks and edges. Your soldiers will now be ready for painting, according to the uniforms and emblems you have chosen.

Erling has now reached the stage when he can start painting his new soldier. Everything is done with great care and accuracy.

To start the operation, Erling melts the lead for his models in the kitchen, over one of the gas-rings.

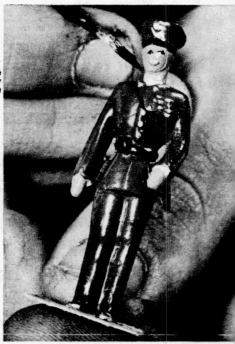

Here are a few caricatures. The bald gentleman in the middle, busy quenching his thirst, is a police officer. Also pictured are an Indian General and a British officer.

Staff officers study the situation at H.Q.! Notice the details: a man on the left is on the telephone, and several of the attendant officers are smoking cigarettes.

NEXT WEEK'S Hobbies Corner: Fishing No.

Another flame-thrower used at Normandy was the *Crocodile*. Mounted on *Churchill* tanks, this weapon could fire a torrent of blistering flame 150 yards.

The *Flammenwerfer* consisted of a steel cylinder (A), with high-pressure gas at the top (B) and oil at the bottom (C). The gas forced the oil through the hose (D), which led to a tube (E) mounted on a rifle butt (F). A trigger (G) controlled the flow of high-pressure oil which, when ignited, emerged as a flame (H) from the muzzle (I). A hand-grip (J) and shoulder straps (K) enabled the weapon to be carried.

SEE PAGE 19

RMS THROUGH THE AGES
No. 47. BIG BERTHA

g Bertha fired a shell 8.26 inches in diameter, eighing 228 lb. and about three feet long. The arge that propelled it on its 67-mile flight was three containers. The lower container (1) was brass and held 154 lb. of powder; next came e middle container (2), which consisted of a k bag holding 165 lb. of powder; the top ntainer (3) was filled with 112 lb. of powder. e lower part of the shell had two grooved rings ich screwed into the rifling of the barrel, so at when the gun was fired the shell screwed its ay out of the barrel at the rate of 100 turns a cond. This kept the shell steady in flight. The awing shows the height of the shell and the ree charges compared with the height of a six-ot gunner.

URN TO PAGE 19

No. 15 THE MOLOTOV COCKTAIL

The Molotov Cocktail was simply a wine bottle filled with inflammable liquids which burst into flames when it shattered against the side of a tank. The later 'Sticky-bomb' was a globe filled with nitro-glycerine jelly. The globe was covered with a powerful glue, which stuck against the side of the target. A fuse ignited the nitro-glycerine to produce an intensely hot flame.

TURN TO PAGE 17

CORK
STRING
GRIP
AIR
CHEMICAL
WATER

KNIGHTS of the ROAD

Meet the Knights – trusty 'Sir' Ted, one of a team of tough, long-distance lorry drivers working the trunk roads for **STRAITWAYS HAULAGE LTD.**: and his gay, irresponsible schoolboy brother, Frank, budding engineer and mouth-organ instrumentalist! They share a flat off the Commercial Road, in East London . . .

Story by GORDON GRINSTEAD
Drawn by GERALD HAYLOCK

. . . where their fussy Auntie Vi comes in to 'do' for them from time to time . . .

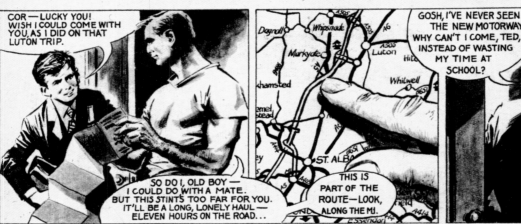

Frank decides to 'cut' school . . .

But the lad is spotted as he darts into Broad Street Station to catch a train to Watford . .

TO BE CONTINUED

161/166 FLEET STREET, LONDON, E.C.4

NEWS FROM EAGLE

Frank Bellamy, at his drawing-board, studies the head of a leopard. Note the African drum, witch-doctor's beads and Ona's (Masai) spear in the background

If you want to meet an artist whose whole interest in life, apart from his work, is devoted to Africa, Frank Bellamy – who draws *Lost Safari* for EAGLE – is the man for you.

I visited him at his Morden, Surrey, home the other day, and Terry Hardy had an exciting time photographing Frank with some of his much-prized African possessions, as you can see in the two pictures which accompany this letter.

Born at Kettering, Northamptonshire, 43 years ago, Frank – who never had training at an art school – worked in an advertising studio until 1940, spent six years in the Royal Artillery, and then returned to his old job, before becoming a free-lance artist in 1953.

The African 'bug' bit Frank, however, as early as 1925, when he drew his first illustration of a hunter with elephants. He's got a wonderful collection of books on the subject of wild life in Africa, as well as all the authentic objects pictured here, and some of them are pretty rare.

"I eat, drink, and dream drawing, Africa and Big Game," Frank told me, "but have still to accomplish my great ambition of a visit to East Africa – even for just one day!

"Kilimanjaro and a close up of a wild lion are 'musts' for me," he added. "So far, I've only got as far as Morocco."

Frank Bellamy already draws *Fraser of Africa* as if he'd lived in the continent all his life, but let's hope that he gets an opportunity soon of visiting his heart's desire in person.

Yours sincerely,

Clifford Makins

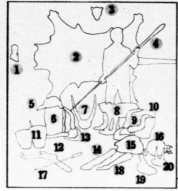

KEY TO PHOTOGRAPH

1. Wakamba wood carving of a Masai; 2. Leopard's skin; 3. Leopard's head; 4. Masai spear (for lion-hunting); 5. Style of hairdressing used by the Masai; 6. African drum (very old); 7. Waterbuck horns; 8. Young leopard; 9. Hartebeeste horns; 10 and 11. Uganda drums; 12. Masai belt and scabbard; 13. Lechwe horns; 14. Leopard's tail; 15. Leopard's head and skin; 16. Ostrich egg water-bottle; 17. Masai sword (called a Simi); 18. Rhinoceros' tail; 19. Elephant's tail; 20. Oribi horns.

One of Sean Connery's early films was *Hell Drivers*. It was made in 1957 and was set in a haulage yard. Three years later *Eagle* followed suit in this tale of a long-distance lorry driver.

KNIGHTS OF THE ROAD

HARRIS TWEED — SUPER SLEUTH

NOTHING LIKE JUGGLING TO KEEP FIT, BOY— AND EASTER EGGS ARE JUST THE THING!

RING! RING!

IT'S THE POLICE, SIR — THEY SAY SOMEONE HAS SENT YOU A BOMB IN AN EGG...

YOU MUST THROW IT INTO THE RIVER — AND, WHATEVER YOU DO, DON'T DROP IT, SIR!

WH–WH–WHAT?

BY JOVE — I BET THERE AREN'T MANY PEOPLE WHO COULD JUGGLE WITH SIX EGGS!

BY THE WAY, HOW MANY EGGS ARRIVED THIS MORNING?

SEVEN, SIR!

BANG !!

Build them all!

REVELL CADETS

at only **2/11** each

For only 2/11 you can create the excitement of modern motoring by
building these superb Revell Cadet car kits.
Each one is packed with true-to-life details – including wheels
that turn, acetate window strips, silver parts and a host of others.
Included free with every kit is the
essential Road Safety Booklet 'Nine Lives'. Buy and build
these Cadet car kits today.

ROVER 3 LITRE   JAGUAR 2·4   MORRIS 1000 TRAVELLER   FORD CONSUL

KARMANN GHIA   VAUXHALL CRESTA   VOLKSWAGEN DE-LUXE SALOON   TRIUMPH TR3

IN YOUR LOCAL HOBBY, TOY OR MODEL SHOP

Revell
Authentic Kits
MANUFACTURED IN GREAT BRITAIN

Really build a Model World

REVELL (Great Britain) LTD.
Maidstone House
25/27 Berners Street, London W1

PLANES · SHIPS · CARS · GUNS · MISSILES

TELEVISION'S UNSEEN MAGICIANS

by BILL EVANS

In the first episode of this new series, which will appear from time to time in EAGLE, the author takes you behind the scenes of a Television Studio, to reveal how some scenic effects are produced . . .

THERE'S a house on fire in Shepherd's Bush – but no one sends a fire-engine racing to put it out. It's snowing, too, and that's a bit odd – for this is a summer's day.

These are two frequent happenings behind the scenes of B.B.C. Television, where, in their TV Centre office, Jack Kine and Bernard Wilkie devise and build scenic effects that add reality to many programmes.

These two 'magicians' can make anything from a 'devil's brew' to a mist that can blot out a whole studio.

Let's take a closer look at that snow. A downfall of false snow used to be an unloading of torn paper or sacks of feathers: "But we try to keep up with the times," explained Jack, showing me a box of tiny, white balls resembling popcorn. This is plastic snow, used in making a light insulator, but more useful to us in the intermediate stage – it can turn a studio into an Arctic waste . . ." He demonstrated this by putting some down a funnel and switching on a hair-dryer at the other end.

"Burn a house down? Certainly," he said, rising from a model he and Bernard were building. "The biggest problem with fire is slowing it down. When we've finished this model, we could set it alight and film the blaze in slow-motion. Better, because it appears to burn slower, is to remove the windows, light some material several feet behind, and let the camera peep through the openings at the blaze."

He showed me a set of charges that any boy would love to get his hands on around 5th November. "These are pyro-

Jack Kine (left) and Bernard Wilkie practise making a blizzard with a hair-dryer, funnel – and thousands of balls of 'plastic snow'.

technic effects, some of which we designed ourselves, made by a famous fireworks firm. This one is a smoke-pencil" – it was about five inches long – "which can be very handy when we want a small amount of smoke. It burns for about ten minutes.

"For bigger explosions, we use maroons containing about a quarter-pound of gunpowder. They are in a cardboard carton, wound-up with very heavy string and then varnished. You don't want to be around when they go off!"

Jack and Bernard smile when they think how they nearly 'blew up' the Army. "We had to create the effects of a 250-pounder in a programme about the Bomb Disposal boys. We coupled a big flash-pot with a maroon, which makes a mighty flash with a loud bang and looks quite convincing. Normally, no one gets hurt but, that day, some high-ranking officers were standing round, drinking tea; to them, it was all rather feeble to use cardboard and string!

"We doubled the charge and I fired it," said Bernard. "We got the bang and the flash with a mighty wallop – but one of the jiggers didn't explode. The detonator went off, but the silver flash-powder, instead of flashing, went up in the air in a great cloud of silver dust, settling on the officers – and their tea."

Talking of drinks, Kine and Wilkie could concoct one to make you foam at the mouth – yet leave you unharmed. "It's easy enough to knock-up a devil's brew – but, when someone has got to drink the stuff, it's more difficult. We apply our own knowledge of chemistry," said Jack, "but we try out the results on ourselves first. If neither of us die, we send it to a chemist friend who vouches for it. We then scrap our 'prescription', and he makes a given quantity bearing

Jack Kine looks like being space-borne at almost any moment, with the working model of a rocket which he constructed for a space series.

his own label. This gives confidence to the actor who has to drink it."

Ever wondered how those misty dream sequences on TV are done? Not, as some viewers think, by a man breathing heavily on the camera lens to give that floating effect. Kine and Wilkie produced a large-scale mist for *The Sleeping Beauty* ballet, which starred Dame Margot Fonteyn. Said Bernard: "We obtained some carbon-dioxide in solid form, then passed steam over it. This produced a liquefied vapour which, on the screen, appeared exactly like a mist. It is, in fact, the same process that Nature herself uses."

From mist, it is not a great step to fog. "We pump oil and carbon-dioxide together to produce a dense, white smoke – which could be pretty horrible if we left it at that. But artistes don't mind our brand of fog, because we pump perfume with it. That's quite a joke in the studio."

They teamed-up six years ago when Kine, a scenic artist and model-maker, met Wilkie, an engineer with a flair for art. From a few effects a week, they now have a large workshop with four assistants. "We are at producers' beck and call to rustle-up

This looks like the biggest fishing story of all time – but the 'catch' Bernard Wilkie is measuring is made of rubber. It was used, with a head added later, in the TV opera Tobias and the Angel. The frogman is Jack Kine, who had the job of testing its flexibility in a large pool.

anything at a moment's notice. When a magician wanted a match that would burn for fifteen minutes, we made it. We gave it a hard wax exterior, with a thin cord interior down the middle. It was like a miniature candle. The magician struck it, and it stayed alight for his whole act."

An unusual call on their services came when a huge fish was wanted for the opera *Tobias and the Angel*. "We made it of rubber, so that it could be manipulated in a large water tank at Ealing Studios. The water represented the River Tigris, and singer John Ford had to 'find' the fish while swimming." The colourful fish, over 6 ft. in length, offered the singer no chance of accidentally swimming past! But, to make sure it would perform as the producer required, Jack had to don frog-

If you have a headache, we are not sure whether Bernard Wilkie's concoction will help much. It is made from bicarbonate of soda and glue – an ideal devil's brew.

man's outfit and carry it into the tank, to test its movement and durability.

As boys, chemistry was one of their best subjects. "But, for TV, our effects can never really be decided until we get on the site, for they have to be designed in relation to actual surroundings," said Jack. "That's why it is dangerous to play around without knowing exactly what you are doing. When I was eleven, I remember trying to make a boy airborne in a kite, by running along, towing it to make it take off. It rose to about 8 ft. – I'm glad now that it didn't go up any farther!"

Another exciting story in our series 'Strange Tales of the Coast' appears on this page next week !

EAGLE introduces . . .

FRASER of AFRICA

LOST SAFARI

NAIROBI, Tuesday. JED Brewster, star in many Hollywood 'tough' roles, has now officially been declared missing while on safari in the little-known Kasu district of Tanganyika.

With him was an experienced White Hunter, Robert E. Evans, and it is understood that an expedition has been organized to trace the missing men.

The district c...

+ STILL NO NEWS OF JED + +

...from ...heard ...re

MARTIN FRASER, KNOWN AS FRASER OF AFRICA, JIM LLOYD HIS ASSISTANT, AND THREE NATIVE BOYS, ARE ON THE TRAIL OF THE LOST SAFARI.

WE SHOULD STRIKE THE KASU RIVER VERY SOON, SIR. HOW NEAR ARE WE TO THE LAST CAMP?

LET'S HAVE A LOOK AT THE MAP.

THE SAFARI WAS LAST HEARD OF THERE, FORTY-FIVE MILES AS THE CROW FLIES.

HOW D'YOU RECKON...?

ENGINE'S STALLED! JUMP FOR IT!

LOOK OUT! RHINO!

THE RHINO'S NOT COMING BACK, AT ALL EVENTS.

BWANA! LLOYD HURT BAD.

JUST MY LUCK - A BROKEN LEG! THAT'S WRECKED EVERYTHING AT THE START!

WHAT ON EARTH DO WE DO NOW, SIR?

JEROGI WILL DRIVE YOU BACK. I'LL TAKE M'KUKI AND HASH, AND WE'LL GO IT ALONE, ON FOOT.

JUST LIKE OLD TIMES, M'KUKI!

FRANK BELLAMY

TO BE CONTINUED

36   Story by George Beardmore ● Drawn by Frank Bellamy

HORSE BOXES FOR HORNBY-DUBLO

No. 4315 Horse Box (with horse) B.R. Price 9/6.

Among the latest goods rolling stock in Hornby-Dublo are two horse boxes, one in British Railways maroon, the other in Southern Region green. Both are supplied with a horse to travel inside.

The stable-type doors open and the bottom half of the door lowers to form a ramp onto the platform.

Racehorses have to do a lot of travelling from their stables to race meetings all over the country. And this is how they do it. In style on British Railways.

These two models are further examples of accurate detail and smooth running of the Hornby-Dublo "Super-Detail" range. Each vehicle has a die-cast metal base and body made of moulded polystyrene. Add a horse box to your Hornby-Dublo layout!

No. 4316 Horse Box (with horse) S.R. Price 9/6.

HALLO, THERE!

I'm back with the answers to some more interesting questions.

Which is fastest British aircraft now in production?
The P1 B English Electric "Lightning" fighter has flown at twice the speed of sound, and is the fastest. Exact performance details are secret. It's a Dinky Toy (No. 737). Price 2/-.

When was Hornby-Dublo introduced?
Just before the war, in 1938.

When was Walschaerts' valve gear invented?
This is the name given to the arrangement of rods and levers which control the steam passing through to the cylinders on a loco- motive. Invented in 1844 by a Belgian called Walschaerts. Still the most widely used valve gear throughout the world. Walschaerts' valve gear is faithfully reproduced on most Hornby-Dublo steam type locomotives.

Dinky Toy Service Station with Tyre Rack, Pump Station and Esso Tanker in foreground, Breakdown Lorry on left.

NOW—BUILD-IT-YOURSELF SERVICE STATION FOR YOUR DINKY TOYS

THIS magnificent Service Station is the latest Dinky Toy accessory. It's made of moulded polystyrene and comes in a "build-it-yourself" kit. You can put it all together in only a few minutes.

The roof is brick red, with realistic skylights made from transparent plastic. The walls are buff-coloured to look like concrete, and the floor is grey. There are upward-sliding doors in dark blue at the front and back, and there are several large windows all round the building. There is even a clock on the fascia board.

Another new accessory from Dinky Toys is the Dunlop Tyre Rack. This device for displaying tyres for sale helps the realism of your Service Station if it is placed in the forecourt.

The Petrol Pump Station with the Esso sign, and the Leyland Octopus Esso Tanker, are two more Dinky Toys which fit the scene well, together with the Commer Breakdown Lorry, its miniature working crane mounted on the back.

Prices of all these items are: Service Station kit 27/6; Tyre Rack 2/11; Esso Pump Station 4/5; Esso Tanker 10/6; Breakdown Lorry 5/9.

Get along to your Dinky Toy dealer now and ask to see this fine range of models!

FAMOUS LOCOMOTIVES OF THE PAST : 2

Courtesy, Railway Museum, York

"Columbine" This 2-2-2 locomotive was the very first to be built at Crewe works, in 1845. It was designed by Francis Trevithick, son of Richard Trevithick, the first man to build a full-sized railway locomotive. The single driving wheels are 6 ft. 3 in. across. This loco was in continuous service until 1902.

NEW STYLE FIRE-FIGHTING SET

No. 957 Fire-fighting set costs 23/6.

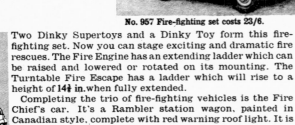

Two Dinky Supertoys and a Dinky Toy form this fire-fighting set. Now you can stage exciting and dramatic fire rescues. The Fire Engine has an extending ladder which can be raised and lowered or rotated on its mounting. The Turntable Fire Escape has a ladder which will rise to a height of 14½ in. when fully extended.

Completing the trio of fire-fighting vehicles is the Fire Chief's car. It's a Rambler station wagon, painted in Canadian style, complete with red warning roof light. It is from here that fire-fighting progress is directed, using two-way radio.

JUST OUT!

STATION TRACTOR AND TRAILER

Here's a Dublo Dinky Toy that's perfect for your 'OO' gauge station platform. It's the Lansing Bagnall Tractor and Trailer used for transporting luggage and heavy parcels on railway stations. Dublo Dinky Toy No. 076. Price 2/9.

EAGLE 21 May 1960

EAGLE

COMPANION TO GIRL, SWIFT AND ROBIN **5d**
21 MAY 1960 Vol. II No. 21 EVERY WEDNESDAY

EXTRA PAGES
EAGLE VISITS THE GUARDS AND THE ZOO

DAN DARE
PILOT OF THE FUTURE
Project Nimbus

THE STORY SO FAR

Dan Dare, piloting the new ship *Nimbus Two*, has tracked marauding aliens to the system of Jupiter. Landing on one of the moons, and leaving Hank and Pierre to guard the ship, Dan and Digby are heading for an old mine – long abandoned by Earth prospectors – when they encounter a robot sentry left by the aliens. In putting this out of commission, the Earthmen reveal their presence to the enemy, up in space, who promptly dispatch two of their number to investigate . . .

THE ERG-BOAT IS DISPATCHED, O COMMANDER !

OF COURSE IT IS, FOOL OF A *SNATHLAP*! DID I NOT ORDER IT TO BE SO ?

WE MUST NOT FAIL, O SIX—THE COMMANDER WOULD MAFFLUNK US !

FEAR NOT — THE PINK CREATURES ARE EASY TO DESTROY. SWITCH ON THE SCANNER.

THAT'S THEIR HANDIWORK, ALL RIGHT — BUT WHATEVER IN THE NAME OF FORTUNE IS IT ?

FRANK BELLAMY

THE ERG-BOAT SPEEDS TOWARDS THE JOVIAN MOON . . .

LOOK—IT IS THE PINK ONES ! THEY ARE ENTERING THE MINE.

THEN WE WILL USE THE SECOND ENTRANCE. THEY WILL NOT KNOW OF ITS EXISTENCE , SINCE WE BUILT IT . . .

THE ALIENS WATCH DAN AND DIGBY . . .

I WILL PREPARE THE *VORKAD*. WHAT ARE THEY DOING NOW ?

THEY HAVE TAKEN WEAPONS FROM THEIR GARMENTS — THEY ARE GOING ALONG THE SHAFT . . .

GREAT RACKETING ROCKETS !

IT'S A FACT

HAVE you ever collapsed a tin by using the normal air around us? To be more correct, one uses the *pressure* of the air.

Take a tin that can be tightly closed with a screw cap – an old oil-drum is ideal for this purpose. Put into it a little water – just enough to cover the bottom of the tin – place it over a source of heat and boil the water. When it boils, remove the tin from the heat and quickly screw on the cap. Now place it on something cold – a pile of snow, for instance. As the tin cools down, it will collapse inwards.

Why? Because, when the water boiled, the steam it formed drove all the air out of the tin. As the steam cooled, it condensed back to water, leaving a vacuum in the tin. When this happened, the air-pressure surrounding the tin exceeded that on the inside – and the tin collapsed.

NEW!

FOUR ADVENTURES

Out and About

SPECIAL FEATURES

ATLANTIC LINER

START 1961 with a NEW DAN DARE ADVENTURE

STONEWALL JACKSON
A HERO OF THE AMERICAN CIVIL WAR

This is the story of a strange and wonderful man. From a poor, bare-foot orphan, he rose to become one of the greatest warriors of all time. Tom Jackson was of English-Irish descent. He first saw light of day on 1st January, 1804, in a little three-roomed cottage in the village of Clarksburg, Virginia. He was the third child of Julia and Jonathan Jackson, who was a man of good intentions but waning fortunes, for he was a reckless gambler. By the time Tom was seven, he had lost both his father and mother, and he and his younger sister, Laura-Anne, were taken to live in the home of their uncle Cummins Jackson, by a negro slave ...

YO' UNCLE SAYS YO'M TO MAKE YO' HOME WID HIM FO' ALLUS NOW, CHILLUN. MASSA CUMMINS AM A STERN MASSA BUT HIM AM A KIND GOOD MAN SHO' 'NOUGH. YO'-ALL WILL BE HAPPY --- MIGHTY HAPPY, YO' SEE.

AND HAPPY THE CHILDREN WERE ON THE GREAT TRACT OF LAND WHERE LIVED CUMMINS JACKSON, A MAN OF MANY PARTS --- MILLER, FARMER, LUMBERMAN, HORSE-BREEDER. HE WAS A STRONG FELLOW WHO BELIEVED IN HARD WORK FOR EVERYONE, EVEN HIMSELF. AND HE WAS PLEASED TO SEE THAT HIS YOUNG NEPHEW WAS NO SHIRKER.

TAKE IT EASY NOW, TOM. THAT'S A BIG SACK OF FLOUR FOR A LITTLE BEAVER LIKE YOU!

I TH-THINK I CAN C-CARRY IT, SIR!

AT CHOPPING FIRE-WOOD, TOM WAS A PAST-MASTER. HIS SISTER LAURA WOULD SIT AND CHATTER TO HIM WHILE HE LUSTILY ATTACKED LOG AFTER LOG WITH HIS GLEAMING AXE.

COME ON, TOMMY. YOU'VE CHOPPED ENOUGH WOOD FOR TODAY. COME AND PLAY DOWN BY THE OLD MILL-STREAM.

NO, SISTER! WE WILL NEED MANY MORE LOGS FOR THE WINTER FIRES. YOU RUN AWAY AND PLAY BY YOURSELF - BUT KEEP AWAY FROM THE MILL-STREAM.

THE TWO CHILDREN SETTLED DOWN TO THEIR NEW LIFE AND TIME WENT BY. HOT SUMMERS FOLLOWED FREEZING WINTERS AND TOM WORKED HARDER THAN EVER. HE LEARNED TO READ AND WRITE AND ON WARM DAYS THERE WAS NOTHING HE LIKED BETTER THAN TO TAKE A COUPLE OF BOOKS DOWN TO THE RUSHING STREAM BESIDE THE MILL AND LIE THERE READING, WHILE HE CHEWED AT A LEMON.

ONE OF HIS BOOKS, WHICH TOM HAD BORROWED FROM A CHUM NAMED JOE LIGHTBURN, RELATED THE STIRRING ADVENTURES OF THE AMERICAN HEROES WHO HAD SUCCESSFULLY FOUGHT THE GREAT WAR OF INDEPENDENCE FORTY YEARS PREVIOUSLY.

"CHARGE!" SHOUTED LIGHT-HORSE HARRY LEE, AND THE SOLDIERS FORWARD CHEERING WILDLY. THE VICTORY WAS COMPLETE LAND-SAKES, DON'T I WISH I COULD HAVE BEEN THERE

TOM'S OTHER BOOK WAS HIS OWN. IT WAS A BIBLE. IT WAS BESIDE HIM NOW — AND IT WAS ALWAYS TO BE BESIDE HIM THROUGHOUT HIS LIFE. HE REJOICED IN THE BATTLES RECOUNTED IN THE OLD TESTAMENT-- HE DEVOUTLY BELIEVED IN THE TEACHINGS OF THE NEW. INDEED IT HAS BEEN SAID OF HIS MILITARY CAREER THAT HE FOUGHT BY THE OLD TESTAMENT AND LIVED BY THE NEW.

TOM JACKSON EARLY LEARNED THE MEANING OF THE WORD HONOUR AND THERE IS A LITTLE STORY TOLD OF HIM WHICH ILLUSTRATES THIS FACT. ONE DAY HE STRUCK A BARGAIN WITH A CERTAIN MR. KESTER, WHO LIVED CLOSE BY.

ALL RIGHT THEN, YOUNG TOM. FOR EVERY FISH THAT SIZE I'LL PAY YOU FIFTY CENTS. IS IT A DEAL?

IT IS, MR. KESTER --- AND THANK YOU.

TOM CAUGHT AND SOLD MANY FISH TO THE KINDLY MR. KESTER. NOT ALL OF THEM WERE THE SIZE UPON WHICH THE CONTRACT HAD BEEN MADE. MOST OF THEM WERE SMALLER, AS TOM TOOK CARE TO POINT OUT.

YOU'RE QUITE RIGHT, TOM. THEY ARE A LITTLE ON THE SMALL SIZE BUT I KNOW YOU SPENT ALL DAY CATCHING THEM. SO I'LL PAY YOU THE FULL FIFTY CENTS FOR EACH OF THEM.

YOU'RE VERY GOOD, SIR, AND I MUCH APPRECIATE YOUR KINDNESS.

ALL HIS LIFE, TOM WAS COURTEOUS TO A DEGREE.

AND THEN ONE DAY --

YA-HOO! WHAT A BEAUTY! IF ONLY I CAN LAND HIM.

IT WAS A LONG STRUGGLE BUT AT LAST TOM HAD THE GREAT FISH SAFELY IN HIS HANDS. HE GRINNED DOWN AT IT.

WON'T MR. KESTER BE PLEASED WHEN HE SEES THIS. I BET HE'LL FAIRLY HOWL WITH JOY.

TOM TROTTED SWIFTLY ALONG THE LANE LEADING TO THE HOME OF MR. KESTER. ROUNDING A BEND, HE WAS HAILED BY A TALL HANDSOME MAN RIDING A HIGH-SPIRITED HORSE. TOM RECOGNISED THE RIDER AS COLONEL TALBOT, A GENTLEMAN OF THE COUNTY.

HALLO, YOUNG JACKSON. THAT'S A FINE BIG FISH YOU HAVE THERE. I'D LIKE TO TAKE IT HOME WITH ME. WILL YOU SELL IT?

I'D RATHER NOT, SIR. IT'S ALREADY SOLD TO MR. KESTER.

COLONEL TALBOT FELT NETTLED AND HE FROWNED SLIGHTLY.

NOW SEE HERE, MY LAD! I'LL GIVE YOU A DOLLAR AND A QUARTER! THERE'S A TIDY SUM. KESTER WONT OFFER AS MUCH AS THAT.

I'M STILL NOT SELLING THE FISH.

THERE WAS A STEADY GLOW IN TOM'S BRIGHT BLUE EYES AS HE LOOKED UP AT THE HORSEMAN. AS EVER HE WAS EXCEEDINGLY POLITE.

YOU SEE, COLONEL, I FIXED IT WITH MR. KESTER TO SELL HIM FISH OF A CERTAIN SIZE FOR FIFTY CENTS EACH. MANY TIMES HE HAS PAID ME IN FULL FOR SMALLER FISH AND NOW HE'S GOING TO GET THIS BIG FELLER FOR FIFTY CENTS, TOO. SO GOOD-DAY TO YOU, COLONEL TALBOT.

AND WITH THESE WORDS TOM RAN OFF DOWN THE LANE WHILE COLONEL TALBOT CHUCKLED AND PUSHED HIS FASHIONABLE TOP-HAT BACK FROM HIS FOREHEAD WITH HIS RIDING CROP.

WELL, I'LL BE HOG-TIED! WHAT A SOLE LITTLE CHAP HIGH-PRINCIPLED TOO. THERE AREN'T MANY BOYS WHO'D HAVE REFUSED MY OFFER

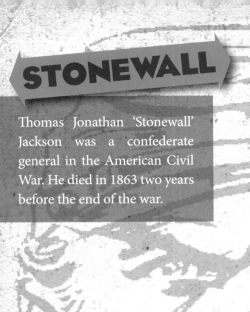

STONEWALL

Thomas Jonathan 'Stonewall' Jackson was a confederate general in the American Civil War. He died in 1863 two years before the end of the war.

The Editor, Clifford Makins, presented the EAGLE Trophy to Bobby Charlton at our Table Tennis Finals last year, and Bobby now treasures two replicas at his home in Ashington, Northumberland. Watch out for news of yet another EAGLE presentation to mark Bobby Charlton's splendid hat-trick of football success

Favourite Sportsman

1st Bobby Charlton 27.48%
2nd Don Thompson 11.21%
3rd Stirling Moss 10.09%
4th Jimmy Greaves 6.40%
5th Brian Phelps 5.09%
6th Johnny Haynes 4.21%
7th Danny Blanchflower ...3.9%
8th Peter Radford 3.8%
9th Bobby Smith 3.6%
10th Jack Brabham 3.5%
11th John Surtees 2.8%
12th David Broome 2.6%
OTHERS 15.32%

Favourite Footballer

1st Bobby Charlton 36.53%
2nd Danny Blanchflower 10.6%
3rd Jimmy Greaves 8.46%
4th Johnny Haynes 7.6%
5th Bobby Smith 6.6%
6th Stanley Matthews ...3.06%
7th Dennis Law 2.46%
8th Jimmy McIlroy 2.4%
9th Dicky Jeeps (Rugby Union) 1.5%
OTHERS 20.79%

Favourite Cricketer

1st Freddie Trueman ..25.85%
2nd Colin Cowdrey 18.30%
3rd Ted Dexter 15.28%
4th Peter May 12.10%
5th Brian Statham 11.0%
6th Trevor Bailey 6.1%
7th Ken Barrington 3.0%
8th Jimmy Parks 2.3%
9th Peter Walker 1.6%
10th Geoff Pullar 1.2%
OTHERS 3.27%

'Other Sports' Favourite

1st Stirling Moss 22.46%
2nd Don Thompson 14.0%
3rd Peter Radford 11.15%
4th Brian Phelps 10.39%
5th Ian Black 8.7%
6th John Surtees 6.0%
7th Jack Brabham 5.3%
8th David Broome 4.0%
9th Terry Downes 3.1%
10th Brian Curvis 2.6%
11th Terry Spinks 2.4%
12th Gordon Pirie 2.3%
OTHERS (which included such personalities as All-in Wrestler Billy Two Rivers)...7.56%

Big news for basketball fans !

AND that means YOU, because basketball is a game that all boys can play and enjoy.

Starting next week, we shall be meeting National Coach Peter Wardale, who is going to describe the main skills and set you on the road to success in this exciting, fast-moving game.

Helping Peter will be the Middlesex County team, the reigning English Schools' champions, with their coach, Ken Charles (pictured here).

Don't miss next week's opening feature !

MIND THE DOORS!

If you weren't a journalist, what would you like to be? The answer was no problem to EAGLE's Assistant Editor, DEREK LORD, whose choice would be a job with London Transport, and who went along, with photographer Howell Evans, to see for himself how the Underground works . . .

This photograph shows an Aldgate-bound train coming out of the tunnel at Baker Street Underground Station. The train 'set' number can be clearly seen on the front centre door

LOOKS easy, doesn't it, driving a train? Well, believe me, there's a lot more to it than meets the eye, as I soon discovered when I rode in the cab of a Metropolitan Line train from Neasden depot to Baker Street. The motorman and his guard booked on duty first at Neasden Station – and that's a story in itself, bound up with an elaborate and complicated system of making sure that the right sort of staff are in the right place at the right time. Then, photographer Howell Evans and I walked down to the depot and tramped along at wheel level, feeling pretty small beside the different kinds of stock which stood awaiting the 'rush hour' call to duty.

Climbing aboard a multiple-unit open saloon ('P') type train, we watched the driver and guard test their equipment to ensure that everything was in working order, particularly to see that the 'continuous' brake was working properly. The guard opened and closed the automatic doors several times, and explained that no train is permitted to carry passengers unless they operate perfectly. If, after the familiar shout of 'Mind the doors!', they fail to close correctly, safety regulations insist that everyone must 'All change', so that the train can be taken out of service.

After an exchange of 'O.Ks' between driver and guard, we moved slowly forward, out of the depot and on to the main Up track, for the through run to Baker Street, and I was surprised to learn that our speed reached 45 m.p.h.; up in the cab, with

a broad landscape before me, we seemed to be moving a great deal slower than that.

At Finchley Road, the train plunged into the tunnel, and all ahead was in darkness except for the one, and sometimes two, green pinpoints of light which appeared to ride towards us out of the blackness. Flashes of daylight from above marked our progress through the unroofed portions of the tunnel at the now disused stations of Swiss Cottage, Marlborough Road and Lords, and then we moved over the points and into platform two at the busy terminus and junction of Baker Street.

We made our way over to the signal-box, and I was fascinated by the lighted diagram, clearly marking the progress of the trains in and out of the six-platformed station, and over the junction of the Circle and Metropolitan tracks. Calmly, easily, the signalman pulled the levers and controlled the points and signalling for the trains – which run at 90-second intervals, in each direction, during rush hours – and I was most impressed at the superb way in which he and his colleagues controlled the passage of the trains carrying London's millions.

It's a real man's job on London's Underground, whatever part you play in the complicated system which moves over 1¾ million passengers a day. Every one of the highly trained staff whom I met carries out his responsible duties with keenness and interest in an organization which has earned the admiration of visitors from all over the world.

View over motorman's shoulder as our train approaches Willesden Green station, where a Bakerloo Line train is standing at the platform

EAGLE's Assistant Editor, DEREK LORD, looks through the rain-spattered window of the motorman's cab as the train leaves Neasden depot. The number plates are used to indicate the running, or 'set', number of the train

The motorman standing at his controls. The Controller-handle is fitted with a safety-device known as the 'dead man's handle'; if the motorman takes his hand away, power is cut off and the brakes are automatically applied

In the Baker Street signal - box. The junction with the Circle Line is shown on the left of the lighted and numbered diagram

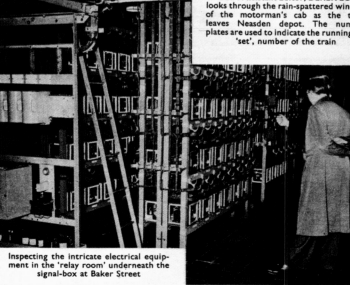

Inspecting the intricate electrical equipment in the 'relay room' underneath the signal-box at Baker Street

HE'S GIVING AWAY

500 EXCITING PRIZES

HOW TO WIN IN THE ROBINSON CRUSOE CONTEST

Imagine you have been shipwrecked on a wonderful tropical island somewhere in the seven seas. Rather like Robinson Crusoe, you are lucky enough to have with you 15 very useful articles that will help you build, hunt and cook. Read through the list of the 15 articles in your entry form below . . . all you have to do then to enter for a prize is CHOOSE THE 5 ARTICLES WHICH YOU THINK WILL BE OF MOST USE TO YOU ON YOUR ISLAND. Just make a tick (✓) against your 5 articles in the "1st Try" column on your entry form. Then, imagine you could CHOOSE 1 EXTRA ARTICLE not already in the list . . . something that would be even more useful for your stay on the island. Print your choice in the space marked on the entry form. If you can't make up your mind which are the most important 5 articles out of the 15, you can use the other columns on your entry form for extra tries. *IMPORTANT:* You can enter this contest if you are under 16 years old on 10th April, 1961, the closing date. For each "Try" column you fill in, you *must* send with your entry a label from *any large tin* of Crosse & Blackwell soup or Baked Beans. Tell your mother about this contest and she will save her tin labels for you. Print your name, address and age clearly on the entry form, and get your mother, father or guardian to sign the entry saying it's all your own work.

ENTER FOR THESE WONDERFUL PRIZES

You see that there are separate prizes for each of three age groups. The age you state on your entry form must be your age on 10th April, 1961, the competition's closing date.

13 to under 16 years

1st Prizes—
5 Sobel Stereo Automatic Record Players.

2nd Prizes—
15 Currys Monte Carlo Tourist Bicycles.

3rd Prizes—
50 Agfa Isola 1 Cameras

7 to under 13 years

1st Prizes—
5 Currys Junior Tourist Bicycles with Dynamo Sets.

2nd Prizes—
15 Junior World Encyclopaedias—16 volumes.

3rd Prizes—
50 Agfa Clack Cameras.

Under 7 years

1st Prizes—
5 Currys Noddy Tricycles & Noddy Dolls.

2nd Prizes—
15 Mobo Rocking Horses.

3rd Prizes—
50 Mobo Desks and Chairs.

300 consolation prizes of

Cricket Bats and Balls.
Fitted Vanity Cases.
Footballs.
Manicure Sets.
C & B Hampers.

Salling Yachts.
Travelling Clocks.
Tool Kits.
Black & White Toy Dogs.
C & B Hampers.

Remote-controlled Cars.
Sewing Machines.
Cranes.
Toy Parrots.
C & B Hampers.

* RULES—READ THEM CAREFULLY

1. First prizes in each age group will be awarded to entrants whose 5 chosen articles are considered most useful and important by an expert panel of judges. All other prizes awarded in order of merit to next-best entries. Usefulness and importance of extra item named on coupon taken into account in cases of ties for any prize. **2.** Contest, open to boys and girls in United Kingdom who are under 16 on 10th April, 1961. Any number of attempts may be sent providing one label from *any large tin* of Crosse and Blackwell soup or Baked Beans is enclosed for each column filled in. **3.** Entries must be made in INK or BALL-POINT on forms cut from Crosse & Blackwell advertisement or leaflet. **4.** Judges' decision in all matters is final and legally binding. **5.** Entries must be posted in sealed envelope (stamped 3d) to: Robinson Crusoe Contest, 18-20 St. Andrew St., London, E.C.4. (Comp). The closing date is 10th April, 1961. **6.** Claims for prizes are not necessary—winners will be notified by post by Monday, 8th May, 1961, and the results will appear in COMP (The Competitor's Journal) issue on sale 8th May, 1961. *Full rules obtainable by sending stamped addressed envelope to Rules, 'Robinson Crusoe Contest', 18-20 St. Andrew Street, London, E.C.4. (COMP).*

CROSSE & BLACKWELL CREAM OF CHICKEN SOUP

CROSSE & BLACKWELL BAKED BEANS IN TOMATO SAUCE

■■■■■■■■■ CUT OUT ROUND THIS LINE ■■■■■■■■■

ENTRY FORM FOR CROSSE & BLACKWELL "CRUSOE" CONTEST

Imagine you are shipwrecked on an island and have saved the 15 items named below. Tick the 5 (and 5 only!) which you think will be most useful and important to you in the "1st Try" column. Other cols. for extra tries.

	1st try	2nd try	3rd try	4th try	5th try
Length of rope					
Scout knife					
Spade					
Box of matches					
Compass					
Axe					
Flag					
Tent					
Torch					
Fishing line					
Distress Rocket					
Blanket					
Telescope					
Radio					
Bucket					

The one extra item I would choose is £1

I agree to accept rules as final and legally binding,

Christian Name .... Surname ....

Address ....

.... Age ....

The above entry is the child's unaided work.

Signature of parent/guardian ....

Dealers name and address ....

CLOSING DATE: 10th APRIL, 1961

SEND TO: ROBINSON CRUSOE CONTEST 18/20 ST. ANDREW STREET, LONDON, E.C.4. (COMP.)

CROSSE & BLACKWELL

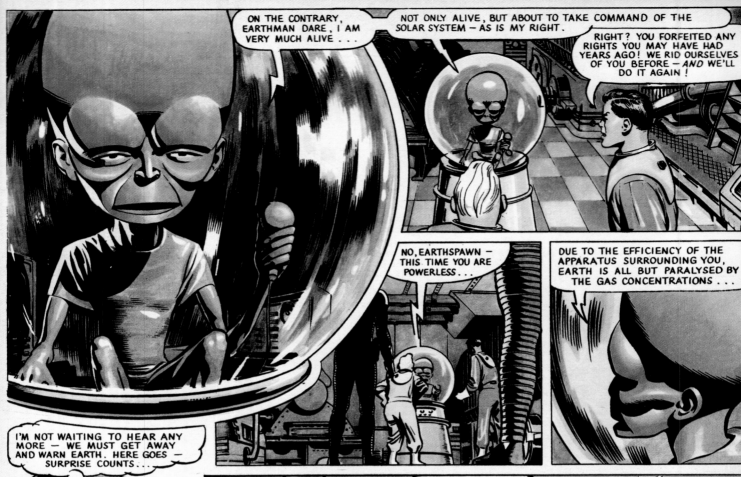

TO BE CONTINUED

Dan Dare, originally created by Frank Hampson, is written by Eric Eden, and drawn by Don Harley and Bruce Cornwell.

RETURN OF THE MEKON

an Dare's arch enemy makes his first
ppearance of the decade. Will we ever
e rid of him?

Readers' Letters

MEANS TO AN END

After reading the three articles on navigation (Fun with a Compass, in EAGLES dated 3rd, 10th and 17th June), I thought some readers might be interested in a method from the book 'Nature is your Guide', by Harold Gatty. It is called the 'intentional error' method, and is used when the destination lies on some kind of definite line – for example, a road or a river.

The navigator aims somewhat askew – for instance, west of the final target –

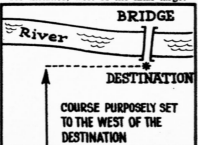

RIVER — BRIDGE
DESTINATION
COURSE PURPOSELY SET TO THE WEST OF THE DESTINATION

and, on reaching the line, follows it eastward till he reaches his destination.

This method is especially useful when the target is small and the distance to be covered is long, because if the navigator uses the direct method and, on reaching the line, finds he has missed his destination, a great deal of time will be wasted if he turns in the wrong direction. I hope this tip will be useful to EAGLE readers. – *John Levett, Bexleyheath, Kent.*

MYSTERIOUS SHAPE

The other day, when out fishing, I experienced quite a rare incident. I was fishing the Teify for a few hours, and the water was quite clear and the river full. I had been fishing for a long time without a bite; then, when casting in a nice swim, I got one immediately. I fought hard and, after it was tired out, I reeled the fish in slowly. It was a fine trout, about five yards away and just under the surface.

I could see the fish plainly and then, to my amazement, a dark shape suddenly grabbed the trout. It was very strong, because I had a high breaking strain line on my reel, and the line was just being pulled off the reel.

Then, just as suddenly as the shape appeared, it let the trout go. The question that puzzles me is, what was the fish that grabbed the trout? Experienced fishermen tell me that it might be a salmon, or a bull trout (*salmo ferox*). When I at last pulled in my catch, the trout had teeth marks all over it. – *R. E. Mansel, Llandovery, Carmarthen, Wales.*

GOOD NEW(T)S

I would like to say how much I enjoy George Cansdale's mature series in EAGLE. The *Out and About* feature on Newts (10th June issue) was of particular interest to me, as I have been keeping newts in captivity for some time, partly as a hobby and partly to study. – *Michael J. Gillingham, Port Talbot, Glamorganshire.*

PICTURE GALLERY

I thought you might like to see this photograph of our play-room, the walls f which have been 'papered' with uttings from three years' issues of AGLE. – *David Payne (aged 11), Portishead, Bristol.*

SPORTSMAN IN THE NEWS

TERRY VENABLES (CHELSEA F.C.)

The England soccer selectors are not the only talent 'spotters' who are keeping an eye on this talented 17-year-old from Dagenham. Terry is also an up-and-coming pop singer in the Johnny Mathis-style, and has written songs himself. He is a useful cricketer, too.

But soccer fans are hoping that he will stick to the game at which he is already a 'star' at right-half for Chelsea, and could become an England regular. As a schoolboy, he was capped six times and heralded as 'another Duncan Edwards'.

ONE-STOP HOP IN THE NEW JET-PROP!

DART HERALD

NEW FEEDER AIRLINER

The Handley-Page Dart *Herald* is a new jet-prop airliner designed for local service and inter-city feeder service anywhere in the world.

This year, a new aircraft shape has been seen regularly in the skies above the Channel Islands, since Jersey Airlines introduced the Dart *Herald* on their Bournemouth-Jersey service. The *Herald* shown here is in the very latest colour-scheme of Jersey Airlines (the inset drawing shows the *Herald* in B.E.A. colours). Series No.

100 *Heralds* are 44-seaters, but the later Series (No. 200) have a 3 ft. 6 in.-extension of the fuselage, and are 50-seaters. Powered by two Rolls-Royce *Dart* turbo-prop engines, these aircraft have a cruising speed of 275 m.p.h. and a range of 1,620 miles. They can also be adapted to carry 6 tons of cargo.

In next week's issue of EAGLE, we shall show a close-up of the world-famous Rolls-Royce *Dart* turbo-prop jet engine, and how it works.

KEY TO NUMBERED PARTS

(1) Retractable nose-wheels. (2) Batteries. (3) Forward end of pressurized fuselage. (4) Elevator and rudder-controls under floor. (5) Aileron and engine-controls in roof. (6) Radio racks. (7) Forward luggage hold. (8) Passenger cabin (44 or 50 seats). (9) Propeller boss and 12 ft. 6 in.-diameter propeller. (10) Compressors of Rolls-Royce *Dart* turbo-prop engine. (11) Combustion chambers. (12) Power take-off for engine accessories. (13) Turbine wheel-casing. (14) Heat exchangers for cabin air and de-icing system. (15) Hot air de-icing pipe in leading edge. (16) Jet pipe. (17) Jet exhaust. (18) Port main under-carriage; this retracts into a space on the inner side of the engine. (19) Fuel tanks in wings; the total fuel capacity is 1,080 gallons. (20) Landing light. (21) Port aileron and trim-tabs. (22) Flap guide-rails and cables. (23) Port wing-flaps, extended for take-off or landing. (24) Toilet and wash-room. (25) Passenger entrance-door. (26) Rear freight-door. (27) Rear freight-hold. (28) Under-floor rudder and elevator controls. (29) Rear end of pressurized fuselage. (30) Hot air de-icing pipes to fin and tailplane. (31) Push-pull rudder and elevator controls. (32) Rudder and trim tabs. (33) Port tailplane and elevators.

HANDLEY-PAGE DART HERALD

Two Rolls-Royce *Dart* turbo-props of 2,100 e.h.p. (equivalent horse power) each. Span, 94 ft. 4½ ins.; length, 71 ft. 11 ins. (Series No. 100); length, 75 ft. 5 ins. (Series No. 200).

EAGLE 7 January 1961

** NEWS *from* EAGLE

THE honorary Deputy Sheriff of Bexar County, Texas – better known to EAGLE readers as Frank Humphris, who draws *Riders of the Range* for us every week – is a real authority on Wild West lore and on guns in particular. Pictured at his drawing-board in his Teddington, Middlesex, home, Frank is surrounded by a few items from his collection of Western gear and antique guns.

He tells me that he has saddles, boots, spurs, chaps, gun-belts – the whole stock-in-trade of an authentic cowboy, and some of his rifles are to be seen on the wall in the photograph. The long rifle at the bottom is an 1857 muzzle-loading Enfield of .577 cal., many of which were used in the American Civil War. Above it is a fine old set-trigger Jager hunting rifle, similar to the Kentucky-Plains rifle, and over that is a Holland deer rifle of 1840. Finally, at the top, you can see a modern .22 semi-auto-

161/166 FLEET STREET, LONDON, E.C.4.

matic sporter, while a gun-belt, Western bridle and Stetson may be seen hanging on the screen alongside.

It is no wonder that Frank Humphris is so good at portraying the adventures of Jeff Arnold and Luke, when he combines such a deep interest in the Wild West with many years of experience as an artist, starting at Gloucester College of Art and leading, via an advertising and display studio, to exhibits at the Royal Academy, Royal Portrait Society, Royal Society of British Artists, Royal Institute of Painters in Water Colour, and Royal West of England Academy.

Yours sincerely,

Clifford Makins

Hobbies Corner — PROGRAMME COLLECTING

Next time you go to a football match or other sporting event, take a look at the programme. Is it interesting enough to keep – or will you throw it away? If you do the latter, it may not reach the ground's dustbin – the chances are that someone else will take it home. For collecting programmes is a big hobby – and the enthusiast will go to a lot of trouble to build a good collection.

League football clubs offer the biggest assortment of programmes, ranging from clubs like Chelsea and Arsenal – pioneers of the move for bigger and better programmes – to the less pretentious programmes of smaller clubs.

Should you collect football programmes only, from matches you visit, it is not only the programme that will be attractive – often it will include the names of Internationals who, one day, you will be proud to say you have seen in action. If you are lucky enough to get their autographs on the programme, so much the better.

Once you start collecting programmes, you will probably find others at school who do so, too. You can swap with them and, very soon, you will find a rate of exchange operating – so many Arsenal programmes, for instance, being worth so many programmes of other clubs. But if you become a collector, concentrate on the *official* programmes – not the unofficial ones, sold outside the ground.

Not only soccer, but Rugby matches, too, are among sporting events where programmes are snapped-up. A good example is the annual Oxford and Cambridge match at Twickenham – for, since 1945, a special programme has been designed for it, showing the traditional colours, and every year it sells out.

The aim of every collector is to build up a range of 'exhibits' representing every football club and, if he can afford it, every other sport as well. He does not, however, have to attend matches personally in order to secure programmes. He can write to the secretaries of football clubs concerned and, provided he sends stamps or a postal order, and a stamped-addressed envelope, can usually rely on getting a desired programme posted to him. It is as well to write before a match is played – you may find all the programmes sold, otherwise.

Though cricket matches do not have programmes, they do have scorecards – which, to the collector, perform the same function. On these informative cards can be found the names of both teams and, if you secure a scorecard when the match has just finished, you can take home the full scores, bowling figures and result.

The same passion for collecting extends to other sports – Wimbledon tennis and the big boxing matches at Wembley are good examples. So, too, are the many excellent programmes produced for athletic meetings, motor-racing, etc.

You can, if you like, add another 'branch' to your collection – theatre programmes. These are often more costly than those you buy at sports events, but the souvenir editions from the West End shows make a memorable keepsake for later years. The ordinary programmes issued by variety theatres are also worth collecting for, after all, many of the stars who are big names today will not always be at the top. Then their names on programmes will be more interesting.

Interest in this side of the hobby could lead to collecting old theatre playbills – a much more difficult, but highly-rewarding, pastime – for playbills bearing the names of old-time stage artists are collectors' pieces that museums and others will often pay for.

A question the young programme collector may well ask is: "What shall I do with the programmes when I have collected them?" One way is to bind them into books – either doing the job yourself, if you are good at handicrafts, or taking them along to a bookbinder. Another idea is to place them in a scrapbook, pasting the corner only to keep them intact. A third, and easier way, is simply to store them in boxes of similar size, like a businessman files his letters.

But for many it is the fun of collecting – hunting, if you like – that will keep up the interest for a considerable number of years.

This design, and those on the left, are examples of programmes available

Reproduced by courtesy of Programme Publications, Ltd.

NEXT WEEK: COLLECTING MATS AND SERVIETTES

Hobbies Corner — PART THREE

Fun with a Compass

This week, the silver arrow of your direction-finder will help you to make a map. It's a method known as the field chart traverse, and you will find it 'spot on' for map-making in your local fields, woods and houses.

The first thing is to wash down the polythene surface of the radar chart you used last week. Now take a chinagraph pencil and draw two lines down the centre to form the 'chain column' of your field chart.

As you see from the sketches, we start surveying from a set point on any quiet road or path. This place is our first station, and so we write (1) at the foot of the chain column.

From here, the young surveyor must now take a *sighted* bearing along the road to the first bend. The number of degrees of this bearing is written immediately above the figure (1) in the chain column.

Taking a sighted bearing is a new technique for many people. It's very easy, however, and is the exact opposite of taking a map bearing.

You hold your direction-finder at eye-level, keep the magnetic needle over 360 degrees, and turn the silver arrow until it points in the required direction. Also, you must remember to *deduct* 10 degrees this time, to allow for the magnetic variation. This is the exact opposite, you will remember, from when you take a bearing from a map.

Before leaving station (1), look on either side of the route ahead for objects you can include on your map. Don't pick too many, though. It's best to keep things simple.

Now pace along in yard measurements. Whenever you see an object clearly, take a bearing and enter it on the field chart. Further on, sight another bearing to *fix* its position.

The first bend in the road is station (2). We take another bearing to the third bend, begin a new section in the chain column, and carry on pacing and sighting objects.

Plotting our map is done on paper ruled with one-inch squares. These act as a good guide for lining up our round protractor.

Choose a scale of so many yards to the inch and draw in the route (road or path) – changing course in the correct direction at each station. From this *route line*, we can next draw, or plot, the bearings to objects.

The maps you make this way will be far more up-to-date than the Ordnance Survey sheets of your area!

Read an introduction to Mapwork and Practical Geography, by John Bygott. University Tutorial Press.

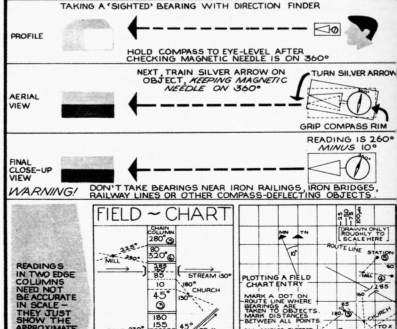

TAKING A 'SIGHTED' BEARING WITH DIRECTION FINDER

PROFILE — HOLD COMPASS TO EYE-LEVEL AFTER CHECKING MAGNETIC NEEDLE IS ON 360°

AERIAL VIEW — NEXT, TRAIN SILVER ARROW ON OBJECT, *KEEPING MAGNETIC NEEDLE ON 360°* — TURN SILVER ARROW — GRIP COMPASS RIM

FINAL CLOSE-UP VIEW — READING IS 260° MINUS 10°

WARNING! DON'T TAKE BEARINGS NEAR IRON RAILINGS, IRON BRIDGES, RAILWAY LINES OR OTHER COMPASS-DEFLECTING OBJECTS.

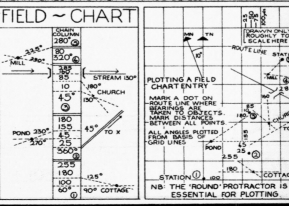

FIELD ~ CHART

READINGS IN TWO EDGE COLUMNS NEED NOT BE ACCURATE IN SCALE – THEY JUST SHOW THE APPROXIMATE POSITION OF OBJECTS.

PLOTTING A FIELD CHART ENTRY
MARK A DOT ON ROUTE LINE WHERE BEARINGS ARE TAKEN TO OBJECTS. MARK DISTANCES BETWEEN ALL POINTS. ALL ANGLES PLOTTED FROM BASIS OF GRID LINES

NB: THE 'ROUND' PROTRACTOR IS ESSENTIAL FOR PLOTTING

NEXT WEEK: CAMPING

BEFORE you have been loco-spotting long, you will get to know engines by their wheel assembly. Your friends will talk about '4-6-0s' and '4-6-2s' – just simple ways of describing an engine's wheels. The first means four wheels in front of the driving wheels, of which there are six, with no wheels trailing. From this it follows that a 4-6-2 engine has a pair of trailing wheels behind the driving wheels. Examples of the latter are the long-distance *Coronation Scot*, while the Southern Region's *King Arthur* class, intended for shorter distances, is a 4-6-0.

The term 'loco-spotters' does not tell the whole story, since there are plenty of things besides engines to interest the railway observer – for instance: stations, level-crossings, signal-boxes, and all the other necessities of railway life.

Many go to great lengths to satisfy their quest for railway knowledge. Some collect the numbers of coaches – even freight wagons. All British Railways coaches carry a number on each side, with a prefix letter showing the region to which they belong. For example, E 5001 belongs to the Eastern Region; M 5000, London Midland Region. Sometimes you see coaches, built prior to nationalization, bearing two letters with the number, like M 106 E. This means

Right: Type A 25kV A.C. electric locomotive built by the G.E.C. This has a Bo - Bo wheel arrangement and develops 3,300 h.p.

Below: 350 h.p. Diesel-electric shunter. Most of British Railways shunting-locos are of this type; about 1,150 are in service.

that the coach was built by the L.M.S., but is now used by Eastern Region.

Photography is becoming increasingly popular among railway fans. On conducted tours, boys with cameras swarm into the loco sheds, snapping everything in sight. Nowadays, more and more interest is being taken in the new Diesel railcars and locomotives which are replacing steam traction generally as part of British Railways modernisation. In some areas, these Diesels are only a stopgap before the electrification of all lines is complete – with the exception of some branch lines, which will eventually be closed.

There are many Diesels running on British Railways, ranging from 200 h.p.

BRITISH LOCOMOTIVE HEADLAMP CODES

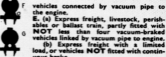

A. Express passenger-train; express Diesel car; newspaper train; breakdown-van train or snow plough going to clear the line; or light engine going to assist disabled train.

B. Ordinary passenger-train; breakdown van train NOT going to clear the line; branch passenger-train or 'mixed' train; rail motor van (loaded or empty); ordinary passenger or parcel Diesel car.

C. Parcels, fish, fruit, horse, livestock, meat, milk, pigeon, or perishables train, composed entirely of vehicles conforming to coaching stock requirements; express freight, livestock, perishables or ballast train fitted throughout with the automatic brake operative on not less than half of the vehicles; empty coaching stock train (not specially authorized to carry 'A' headlamps).

D. Express freight, livestock, perishables or ballast train, partly fitted with NOT less than one third of the vacuum-braked

E. (a) Express freight, livestock, perishables or ballast train, partly fitted with NOT less than four vacuum-braked vehicles linked by vacuum pipe to the engine.
(b) Express freight with a limited load, or vehicles NOT fitted with continuous brake.

F. Express freight, livestock, or ballast train NOT fitted with continuous brake.

G. Light engine, light engines coupled, or engine with NOT more than two brake-vans attached.

H. Through freight, or ballast train not running under class 'C', 'D', 'E' or 'F' conditions.

J. Mineral or empty wagon train.

K. Freight, mineral or ballast train, stopping at intermediate stations; branch freight train.

NOTE: The term 'freight train' applies to loaded, mineral, or empty wagon train.

ROYAL TRAIN

shunters to 2,500 h.p. main-line express locos. They are now used for varied duties, once performed by steam engines. There are also Diesel railcars used on many country routes, for suburban services in most cities, and for some inter-city trains. At present, the most powerful British Diesel loco is the 3,300 h.p. *Deltic*. She was built by English Electric at Preston, and is still owned by them – being on loan to British Railways, who are soon to have 22 new *Deltics* of their own.

The amount of success and enjoyment you get from loco-spotting may depend on where you live. If your home is near one of our great railway lines, you are naturally more likely to see plenty of trains; but a good thing about this hobby is that you are never very far away from a railway track or station of some kind. Some readers may count themselves especially lucky in living near a main-line centre like Crewe, or a big rail town like Swindon.

Even if you live near one of the

engine 'graveyards' at Derby, Crewe, Darlington, or Ashford, in Kent, at least you will have a chance of getting some unrecorded engine numbers as the once-proud giants queue in the breakers' yards.

Other facets of the hobby include the statistics about record-breaking trains, the numbers of trains handled by different stations, and the lengths of British tunnels. In fact, there is more to loco-spotting than merely recording numbers in a tattered note-book. As you get older, loco-spotting could possibly put you on the road to a career; for it tests your powers of observation – a useful quality in any walk of life – and, if you have a natural interest in how things work, the study of railways may start an interest in engineering, or in the many branches of employment offered by British Railways.

There is one book that no keen loco-spotter should be without – the 'EAGLE Book of Trains'. You will be able to learn a tremendous amount about the hobby from its text and illustrations.

In two weeks' time: AUTOGRAPHS

IF you have been studying Motor Index Marks, you will probably have noticed the variety of badges attached to some car radiators.

A collector's dream is the car (shown on right) belonging to Mr Gerald Nabarro, M.P., which has no less than 27 badges attached to three radiator bars! Many of these are foreign – a fact illustrating the scope offered to car-badge spotters.

There are many organizations to which motorists belong, ranging from the Automobile Association and Royal Automobile Club – open to all motorists – to the smaller sports-car clubs and those devoted to special interests; for example, the Motor Caravanners.

The A.A. badge was first introduced in 1906, though it did not at that time display the surmounting wings. In 1910, the A.A. joined with the Motor Union, a powerful rival organization of long-standing, and the next year the wings of the Motor Union emblem became part of the A.A. badge, which has remained unaltered ever since. The A.A. has over 1,500,000 members.

The R.A.C. was formed in 1897 as the Automobile Club of Great Britain and Ireland. Ten years later, it became the Royal Automobile Club by decree of Edward VII. The members' badge shows the monarch's head on the front, with the Union Jack on the reverse side. The more familiar badge, however, is the one issued to associate members. Many local motor clubs are recognized by the R.A.C. and thus accepted in the sphere of motor sport. For this, the special Motor Sport badge illustrated on the right is issued.

One of the most interesting car badges is that of the Veteran Car Club of Great Britain, many specimens of which can be seen in the annual London to Brighton Commemorative Run. The word 'commemorative' refers to the freedom of the road granted to motorists when the red flag carried in front of all cars was abolished in 1896.

Though organized by the R.A.C. and open to all cars of pre-1905 make, about 90 per cent of those drivers taking part are V.C.C. members. There are almost 1,750 members, plus nearly 100 junior members – the latter being boys under 17 whose parents are associate or full members. Incidentally, the London - Brighton run, held the first Sunday in November, is second only to the Mille Miglia in attracting the world's biggest motoring crowd.

Another body with a distinctive badge – this in the shape of a 'V' – is the Company of Veteran Motorists. Strictly limited in membership, it is designed for recognition of motorists with 10 years or more driving experience with no serious convictions. The extent of each member's driving experience is shown by a coloured disc on the badge. The years are displayed in figures as follows: 10-14 years – red; 15-19 years – white; 20-24 years – light blue;

25-29 years – yellow; 30-34 years – black; 35-39 years – green; 40-44 years – grey; 45-49 years – dark blue; 50 years and over – dark blue, with a crown surmounted.

A comparative newcomer among car badges is that of the Institute of Advanced Motorists. Launched in 1956, with the object of securing better standards of driving, would-be members of the I.A.M. have to take a special test lasting nearly two hours. Only if they pass can they claim the Institute's badge.

The House of Commons has its own car club, to which all M.P.s are eligible. The main purpose of the black and red badge – which displays part of the Arms of Westminster – is to enable police on duty near the House to facilitate the approach and departure of Members' cars. For that reason, the badge is attached to the windscreen.

The best way to 'log' car badges is to devote some pages of your car-spotting book to it, and enter each badge as you see it. You can add a short description and the colour; if you do this methodically, you will be amazed to see how many different badges you 'collect'. If you come across a car with a badge you cannot identify, don't be afraid to ask the owner about it. If you ask courteously, he will usually be pleased to tell you all about it.

NEXT WEEK: Ticket Collecting

LUCK OF THE LEGION

MARK OF THE MONSTER

Sergeant Luck, Corporal Trenet and Legionnaire Bimberg, together with a French zoologist named Verdier, are tied to stakes by pygmies, as a sacrifice to their 'gorilla-god'. Luck succeeds in breaking free just as the gorilla appears and, to show the pygmies that he is friendly, uncovers a trap constructed by their enemies to catch the Monster. When the gorilla goes raging after the pygmies' enemies, the beast knocks Luck sprawling with a swipe of its paw. After being released by the pygmies, now anxious to be friendly, the other three fear that Luck has been killed . . .

THE MONSTER HAS KILLED HIM!

NO!

ARE YOU SURE? LET ME SEE!

NO—HE STILL LIV BUT, UNLESS WE GET HIM TO A DOCTOR SOO THERE'S LIT CHANCE— AN IT'S A LON WAY TO G

WE'LL MAKE IT— SOMEHO

And, lurking in the jungle foliage fringing the river . . .

I SWEAR I SAW THE MONSTER JUST NOW—AS THOUGH HE WAS WATCHING US OFF HIS TERRITORY.

Below, in the engine-room, Bimberg gets up steam . . .

THE BOILER'S SINGING FIT TO BUST—BUT WE'VE GOT TO MAKE IT ON TIME.

The next evening, at H.Q. . . . .

STRAIGHT TO THE HOSPITAL BLOCK — QUICKLY!

Story by GEOFFREY BOND ● Drawn by MARTIN AITCHISON

OUT and ABOUT

BY GEORGE CANSDALE ● Drawn by GEORGE BOWE

Since early March, migrating birds have been arriving and, by this week, the last of them should be with us. Have you seen any of them around in your area?

The spotted fly-catcher is a rather plain little bird that you recognize best by its behaviour and way of sitting. It finds its food in the air, and nearly always returns to the same perch to eat its catch.

The nightjar may be found almost all over the British Isles, living on heaths and commons, but it is hard to see, for it becomes active only at dusk. You will hear it rather than see it; its strange, vibrating song goes on for minutes at a time, and carries a long way.

Swifts are noisy birds. As they scream round, you cannot mistake them for swallows or martins. Close up, you will notice that, except for a white throat, the swift is all brown. Swallows and Martins are mostly white underneath.

Another name for the red-backed shrike is the butcher bird, from its habit of sticking its dead prey on spikes in a 'larder'. Like the turtle-dove, it is usually found in southern England, frequently nesting in hedgerows.

The turtle-dove is obviously one of the pigeon family, but it is smaller than the others, and its upper plumage is reddish. You will probably hear its cooing note, almost a purr, before you see it.

NEXT WEEK: Hares and Rabbits

the pygmy village, Bimberg
d the language barrier, a
litter, then a boat . . .

YOU'RE QUITE TALENTED, BIMBERG!

SO I SHOULD BE—MY FATHER WAS A PAVEMENT ARTIST!

A rough litter is hastily prepared, and the race against time begins . . .

GO AHEAD WITH A GUIDE, BIMBERG, AND GET UP STEAM ABOARD THE *SEA EAGLE*.

SHE'LL BE READY TO GO AS SOON AS YOU ARRIVE.

Soon, the pygmies wave good-bye from the tree which they originally felled to stop the Legionnaires...

The three men have a long and anxious wait – then, at midnight . . .

LOOK—A GHOST!

WHAT THE...?

IMBECILE! IT'S THE SURGEON.

WELL, SIR?

TURN IN NOW, MES AMIS— YOU WERE *JUST* IN TIME! THE SERGEANT WILL BE OUT OF ACTION FOR A WHILE, BUT HE'LL LIVE.

Several weeks afterwards . . .

PICK 'EM UP! LEFT, RIGHT, LEFT, RIGHT...!

WHAT'S GOING ON OUT THERE, DOC?

OH, THE CORPORAL'S SWORN TO MAKE A SMART SOLDIER OUT OF BIMBERG IN TIME FOR YOUR RETURN TO ACTIVE SERVICE!

THE END

Starting next week: THE LAST OF THE SAXON KINGS!

Having begun on the 9 May 1952 Luck of the Legion was one of longest running series in *Eagle*. Luck finally ran out for the foreign legionnaires on the 16 September 1961.

LUCK OF THE LEGION

EAGLE 14 January 1961

NEWS

FROM EAGLE

Final details! Our 'Dan Dare' team discuss the finishing touches to cover art-work for EAGLE

PHOTOGRAPHER Terry Hardy caught our *Dan Dare* team at work on the episode of 'The Solid-Space Mystery'- which appears in this week's EAGLE, so let me introduce them. Left to right, they are Bruce Cornwell, Eric Eden and Don Harley – all old-timers so far as *Dan Dare* is concerned. Bruce, a Canadian born at Vancouver, B.C., in 1920, was with Frank Hampson (*Dan Dare's* creator) from the beginning – way back in 1950 – for three years, and rejoined us last year after freelancing. Married, with a 17-year-old son, Bruce served as a Radio Officer in the Merchant Navy during the war; he spends his spare time model-making, painting in oils, motoring and practising judo, at which he has attained the Orange Belt.

Eric, of course, writes the story. Married, with a one-year-old daughter, he met Frank Hampson whilst studying at Southport School of Art and, the end of his course coinciding with the birth of EAGLE, Eric became an assistant on Dan Dare for

161/166 FLEET STREET, LONDON, E.C.4.

a year. He returned to the fold after five years in an advertising studio, and has latterly become a freelance contributor to EAGLE, both as author and artist. Reading - especially scientific books, with a partiality for Space fiction adventures – model-making, drawing, painting and music rank as Eric's main hobbies.

Joining Frank Hampson at his Epsom Studio in 1951, Don worked as assistant until last year, when he took charge of the whole *Dan Dare* drawing operation. Apart from photography, his great spare-time interest is Motor Sport. Don is the proud owner of an Austin Healey 'Sprite' and, as a member of the Mid-Surrey Automobile Club, he takes part in rallies and driving tests whenever *Dan Dare* will let him off the leash!

Yours sincerely,

Clifford Makins

EAGLE

23 DECEMBER 1961
Vol. 12 No. 51
EVERY WEDNESDAY

5d

Wishing you all a Very Merry Christmas

MEN OF ACTION

No. 10— OLEG GONTCHARENKO

Can you imagine what it must be like to be the fastest man on ice? One man who knows is Oleg Gontcharenko, of Russia, who has won the World Championship for Speed-Skating three times. This tremendously powerful Russian first won the title in 1953, in Helsinki; and, at Oslo in 1956, he repeated this victory. In 1957, he continued his fabulous run of success by becoming European Champion. Then, in 1958, Gontcharenko achieved the distinction of winning both the European and the World titles.

The championships are decided by the highest scorer over four events – the 500, 5,000, 1,500 and 10,000 metres, the last being one of the toughest skating tests possible – the competitors must go 'all-out' for more than 15 minutes! This hardy Russian was, however, more than a match for anyone for several years.

DAN DARE

THE EARTH-STEALERS

THE STORY SO FAR: Dan and Digby return from a long absence in Deep Space to find a deserted Earth. When eventually they do find a populated settlement in the Andes, they are shot at and captured. They are told that this is because of the fear of a plague which has swept the Earth and resulted in mass evacuation to Mars. When Dan and Digby are given poisoned 'anti-plague' tablets, they resolve to escape, just as Malvol, the settlement director, approaches with two guards . . .

DANGER UNLIMITED

JAMAICA, British West Indies — land of sunshine and palm-fringed, white-sand beaches ... the pleasure island of the Caribbean

While swimmers, spear-fishermen and skin-divers enjoy themselves in the blue waters of Montego Bay ...

INCIDENT AT MONTEGO BAY

... three men, with a long-standing date, are converging on the 'Palm Hill Hotel'. The first of them arrives ...

... and signs in!

The second man is on the last lap of his journey along the twisting coast road from Kingston ...

... and he is not alone!

The last of the trio heading for the agreed rendezvous circles slowly over Montego Bay Airport ...

FASTEN YOUR SEAT-BELT, PLEASE.

... unaware that he, too, is not alone!

An hour later, Montego Bay witnesses a boisterous reunion ...

ROCKY!

TIGER! TIGER STEELE! 'TIS THE VERY MAN HIS OWN SELF!

GOOD TO SEE YOU, MIDGE — WHAT LITTLE THERE IS TO SEE!

ROCKY, YOU HAVE NOT TAUGHT THE MAN YET — HE'S TO STOP TAKING THE 'MICKEY' OUT OF MICHAEL!

I HAD A CABLE FROM PETE — HE'LL BE IN ON THE AFTERNOON 'PLANE ...

And in the beach cottage the trio are sharing for their holiday, Pete Rogers has already arrived ...

TO BE CONTINUED

Story by STEVE ALEN ● Drawn by MARTIN AITCHISON

53

Mr PRESIDENT

In this special two-part EAGLE feature, Deputy Editor Peter Stephens tells the amazing life story of John Kennedy, youngest-ever occupant of the White House . . .

1928: Aged ten, John Kennedy plays college football for Dexter School, Brooklyn

PRESIDENT John Kennedy was a sickly, bookish boy, who would rather read 'Billy Whiskers' and 'The Last of the Mohicans' by James Fennimore Cooper than take part in the games and exercises which were an every-day part of Kennedy family life. His father, Joseph Kennedy, thought that the boy might become a writer or perhaps a teacher.

"I wasn't a terribly good athlete," President Kennedy now says, "but I participated."

THE KENNEDY FAMILY – RICH, LARGE AND LOYAL

Possibly, like many another boy who belongs to a large family, John Kennedy soon learnt that it was easier to join in than be left out. Later, at Harvard University, he became Captain of the Swimming Team. So much for not liking games!

The Kennedy family is a wealthy one. When John Kennedy's elder brother, Joe Junior, was born in 1915, his father vowed to make the boy a millionaire on his 21st birthday. He made the same vow when John was born in 1917, and the same vow for all the rest of his nine children.

Today, the President's father is reputed to be worth more than $200,000,000 – and all the children have been made millionaires.

While John was still a student, his father was appointed United States Ambassador to the Court of St. James.

So the whole family moved to the American Ambassador's residence in Prince's Gate, London.

Naturally, the nine children of the Ambassador met and came to know, as family friends, the many politicians who frequently visited their home.

Although the children knew they were all going to be very rich after their 21st birthdays, this did not mean they meant to spend an idle life.

"I put them," their father said, "in a position where each one of them could spit in my eye and tell me where to go; and there was nothing to prevent them from becoming rich and idle if they wanted to."

But father Kennedy guessed, rightly, that all the children would devote their lives to being anything but idle. As a family they are all extremely loyal to each other. This doesn't mean that there were no family scraps.

Mr Kennedy and his two older sons once had a violent argument.

"Let 'em fight," he said later. "The important thing is that they fight together. I can take care of myself."

Family rivalry at fiercely competitive games of swimming, sailing, golf and tennis were encouraged.

From family rivalry has grown the legendary Kennedy family unity. Legendary, because of the extraordinary amount of help each member of the family gives another who needs it. From turning out in strength to travel hundreds of miles to young Teddy Kennedy's football match, to political support – the family is always there!

The first to gain his family's help was Joe Junior.

The Kennedy family, by 1940, thought that the likeable and confident Joe Junior, the eldest son, would enter politics and eventually become President of the United States. They did everything to help him on his way.

John Kennedy, by this time having spent a term with Joe Junior at the London School of Economics, returned to Harvard, where he wrote a book called 'Why England Slept'.

This book, dealing with the reasons behind England's unpreparedness for war, became a best seller.

SWIMMING – FOR LIFE

On the night of 2nd August, 1943, John Kennedy – by now a Lieutenant in the United States Navy – was at sea. He was Skipper of a PT-109 motor-torpedo-boat patrolling Blackett Strait in the Solomon Islands.

In the dark, at sea, there is often little enough time to sense danger. For Skipper Kennedy and his crew, there was no time at all.

Suddenly, came a shout "Ship at 2 o'clock!" – but the warning came too late. A Japanese destroyer knifed straight through the PT boat.

The first impact sent Lieutenant Kennedy crashing to the deck, injuring his spine.

It was at this moment, above all others in his life, that he had cause to be thankful for learning to swim.

One of his crewmen, the machinist's mate, lay on the rapidly sinking part of deck alongside Kennedy. Too badly burned and wounded to save himself, this man thought he would be drowned within minutes.

Kennedy, an expert swimmer, took the man's life-belt in his teeth and pushed away from the wreck.

He towed the wounded crewman, clenching the lifebelt in his teeth, for five miles to a small island.

Kennedy's back was now giving him considerable pain, but there was no time to consider his own injuries. As the Skipper in charge, he had a responsibility to his crew.

According to his official Navy and Marine Corps Medal Citation, Lieutenant Kennedy spent the next six days on rescue work. "He succeeded in getting his crew ashore and, after swimming many hours attempting to secure food and water, finally affected the rescue of his men."

Meanwhile, his family received a telegram saying that he was listed as 'missing in action'.

His gallant part in helping his crew to safety has become one of the great tales of South Pacific heroism.

FLASHBACK TO COLLEGE DAYS AT HARVARD

Possibly, as he was swimming for his life in the South Pacific, John Kennedy's memory recalled an incident of his Harvard days.

Kennedy was in bed with influenza. It was the night before an important swimming race against another college. He slipped out of the infirmary to the gymnasium swim-

The first impact sent Lieutenant Kennedy crashing to the deck

1944: Captain Conklin, U.S. Nav[y] inspects the Navy and Marine Cor[ps] Medal awarded to Lieutenant Kenne[dy] for his bravery in the Pacific

ming pool late at night – when no o[ne] could see him or stop him. There, [he] conditioned himself with a br[ief] swimming practice.

As it turned out, he was not call[ed] on. But he was ready – being pre[pared] was as all-important to hi[m] then as it has been since.

A BROTHER'S DESTINY

While John was in the Sou[th] Pacific, his elder brother Joe (still t[he] bright hope of his family as a futu[re] President) was in Europe.

Joe Junior was also a Naval Lie[u]tenant, and had completed two 'tou[rs]' – as a pilot over enemy waters by 194[4].

He was now due for some hom[e] leave to the United States. But t[he] menace of the German V2 launchi[ng] sites meant more to him than lea[ve].

Joe now volunteered to pilot [a] highly secret 'drone' 'plane, who[se] target was an important V2 site.

This 'plane was crammed tight wi[th] explosives. Joe and his co-pilot h[ad] orders to parachute to safety as so[on] as their 'plane was at cruising lev[el].

The 'plane would then be guided [by] radio to its target.

Just before the two men were d[ue] to jump, the 'plane blew up. Th[eir] bodies were never found.

* * *

The news of his brother's dea[th] came to Lieutenant John Kenne[dy] while he was still recovering fr[om] his wounds in a Naval Hospital.

It was now quite clear to Jo[hn] Kennedy what his destiny was to [be].

Brother Joe, the bright hope of [the] family, and already a rising you[ng] Democrat, had been killed.

As the new eldest living Kenne[dy] John's duty would be to step in[to] his brother's place.

Politics would now become his l[ife] – and his ultimate ambition w[ould be] clearer still.

He would aim at the highest hono[ur] his country could offer – Preside[nt] of the United States!

1939: John Kennedy leaves Croydon airport for Rome with his father, Joseph P. Kennedy, at that time United States Ambassador to Great Britain

The White House

*

Next week: DESTINATION WHITE HOUSE

RETIREMENT FOR *MALLARD*   WORLD'S FASTEST STEAM LOCOMOTIVE

Mallard reached a speed of 126 miles per hour on 3rd July, 1938 – a record for a steam locomotive.

Among other railway engines, *Mallard* – a 4-6-2, Class A4 locomotive – is scheduled for preservation by the British Transport Commission as an example of outstanding development in locomotive design.

No. 4468 *Mallard* is shown here in the original livery of Garter blue for the then L.N.E.R. The locomotive's present British Railways number is 60022.

Key to Numbered Parts

(1) Gangway door from leading coach. (2) Corridor tender, used for changing crews on long runs. (3) Safety valves. (4) Outer firebox. (5) Inner firebox. (6) Brick arch. (7) Water level in boiler and over firebox. (8) Steam rises through slots to regulator valve. (9) Regulator valve. (10) Driver's regulator rod. (11) Steam pipe from valve to superheater. (12) Streamlined outer-casing. (13) Superheater flues. (14) Fire-tubes which heat the water. (15) Superheater header. (16) Superheater steam pipes. Steam passes back into the boiler via these pipes inside the flues, and returns superheated. (17) Superheater steam pipe to outside cylinder. (18) Double chimney-cowl. (19) Smoke-box door. (20) Steam pipe to inside cylinder. (21) Double blast-pipe. (22) Inside cylinder. (23) Piston valve motion of inside cylinder. (24) Rocker arm from outside-cylinder's piston valve motion. (25) Exhaust from cylinders to blast pipes. (26) Outside-cylinder piston valve case. The valves admit steam alternatively either side of piston. (27) Outside cylinder and piston. (28) Connecting rod to driving wheels. (29) Piston valve motion arms. (30) Crank driving piston valve motion.

Mallard 4-6-2 Class A4

The locomotive has three cylinders, with a boiler pressure of 250 lb. per sq. in. Tender capacity: coal, 9 tons; water, 5,000 gallons. The total weight of the engine and tender in working order is 167 tons 18 cwt.

RIDERS OF THE RANGE

Jeff Arnold in WEST TO SANTA FÉ

Unknown to Jeff Arnold and Luke, Dutch Leuter — a 'wanted' man — and his gang of thugs are on their way to Eagle Pass. They aim to annex the pass and, by force of arms, hold it for the Denver Railroad. In this way, Dutch hopes to ensure that work on the Santa Fé line will come to a halt for, without possession of the pass, Jeff Arnold's concern cannot hope to complete the laying of the line in Colorado . . .

However, Leuter's Chinese workers desert him during the night and, to Jeff's surprise, head for the Atchison, Topeka and Santa Fé camp, with most of Dutch's supplies.

GOLDARN IT! IT'S THE SAME GALOOT WE FOUND IN THE MOUNTAINS — SAID HE WORKED FOR THE DENVER RAILROAD... REMEMBER?

YES, LUKE — YOU'RE RIGHT.

OLD MAN VERY GOOD MEMORY — ME AH WONG!

WE ONCE WORK FOR DENVER RAILROAD, BUT BOSS NOT GOOD MAN TO CHINESE. SANTA FÉ BOSS VERY KIND TO AH WONG OTHER DAY — NOT KICK HIM OR BEAT HIM. AH WONG SAY TO OTHER CHINESE, 'NO WORK FOR DENVER — WORK FOR SANTA,' SO WE COME. VERY GOOD COOKS — HARD WORKERS — WE LIKE — YOU LIKE — EVERYBODY HAPPY!

SEEMS THEY ALL WANT A CHANGE OF EMPLOYMENT. SORRY, AH WONG, BUT WE HAVE ALL THE WORKERS WE NEED — WE'RE FULL UP.

EAGLE PASS ALSO FULL UP! DUTCH LEUTER MEN ALL THERE, WAITING TO KILL SANTA FÉ WHEN IT REACHES PASS — BUT WE WORK FOR YOU, TELL YOU ALL DUTCH DO. DUTCH BIG, BAD MAN — KILL YOU ALL AND RUIN RAILROAD!

WHAT'S THAT? TELL ME MORE, AH WONG. MAYBE YOU CAN WORK FOR US, AFTER ALL.

AH WONG VERY HAPPY TO TELL — VERY HAPPY TO WORK FOR YOU.

YES, YES — CUT OUT THE HAPPY STUFF AND TELL US ABOUT DUTCH LEUTER!

It doesn't take long for Jeff to learn the full story from Ah Wong, who willingly allows Paddy and Luke to examine the contents of the boxes which he has brought from Dutch Leuter's party . . .

NO DOUBT ABOUT IT, JEFF. ALL THESE BOXES ARE FULL OF AMMUNITION AND DYNAMITE — JUST WHAT ANYBODY PLANNING TO HOLD EAGLE PASS AGAINST US WOULD NEED!

WELL, THAT'S ALL THE PROOF WE NEED, I GUESS . . .

FROM NOW ON, AH WONG, YOU AND YOUR BOYS ARE WORKING FOR THE SANTA FÉ — AND, JUST AS SOON AS I GET ENOUGH MEN TOGETHER, YOUR FIRST JOB WILL BE TO LEAD US TO WHERE DUTCH LEUTER'S HIDING UP IN EAGLE PASS.

AH WONG AND OTHER CHINESE ALL SURE VERY HAPPY TO OBLIGE. AH WONG OVERHEAR ALL DUTCH'S PLANS — I TAKE YOU TO VERY PLACE . . .

A day or two later, in Dutch Leuter's camp at Eagle Pass.

WELL, THOSE CHINESE CERTAINLY MADE OFF WITH THE BULK OF THE AMMUNITION, THOUGH WHAT THEY PROPOSE TO DO WITH IT, BEATS ME — THEY HAVEN'T A GUN BETWEEN THEM!

WE'LL SOON MAKE UP THE LOSS WITH NEW SUPPLIES FROM BASE. MEANWHILE, WE'LL HAVE NO TROUBLE IN HOLDING THE PASS — WE COULD PIN DOWN AN ARMY FROM UP HERE . .

HEY, BOSS — SOMEBODY COMING!

ALREADY? GOLDARN IT — NOT EVEN THE SANTA FÉ CAN LAY TRACK THAT FAST!

COME ON!

THERE YOU ARE, BOSS — A DOZEN OF 'EM OR MORE!

LET'S TAKE A CLOSER LOOK AT 'EM . . .

WELL, AS I LIVE AND BREATHE — JEFF ARNOLD — AND RIDING STRAIGHT INTO OUR AMBUSH!

TAKE IT EASY, FELLERS. DON'T FIRE UNTIL THEY'RE GOOD AND CLOSE — I DON'T WANT ANY OF YOU TO MISS!

Story by **Charles Chilton** ● Drawn by **Frank Humphris**

TO BE CONTINUED

DOWN TH

Eels galore — 12½ miles of them every week — slip down appreciative throats in this country!

A wooden Dutch ship waiting in the lock before discharging its cargo of live eels

The amount of eels consumed in Britain is really ama[...] weekly average of 40,000 lb. of these fish are sent to Bill[...] Market for distribution to London, Southend, Blackp[...] other places. The majority will appear 'jellied', as we s[...] on stalls at the seaside or in the East End of London, b[...] will be served in the best hotels 'smoked', as in Holla[...] Germany. Eels, in fact, appeal to all tastes.

* * * * *

At Heybridge Basin, in Essex, Mr Kuitjen has an e[...] Here, the freshly-caught live eels, from Ireland, North [...] Greece and Turkey are stored in specially-construc[...] barges to await shipment to Billingsgate, still alive. Mr [...] also supplies European countries too, including Pola[...] East Germany. The eel ships are met at the continent[...] by a fleet of large tankers (like petrol lorries) which co[...] eels live to the fish markets.

The eel is a fascinating fish. Beginning life in the S[...] Sea, it travels with the Gulf Stream and arrives in ab[...] years at the coasts of Europe. Eels are about 1½ in. lo[...] subsequently develop into elvers; then, in their thousan[...] swarm up the rivers, looking for the lakes where they [...] for approximately four years. By this time they are abo[...] years old, and anything between 12 in. and 24 in. long[...] autumn, these seven-year-olds start their journey do[...] rivers back to the Sargasso Sea, where they will spa[...] die. But along the rivers of Europe, and as far away as [...] fishermen will be waiting for them, because the eels on[...] down the rivers in the autumn, and then only after a fu[...]

So, when you next enjoy a mouthful of jellied eels, [...] stun your friends by rattling off some facts and figure[...] them – but not with your mouth full!

"A little of what you fancy does you good..."

The crew are busy on the deck of m.v. *Helene*, sorting eels into their different sizes

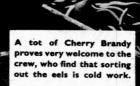

A tot of Cherry Brandy proves very welcome to the crew, who find that sorting out the eels is cold work.

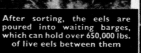

After sorting, the eels are poured into waiting barges, which can hold over 650,000 lbs. of live eels between them

All compartments of the barges are searched da[...] for dead eels. The water is aerated and kept movi[...] by means of pumps

HATCH!

Written and photographed by
HOWELL EVANS

m.v. *Helene* unloads its cargo of live eels into a modern barge

Unloading the eels from the barges in Heybridge Basin, where they have been kept for anything up to six months

ooden barges, full of e eels, lie in the ackwater Canal at Heybridge Basin

Eels are hoisted from the barge, emptied into bins and weighed, prior to crating and sending off to Billingsgate

Live eels being crated for dispatch to Billingsgate, from where they are distributed to cities and seaside resorts throughout the country

Next week: Behind the scenes at Ogwen Cottage

NEWS FROM EAGLE

161, Fleet Street, London, E.C.4.

Four EAGLE readers from Edmonton check the accuracy of the yard measurement of a tape measure—it was very slightly over 36 ins.

WHEN you're next in Trafalgar Square, go and have a look below the parapet built into the wall on the National Gallery side, where the Imperial Standards of Length (shown here) are situated. These lengths – one foot, two feet, the Imperial yard and one hundred feet – were placed there by the Standards Department of the Board of Trade in 1876, following a report by a Commission set up to inquire into various standards of weight, length, etc., a few years previously. The public were thus able to check any length which seemed inaccurate. There are similar plaques in other cities in Great Britain, and the lengths are correct at 62° F., but naturally vary slightly in very hot or very cold weather.

Not many people know of the existence of these lengths, so you can airily lay claim to superior knowledge by pointing them out to your pals!

Yours sincerely,

Clifford Makins

The Man from Eagle

Each week, EAGLE's MAN-ON-THE-SPOT will visit somewhere new and exciting – including many places where the general public are never allowed! This week – JODRELL BANK!

The telescope you listen to!

Like many who have in them a spark of adventure, I find space and its mysteries a fascinating study. So it was with great enthusiasm that I accepted an invitation from Manchester University to pay a visit to the Nuffield Radio Astronomy Laboratories at Jodrell Bank, on behalf of EAGLE.

As my car approached the famous observatory, the world's largest fully-steerable radio telescope soon became visible, its great bowl towering above the Cheshire countryside. This huge telescope can be seen glistening in the sun from over 30 miles away!

'Dan Dare' fans!

Inside the laboratories, a team of highly specialized scientists work under the Directorship of Professor Sir Bernard Lovell, who has developed the Establishment from its humble beginnings 16 years ago.

I was delighted to discover that most of Sir Bernard's staff were acquainted with the doings of 'Dan Dare' – and seemed just as interested in EAGLE as I was in Jodrell Bank!

Sputniks and Satellites

The radio telescope was first ready for use in September, 1957. Since that time, over 15,000 hours of fundamental astronomical research have taken place. Although Jodrell Bank's name is known throughout the world for its tracking of Russian and American satellites, only 5% of all its time is spent on such projects.

Outstanding among these space-age achievements was the radar observation of the carrier rocket of SPUTNIK 1 and of the satellite SPUTNIK 2, the tracking of LUNIK 2 until it hit the moon, and the tracking of the American PIONEER series of space probes. Particularly noteworthy was Jodrell Bank's share in tracking PIONEER 5 – the American Venus probe.

The observatory transmitted the command signals which brought about the separation of the final stage, and received information from it over greater distances than had ever been imagined possible before!

When Princess Margaret visited the establishment, she switched on the space probe's own radio by remote control, and heard it sending back its information from nearly a million miles away. Contact was maintained until 26th June, 1960; and, by this time, the probe was 23 million miles away!

Mapping the 'Radio Universe'

What of the remaining 95% of Jodrell Bank's work? The team of astronomers' normal programme is mainly devoted to 'mapping the radio universe'.

The importance of such 'mapping' is that, previously, only those objects in space emitting sufficient light to be

The Man from EAGLE stands before the huge radio telescope at Jodrell Bank

seen on earth have been known and classified. The short history of radio astronomy has already proved that we formerly had a very incomplete picture of space.

At Jodrell Bank, enough radio information has been collected to reveal the existence of countless sources of radio emission not previously known. Thus Jodrell Bank is helping to reshape scientific theory.

Galaxies in collision

Here is just one example of how the researchers at Jodrell Bank are making us 'think again' about traditional ideas.

A very strong source of radiation was discovered in an area of space where nothing had ever been known to exist before. The information was conveyed to the Palomar Observatory in America, where the great 200-inch-diameter Reflecting Telescope was used to photograph the area. The exposure time of the photograph was nine hours! This produced an amazing picture of two galaxies in collision, at a distance of 700 million light years from earth.

These galaxies are known to be rushing through one another at something like 1 million miles per hour, and the release of energy in this tremendous collision is the greatest known to man.

How distance is measured in space

When the 'Radar' method is used, radio signals beamed out into space and received back, having been reflected by the distant object. A measurement of time interval then enables the distance to be calculated since it is known that the speed of radio waves is 186,000 miles per second.

By this method, echoes have been received from the planet VENUS, enabling its distance to be measured with much greater precision than ever before. In this way Jodrell Bank has provided a scale by which the whole of the Planetary System can eventually be measured. Its proportions, of course, are already known. This highly-skilled work will pilot the way for interplanetary navigation of the future.

It is hoped that surveys by the Radar method will soon produce a better understanding of the surface features of such planets as VENUS, which is perpetually enveloped in cloud. Who knows? – perhaps even MARS will be persuaded to reveal some of its secrets.

From what I saw at Jodrell Bank, I am quite sure that future generations will regard its work as among the greatest contributions towards man's knowledge of the universe and what lies beyond.

FACTS AND FIGURES
about the Radio Telescope at Jodrell Bank

DIMENSIONS: Total weight, 2,000 tons; weight of bowl, 750 tons; height to the top of towers, 185 feet; height to the top of bowl, 215 feet; maximum height when bowl is tipped, 300 feet; diameter of bowl, 250 feet; height of aerial mast, 62½ feet.

The two main elevating racks are taken from the gun turrets on the battleships H.M.S. Royal *Sovereign* and H.M.S. *Revenge*.

Maximum speeds of movement of the telescope are:—

in azimuth, 20 degrees per minimum

in elevation, 24 degrees per minimum

TALKING POINTS

FIRST SPACEMEN!

A short while ago, my form-master at school asked us the following question: 'Who were the first two men to go into orbit round the Earth?' Imagine the laughter when one of the boys answered: "Dan Dare and Digby, sir!"

Alan Wrate, Leeds.

Of course if the teacher had known his Dan Dare a bit better he would have pointed out that when Yuri Gagarin became the first human to travel into space, launching into orbit aboard the Vostok 3KA-2 on 12 April 1961, he was actually a number of years ahead of Dan Dare, who wasn't even born until 1967.

THE BULLDOG BREED

Ever wondered what it's like to live a life on the ocean wave? You'll certainly get a good idea of what it's *not* like by following the crazy antics of Norman Wisdom in the Rank Organization's latest laughter-maker, now on general release. Shades of Nelson! But, to begin at the beginning . . .

WHEN a flotilla of destroyers of the Home Fleet, commanded by Admiral Sir Bryanston Blyth, sails from Portland Harbour, the admiral does not expect to see a ramshackle little sailing craft, piled high with wire wool, butter, ham, eggs, marmalade and other groceries, sail slap under the prow of his vessel, and refuse to give way.

"Sail before steam!" yells the man at the helm of this strange-looking craft. "Sail before steam!"

The admiral glares. He is in a spot – so is the captain, Commander Clayton. Who would have the effrontery to impede Her Majesty's Navy by insisting on this rule of the sea?

Sirens wail, sailors shout – a collision is imminent. But Norman Puckle, the little man in the boat, is a member of the Bulldog Breed. He knows his rights; let the Navy wait.

Norman, who delivers groceries to the innumerable craft dotted about the harbour, has won a famous victory – but it doesn't do him any good. For Norman is destined to serve under the self-same admiral, in the very destroyer whose right of way he has challenged.

It's all the fault of Marlene, a haughty blonde in the local cinema box-office. She refuses Norman's chocolates, his solitaire, and his heart – in that order. So Norman tries to hang himself, drown himself, throw himself before a train, and over a cliff – in *that* order.

He fails – as he does at everything – so he joins the Navy.

Norman boards the destroyer *Dorchester*, just as the admiral is presiding – assisted by Bosun, his magnificent bulldog – over a small conference to consider details of a scheme to put a rocket into orbit. It is called 'Interplanetary

Projectile Bosun' – after the bulldog.

Mr Philpots, the smug senior Civil Servant, wants his scientific nominee, Carruthers, to man the rocket – but the admiral is all out for the glory of the Navy. He wants an ordinary, simple-hearted sailor with initiative and guts to be the first to travel in space, so that he can say: "The Navy did it first."

Norman Puckle, as the Navy's newest recruit, gets the job – not, however, before he has disorganized the whole ship's company.

When Norman is brought before the admiral, as the man who will travel in Interplanetary Projectile Bosun, the admiral recognizes his enemy of the sailing boat. He also recognizes him as a man of the bulldog breed, who refuses to give an inch of ground, even to the might of the Royal Navy.

Norman takes diving instruction, nearly killing the instructors headed by Petty Officer Knowles. He takes mountaineering instruction and, as a result, puts the whole party in danger.

He does everything wrong so consistently and so well, that the admiral has to give way to the boffins and cancel his scheme to put a Navy recruit into Interplanetary Projectile Bosun.

Norman is reduced to the job of looking after Bosun, the bulldog, and it is Bosun who guides Norman to glory.

When the bulldog chases a rabbit, Norman chases Bosun. The rabbit takes refuge in the Interplanetary Projectile Bosun, the bulldog follows – and so does his keeper, Norman.

This is at the exact moment when the rocket, manned by the scientist Carruthers, is due to take off. But Carruthers is unavoidably detained, and it is Norman who is launched into space. Then comes the discovery that the space-pilot has no chance of getting back to earth.

But trust Norman to do the wrong thing – with the right result!

WANTED – SIX BOYS TO SPEND 3 DAYS WITH THE FLEET!

Double up, there! If you've got just one drop of salt in your blood, you'll thrill at this chance of spending three exhilarating days as guests of the Royal Navy. The top six winners of this special 'Bulldog Breed' competition, organized in association with the Rank Organization, will spend the three days on board aircraft-carriers, submarines, destroyers, cruisers, etc., seeing just how the Senior Service goes about its daily tasks. Rail fares will be paid for by the Rank Organization, who will see that the prize-winners are safely delivered to the Navy, and also collected and returned to their homes. So weigh anchors and get cracking!

1. What do the chevrons on a rating's left arm mean?
2. Do the three white tapes on a sailor's collar have any particular meaning?
3. On the home station, during what months do sailors wear blue-topped caps?
4. What flying badges are worn by officers?
5. What class of rating wears a spider's web crossed by a lightning flash on his right arm?
6. Which medal, decoration, or order is worn first?

~~~~~~ WHAT YOU HAVE TO DO ~~~~~~

Write your answers to the six questions neatly on a postcard, or as a letter; then say – in not more than 20 words – why you would like to become a member of the 'Bulldog Breed'. Add your name, age and address in the top, right-hand corner, in block capitals, and send to: 'Bulldog Breed' Comp., EAGLE Reader Services, 5 Dryden Street, London, W.C. 99 (Comp.), to arrive by 20th January, 1961. Neatness and age will be taken into consideration when selecting the six winning entries, and the age limit is 16. No correspondence can be entered into, and the Editor's decision is final.

One of the things *Eagle* did really well was to tell stories using an interesting and exciting mix of words and pictures. Here we can see just this combination serving a topic *Eagle* revelled in: fiction presented as historical fact.

THE LAST OF THE SAXON KINGS

UNDER THE GOLDEN DRAGO

On a storm-lashed Winter's night in the year A.D. 1042, a war-horse came thundering down the road to Winchester, capital of Wessex . . .

AT LAST! HEAVEN BE PRAISED — WINCHESTER!

The horseman drew rein under the walls of a grim, grey castle overlooking the city . . .

HO THERE, WITHIN! OPEN UP! OPEN UP IN THE KING'S NAME!

Then mighty bolt and the great doo

WH KIN A K

IT IS I, EDRIC OF DOR I BRING NEWS FOR E OF WESSEX — NEWS S IF HE WERE AT THE O THE EARTH, I WOULD AND DAY TO REACH H

The Sword of F

One morning in the early summer of the year 1553, Paul Quincey, the Earl of Bristol, paced restlessly in one of the rooms of the Tower of London. Ever since he had unwittingly incurred the displeasure of King Henry VIII, long years before, the Earl had been a prisoner within the Tower, and remained so even though Henry was now dead and his young son, Edward, reigned instead. But two days ago, he had been told he was now to prepare himself for a summons to the scaffold.

SO THE LONG YEARS OF UNCERTAINTY, HOPES AND DESPAIR ARE OVER, AND I KNOW MY FATE AT LAST. SINCE I AM TO DIE THIS DAY, I TRUST THEY WILL COME EARLY FOR ME, AND NOT LEAVE ME TOO LONG ALONE HERE WITH MY THOUGHTS.

The Earl swung round as a key rattled in the lock . . .

AH — MY ESCORT IS HERE ALREADY, BUT IF THEY HOPE TO SEE FEAR IN MY FACE, THEY SHALL BE DISAPPOINTED!

The heavy door op face relaxed into be smiling, well-dresse came in was his y

EXPE A

BEC WONDER YOU A HEAR

CAPTAIN HORNBLO

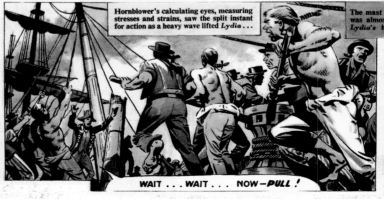

In the Pacific, Captain Horatio Hornblower, R.N., commanding the frigate *Lydia*, had fought a damaging sea battle with the *Natividad*, an ex-Spanish ship which was now part of a rebellion against Spain, England's new ally in the war against Napoleon.

A storm separated the battered ships, and Hornblower carried out urgent repairs at sea. In attempting to erect a new mizzen mast, the critical point of danger had been reached . . .

If the new mast slipped from its hoisting tackle now, it would cause crippling damage to *Lydia* . . .

AN OUNCE TOO MUCH STRAIN FORWARD OR ABEAM, AND SHE'LL SLIP AT TOP OR AT BOTTOM!

THE CAPTAIN'S WAITING FOR THE SHIP TO HEAVE — THAT WILL SPEED UP THE PULL THROUGH THE DANGER ANGLE!

Hornblower's calculating eyes, measuring stresses and strains, saw the split instant for action as a heavy wave lifted *Lydia* . . .

The mast was almo *Lydia's*

WAIT . . . WAIT . . . NOW — *PULL!*

E THRILLING TRUE STORY OF THE NORMAN CONQUEST

Edric of Dorchester was led to the Great Upper Hall of the castle, where three tall, powerfully-built men sat. The eldest of the three rose in surprise, as the mud-stained messenger dropped on one knee before him . . .

EDRIC! WHAT BRINGS YOU HERE? YOU — THE CAPTAIN OF THE KING'S BODYGUARD — SWORN TO WATCH OVER HIM DAY AND NIGHT!

O MIGHTY EARL — ONLY PRIESTS AND MONKS GUARD MY MASTER NOW. THE KING IS DEAD!

Earl Godwin turned to his companions.

DO YOU HEAR THAT, MY SONS! HARDACANUTE IS DEAD! FOR TWENTY YEARS, I, GODWIN, OF WESSEX, HAVE FOUGHT TO BRING PEACE AND PROSPERITY TO SAXON ENGLAND. THE DEAD KING AND HIS FATHER WERE DANES, IT IS TRUE, BUT UNDER MY GUIDANCE THEY DID MUCH TO REDUCE THE WAR AND SUFFERING WHICH HAVE TORN THIS LAND. AND NOW MY WORK LIES IN RUINS — FOR HARDACANUTE HAS NO SON TO SUCCEED HIM.

Godwin dismissed the messenger – then, watched by his two sons, Sweyn and Harold, he looked out from the window over the frozen roofs of Winchester . . .

THERE IS NOTHING ELSE FOR IT — WE MUST ASK HARDACANUTE'S STEP-BROTHER, PRINCE EDWARD, TO BE OUR KING!

BUT, FATHER, EDWARD IS HALF-NORMAN, AND HE HAS LIVED IN NORMANDY ALL HIS LIFE!

BE QUIET, SWEYN! FATHER IS RIGHT! PRINCE EDWARD IS OUR ONLY HOPE — AND THINK OF IT — THE BLOOD OF ALFRED THE GREAT RUNS IN HIS VEINS.

Simon's voice ran on excitedly, but Paul hardly heard, for his brain was reeling from the shock. He hardly looked up as the Lieutenant of the Tower entered the room.

YOUNG KING EDWARD IS DEAD AND HIS SISTER, QUEEN MARY, RULES ENGLAND NOW. BY HER GRACIOUS MERCY AND IN CELEBRATION OF HER ACCESSION, YOU AND SEVERAL OTHER PRISONERS ARE TO BE RELEASED.

IT IS TRUE, MY LORD. YOU HAVE BEEN GRANTED A FULL PARDON.

The formalities were quickly completed, but not until he and Simon were outside the Tower did Paul really feel free.

A THIRD OF MY LIFE HAS BEEN SPENT WITHIN THOSE WALLS — I HAVE ALMOST FORGOTTEN WHAT THE OUTSIDE WORLD IS LIKE.

HA! BUT WITH MY ASSISTANCE YOUR MEMORY WILL SOON RETURN, I PROMISE YOU. STEP INTO THE CARRIAGE, PAUL, AND LET US HOPE THAT NEITHER OF US EVER SEES THE INSIDE OF THE TOWER AGAIN.

ER, R.N.

Adapted from the famous book 'The Happy Return', by C. S. Forester

A MAGNIFICENT PIECE OF WORK, SIR! SHALL I GET THE SAILS SET, SIR?

Again a vital decision for Hornblower – whether to crowd sail and try to find the *Natividad* in the raging storm – or . . .

NO — WE'LL STAY HOVE TO UNTIL THE STORM DROPS . . .

Hornblower did not see the admiration in Bush's eyes – for if the *Natividad* escaped, it meant certain ruin for Hornblower!

Darkness was closing in on the gale-lashed sea. Hornblower knew that no more could be done as he rested in a hammock chair.

THE WIND IS VEERING ROUND TO THE SOUTH—*NATIVIDAD* WILL DRIFT FASTER THAN *LYDIA*, AND SHE'LL TRY TO MAKE FOR HER BASE AT THE GULF OF FONSECA! AT DAWN, THAT'S WHERE WE HEAD!

Horatio Hornblower's adventures and The Sword of Fate could just as easily be the retelling of Wellington's life or Churchill's. An alien picking up an old copy of *Eagle* would have trouble knowing where truth ended and imagination began.

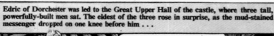

EAGLE

THE TOP PAPER FOR BOYS

5 May 1962 Vol. 13 No. 18

EVERY WEDNESDAY 5d.

MONTGOMERY OF ALAMEIN
Allied assault troops swarm ashore on the Normandy beaches! (See pages 10-11)

THE LOST WORLD
by Sir Arthur Conan Doyle
Four English explorers are trapped in a nightmare world of prehistoric monsters and savage ape-men! (See page 3)

HOME OF THE WANDERERS
A leading football club battles for survival! (See page 2)

ONLY THE BRAVE

No. 9 – First Officer Thomas Bennett

Tom Bennett enjoyed his life as a pilot for Trans-Australian Airlines. One of his favourite routes was Sidney to Brisbane . . .

ON THIS PARTICULAR TRIP, FIRST OFFICER BENNETT WAS FLYING AS CO-PILOT . . .

ONLY ANOTHER FIFTEEN MINUTES, TOM, AND WE'LL BE TOUCHING DOWN AT BRISBANE.

PRETTY UNEVENTFUL THIS TIME. NOT EVEN ANY BUMPS. I'LL TAKE A LOOK AT THE PASSENGERS.

BENNETT LITTLE REALIZED THAT THE NEXT FIFTEEN MINUTES WOULD BE THE MOST EVENTFUL OF HIS LIFE!

IT BEGAN WHEN A PASSENGER TUGGED WILDLY AT HIS SLEEVE.

YES, SINGAPORE . . . SINGAPORE . . . IF WE DON'T BY-PASS BRISBANE, THIS GELIGNITE WILL BLOW US ALL TO BITS. UNDERSTAND?

The George Medal was instituted in 1940. There is a hierarchy with medal awards and this comes just below the George Cross. Only the Brave honoured in strip form recipients of this medal, who could be military or civilian.

CAN I HELP YOU, SIR?

DON'T 'SIR' ME! YOU JUST LISTEN. TELL THE PILOT TO DIVERT THE PLANE. WE'RE NOT LANDING AT BRISBANE – WE'RE GOING ON TO SINGAPORE. DO AS I SAY! TELL HIM THAT!

BENNETT REALIZED HE MUST HUMOUR THIS PASSENGER IF THE LIVES OF EVERYONE ON THE PLANE WERE NOT TO BE ENDANGERED!

RIGHT, SIR. I'LL GET THE PILOT TO CHECK WEATHER CONDITIONS AT SINGAPORE.

BENNETT HELD A LIGHTNING CONFERENCE WITH THE CAPTAIN AND ANOTHER T.A.A. PILOT, CAPT. DINNY LAWRENCE, WHO WAS FLYING AS A PASSENGER . . .

I'LL TRY TO DISTRACT HIM WHILE YOU GET HIS GUN.

BENNETT AND LAWRENCE, FULLY AWARE THAT THEIR LIVES WERE IN DANGER, QUICKLY MADE THEIR WAY BACK TO THE CRAZED GUNMAN . . .

NOW, SIR. ABOUT SINGAPORE . . .

HEY! LOOK OUT!

WHAT THE . . .?

BY SOME MIRACLE, THE BULLET SHOT PAST BENNETT'S EAR THROUGH THE ROOF OF THE AIRCRAFT . . .

WHILE AIR-HOSTESSES CALMED THE TERRIFIED PASSENGERS, BENNETT OVERPOWERED THE GUNMAN . . .

THANKS, DINNY. TELL THE SKIPPER THAT EVERYTHING IS UNDER CONTROL, AND RADIO THE AIRPORT POLICE AT BRISBANE.

CREW ONLY

I'LL TAKE THESE TROUBLE-STICKS WITH ME.

THE PLANE LANDED SAFELY AT BRISBANE . . .

SINGAPORE, EH? IT WILL BE SOME TIME BEFORE THAT SCREWBALL SEES SINGAPORE – OR ANYWHERE ELSE!

THE HEROISM WHICH HAD BEEN WITNESSED BY THE AIRCRAFT'S FIFTY PASSENGERS, EARNED BENNETT A WELL-DESERVED GEORGE MEDAL!

ANOTHER TRUE TALE OF HEROISM NEXT WEEK!

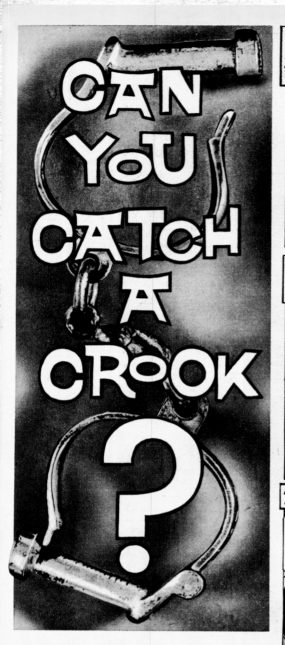

CAN YOU CATCH A CROOK?

You can actually help Bruce to solve this crime — if you're smart enough to spot the clues!

No. I. THE CASE OF THE STOLEN PAINTING

THE CASE OF THE STOLEN REMBRANDT BEGAN WITH A FRENZIED EARLY-MORNING CALL TO THE MANNINGHAM C.I.D...

...YES...YES... I'VE ONLY JUST DISCOVERED THE THEFT! IT WAS STOLEN SOME TIME LAST NIGHT! THE MOST VALUABLE POSSESSION I HAVE...!

AT ONCE, CHIEF-INSPECTOR WADE ASSIGNED SERGEANT DAVE BRUCE, AND HIS WORKING PARTNER, DETECTIVE-CONSTABLE BILL PRIOR, TO THE CASE...

THIS CHAP HENRY BREEN ONLY MOVED TO THE DISTRICT A WEEK AGO! AND THIS HAPPENS! IT LOOKS BAD FOR MANNINGHAM — AND THAT'S WHY I WANT THIS SOLVED—WITHOUT DELAY!

WE'LL DO OUR BEST, SIR. WE'LL DRIVE OUT TO OAK GRANGE STRAIGHT AWAY!

A SHORT, FAST DRIVE BROUGHT THEM TO THE SCENE OF THE CRIME...

THIS IS OAK GRANGE, DAVE. LOOKS AS IF MISTER HENRY BREEN HAS PLENTY OF MONEY, ALL RIGHT.

SEEMS LIKE IT, BILL, BUT YOU NEVER CAN BE SURE. THAT MUST BE HIM WAITING FOR US!

HENRY BREEN'S HEAVY FEATURES WERE FLUSHED WITH ANGER...

WELL, AT LEAST YOU DIDN'T WASTE ANY TIME GETTING HERE! YOU'VE GOT TO FIND THE THIEF WHO STOLE MY REMBRANDT. I'LL LOSE A FORTUNE IF THAT PAINTING IS NOT RECOVERED!

IF IT WAS ONLY STOLEN A FEW HOURS AGO, WE HAVE A GOOD CHANCE, MISTER BREEN. BUT SURELY SUCH A VALUABLE PICTURE WAS INSURED?

BREEN EMITTED AN ANGRY SNORT...

'COURSE IT WAS INSURED! BUT SOMEONE WAS PREPARED TO BUY IT FOR TWICE THE AMOUNT I PAID FOR IT. ONLY LAST WEEK HE SENT AN EXPERT DOWN HERE TO LOOK AT IT!

I SEE. BUT NOW CAN YOU TAKE US TO THE ROOM FROM WHICH IT WAS STOLEN, MISTER BREEN.

DIDN'T REALIZE THE WALLS WERE SO DUSTY, BUT YOU CAN SEE WHERE THE PICTURE WAS —AND THAT OILY PALM PRINT MUST BE THE THIEF'S.

THE WINDOWS HAVEN'T BEEN OPENED, SIR—SO IT WAS SOMEONE WHO WAS ABLE TO GET THROUGH THE FRONT DOOR!

HENRY BREEN GAVE A SUDDEN CRY...

THAT'S IT! WHY DIDN'T I THINK OF IT BEFORE? THE ONE PERSON WHO HAD A KEY APART FROM MYSELF WAS STUBBINS — MY NEW CHAUFFEUR!

YOUR CHAUFFEUR? BUT WHY SHOULD YOU THINK *HE* STOLE YOUR REMBRANDT? DON'T YOU TRUST HIM?

THAT'S JUST IT! I DON'T KNOW ANYTHING ABOUT HIM! HE CALLED HERE YESTERDAY AND ASKED ME FOR A JOB. I ONLY KNOW HIS NAME. OH, WHAT A TRUSTING FOOL I WAS...!

I THINK WE'D BETTER SEE THIS CHAUFFEUR OF YOURS—RIGHT NOW!

CONTINUED ON PAGE 8

WERE YOU AS SMART AS BRUCE? — IF NOT YOU

CLUES

1. Bruce guessed which turning Stubbins had taken because . . . ONE ROAD HAD TRAFFIC SIGN WITH BARRED GATE ON IT – DENOTING LEVEL-CROSSING AHEAD. Any experienced driver on the run from the police would know this meant there was a danger of being forced to stop until railway line was clear.

2. BRUCE SAW THAT STUBBINS HAD ONE FINGER MISSING ON LEFT HAND. YET ON WALL OF OAK GRANGE, THE PERSON WHO HAD REMOVED THE REMBRANDT PAINTING HAD LEFT A PERFECT LEFT HANDPRINT.
(This would not be in any way a conclusive clue, but enough to make Bruce suspicious.)

3. Henry Breen made two slips when the police car returned to Oak Grange. He called Stubbins a 'jailbird', yet earlier had told Bruce that all he knew about his new chauffeur was his name. Also, Breen knew, without anyone telling him, that Bruce had not brought back the stolen picture – obviously, because Breen himself had the picture and had tried to destroy it.

CAN TRY SOLVING ANOTHER MYSTERY NEXT WEEK!

THE MAN FROM EAGLE VISITS 'FRIENDSHIP 7'

As the time the Mercury spacecraft, *Friendship 7*, is being shown in London is too short to allow many of you to see it yourselves, I have, as the Man from EAGLE, made a special visit to the Science Museum in South Kensington to describe for you my impressions of the space vehicle in which astronaut Lt.-Colonel John Glenn made the first U.S. manned orbital space flight on 20th February, 1962.

Col. Glenn on his way to the rocket, carrying his portable air conditioner for his space-flight suit

SPACECRAFT INTERNAL ARRANGEMENT

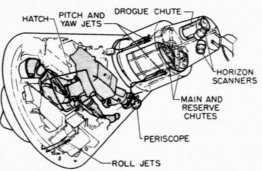

HATCH — PITCH AND YAW JETS — DROGUE CHUTE — HORIZON SCANNERS — MAIN AND RESERVE CHUTES — PERISCOPE — ROLL JETS

Astronaut John Glenn poses in his space-flight suit at Cape Canaveral

MERCURY-ATLAS COMBINATION. The Atlas rocket with *Friendship 7*, the Mercury capsule, mounted on top, at Cape Canaveral, Florida, before blast-off

★ ★ ★

This is a drawing of the internal arrangements of the Mercury spacecraft which carried the first U.S. astronaut into orbit

THE CAPSULE

AT first glance I was struck by the smallness of the spacecraft, which is just large enough to contain the astronaut and the equipment necessary to sustain and protect him in space.

The main cone-shaped section contains the cockpit and control systems, and the smaller cylindrical section houses the parachute-landing equipment.

The large face of the spacecraft, part of which has been melted and burned away during the re-entry of the spacecraft into the atmosphere, originally carried the heat-shield – a thick pad of resin and glass fibre which was designed to burn and boil away during the descent, taking with it much of the heat which is generated. The heat-shield reaches a maximum temperature of 3,000 degrees F. during re-entry. Also mounted on the heat-shield and burned away during re-entry was the retro-package containing the three retro-rockets which are fired to decrease the speed of the spacecraft and bring about its re-entry into the earth's atmosphere.

The Interior of the Spacecraft

The cockpit of *Friendship 7* is much like the cockpit of any high-speed aeroplane. The instruments are mounted on a main panel in front of the pilot and on consoles to left and right of him, and the periscope is mounted in the centre. This enables the astronaut to see the surface of the Earth, providing a full view of the horizon in any direction. A window is also provided above the space-pilots head.

Control Systems

A control lever is operated by the pilot to control the spacecraft's altitude. It does this by releasing short bursts of superheated steam (hydrogen peroxide) from nozzles on the outside of the capsule. There is also an automatic system which operates without any independent action by the pilot.

Life Support System

To absorb accelerations during the launching and re-entry, the astronaut is supported by a moulded couch constructed of a crushable honey-comb material lined with foam-rubber padding. Each of the Project Mercury astronauts has an individually-moulded couch made to suit his own body. A system of reclaiming straps keeps the pilot firmly in position during deceleration.

A complete pressure-suit was pro-vided for the pilot to ensure his safety in the event of a failure of the cabin-pressure system.

As the cabin-pressure system worked well, the suit was, in fact, used only as a flying suit.

The cabin temperature is controlled by a water evaporation heat exchanger, and the suit by a system which cools the oxygen that is fed to it, thus providing for ventilation and emergency breathing.

Communication Systems

Throughout the flight, the pilot's physical condition was monitored and relayed to surgeons on the ground.

Ground stations and Colonel Glenn kept in touch by means of ultra-high-frequency radio, and the whole of the flight was followed by a chain of radar stations right round the world.

Pilot's Report

Here in his own words are some extracts from Colonel Glenn's report on his historic flight.

"As the Atlas was released, there was an immediate gentle surge that let me know I was on my way.

"Weightlessness was a pleasant experience . . . I felt fine.

"Over the Atlantic, I saw what I assume was the Gulf Stream. The different colours of the water are clearly visible.

". . . off the coast of Africa were two large storm areas. Lightning could be seen flashing back and forth between the clouds – illuminating them like light bulbs.

"The success with which I was able to control the spacecraft at all times was, to me, one of the most significant features of the flight."

In touch with History . . .

Even to stand next to *Friendship 7*, at this point in space exploration, is akin to having been near the *Santa Maria* when Christopher Columbus discovered America.

No one can tell what new worlds will be opened by man's latest inventions – but these are the curiously-shaped vehicles which will take him to them!

NEXT WEEK: The Man from EAGLE visits SCOTLAND YARD!

EAGLE

1 September 1962 Vol. 13 No. 35

EVERY WEDNESDAY 5d.

KINGS OF THE ROAD

GRAHAM HILL DRIVING the 1½ litre V.8. B.R.M. to victory in the European Grand Prix at Zandvoort, in Holland. (See page 19)

-CROSS-

THE COOPER / CLIMAX V/8

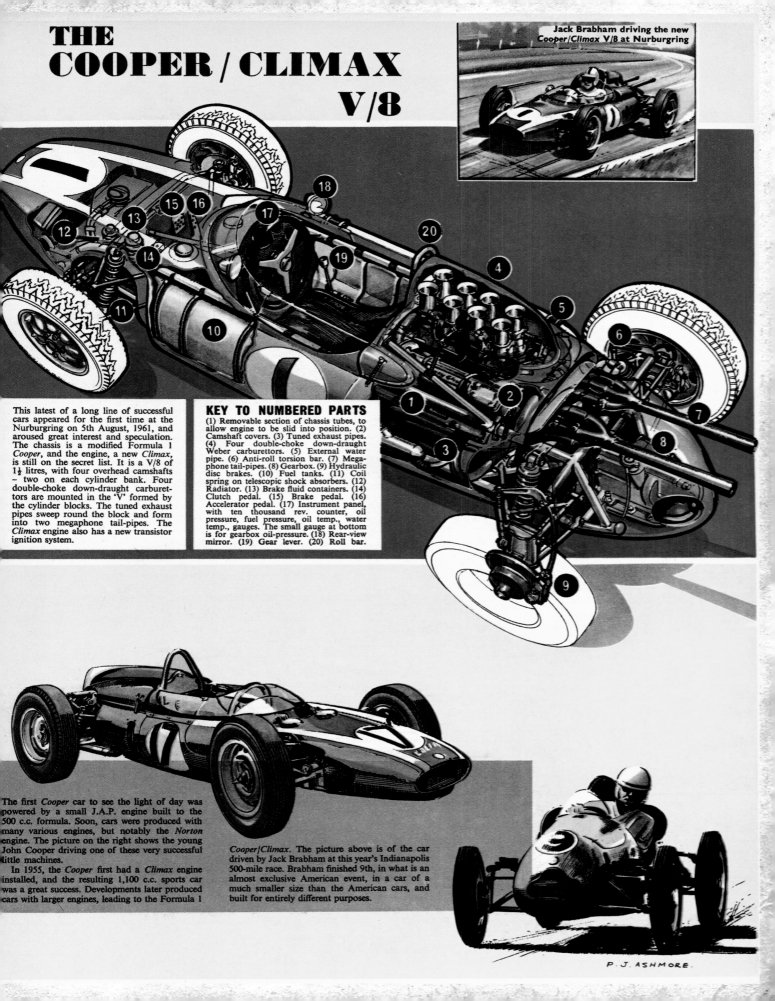

Jack Brabham driving the new Cooper/Climax V/8 at Nurburgring

This latest of a long line of successful cars appeared for the first time at the Nurburgring on 5th August, 1961, and aroused great interest and speculation. The chassis is a modified Formula 1 *Cooper*, and the engine, a new *Climax*, is still on the secret list. It is a V/8 of 1½ litres, with four overhead camshafts – two on each cylinder bank. Four double-choke down-draught carburettors are mounted in the 'V' formed by the cylinder blocks. The tuned exhaust pipes sweep round the block and form into two megaphone tail-pipes. The *Climax* engine also has a new transistor ignition system.

KEY TO NUMBERED PARTS

(1) Removable section of chassis tubes, to allow engine to be slid into position. (2) Camshaft covers. (3) Tuned exhaust pipes. (4) Four double-choke down-draught Weber carburettors. (5) External water pipe. (6) Anti-roll torsion bar. (7) Megaphone tail-pipes. (8) Gearbox. (9) Hydraulic disc brakes. (10) Fuel tanks. (11) Coil spring on telescopic shock absorbers. (12) Radiator. (13) Brake fluid containers. (14) Clutch pedal. (15) Brake pedal. (16) Accelerator pedal. (17) Instrument panel, with ten thousand rev. counter, oil pressure, fuel pressure, oil temp., water temp., gauges. The small gauge at bottom is for gearbox oil-pressure. (18) Rear-view mirror. (19) Gear lever. (20) Roll bar.

The first *Cooper* car to see the light of day was powered by a small J.A.P. engine built to the 500 c.c. formula. Soon, cars were produced with many various engines, but notably the *Norton* engine. The picture on the right shows the young John Cooper driving one of these very successful little machines.

In 1955, the *Cooper* first had a *Climax* engine installed, and the resulting 1,100 c.c. sports car was a great success. Developments later produced cars with larger engines, leading to the Formula 1

Cooper/Climax. The picture above is of the car driven by Jack Brabham at this year's Indianapolis 500-mile race. Brabham finished 9th, in what is an almost exclusive American event, in a car of a much smaller size than the American cars, and built for entirely different purposes.

P. J. ASHMORE.

Luxury Car in Miniature   THE RILEY *ELF*

Over the past two years, the famous B.M.C. range of Mini-cars has been progressively enlarged to include station wagons, de luxe and sports versions, vans, and now a model furnished in the style of the traditional, expensive English car. Basis of the brilliant original design was the grouping of engine, gearbox and transmission into one forward unit, with front wheel drive and the power unit mounted transversely across the body (1). This innovation resulted in exceptionally-roomy passenger accommodation for a miniature car, and a low, flat floor. Small wheels placed at the corners, and sprung independently all round with rubber cones (2), provide exceptional stability and road holding. On the *Elf*, a traditional Riley radiator grille has been moulded on to the front (3), and the boot has been extended rearwards to form a conventional tail end (4), with a noticeable improvement on the previous Minis' rather boxy shape.

The interior of the *Elf* is luxuriously furnished with leather, pile carpets and a polished walnut dash-panel (5), mounting oil-pressure and temperature-gauges, as well as the combined speedometer and fuel-gauge. Extra-sound insulation is fitted throughout to deaden power-unit and road noise. The boot has a carpeted floor, beneath which are the battery (6) and spare wheel (7); it also houses the fuel tank (8). However, Riley enthusiasts accustomed to above-average performance will perhaps be disappointed, for the car is heavier than the standard Minis, yet retains the same 848 c.c. engine devoid of any tuning, and the price seems rather high at £693 18s. 11d. Other features shown on the drawing are: (9) sideways-placed radiator, to keep engine compartment as small as possible; (10) wide, single doors, each side; (11) extra space for small cases beneath rear seat; (12) upward-opening boot-lid with telescopic stay.

It's different   It's inexpensive

It's fun

On our 1962
EAGLE ADVENTURE HOLIDAYS

If you are between 11 and 15 years of age, these are just the holidays for you.

We proudly announce our 1962 Holiday brochure. This year, it covers not only a wonderful selection of tours for the summer, but special holidays during Easter too.

Adventure holidays, specially arranged in co-operation with the Youth Hostels Association of England and Wales, are full of excitement and fun, with the wonderful sense of freedom which only the great outdoors can

give – plus the companionship of boys of the same age and interests.

With the experience of seven successful years behind us – and with hundreds of letters from our readers, all saying 'this is the perfect way of spending a week's holiday' – we can guarantee that, whatever tour you select, it will be a holiday you will always remember.

The cost of holidays will range from

£6.0.0d. for a standard walking or cycling tour, to £11.0.0d. for a specialized tour.

Write NOW to:– Holiday Brochure, EAGLE Tours, Y.H.A. Trevelyan House, 8 St. Stephen's Hill, St. Albans, Herts., enclosing a self-addressed gummed label bearing a 2½d. stamp. Don't worry if there is a little delay – it takes some time to deal with all your applications.

The choice is yours

AT EASTER
Walking in the Wye Valley, or on the High Peak – Cycling on the South Coast and the rolling Downs, or in the lovely Yorkshire Dales.

DURING THE SUMMER
WALKING
Wye Valley – Gower Peninsula – Isle of Wight – North Yorkshire Moors and Coast – Lakeland – The High Peak – Devon – The Yorkshire Dales – Loch Lomond – Isle of Man – The Pilgrim's Way – Wild Wales – Snowdonia – The Mendips – Exmoor.

CYCLING
South Coast and Downs – The Yorkshire Dales – The Garden of England – Dorset – Wild Wales – North Yorkshire Moors and Coast – Devon – West of the Wye – Heart of England – The Thames Valley – East Anglia.

SPECIAL ACTIVITIES
Holidays with a Camera – Skin Diving in Devon – Sailing on Lake Bala – Fishing – Looking at Birds – Hillcraft – Train Spotting.

CONTINENTAL HOLIDAYS
The Grand Duchy of Luxembourg – Sparkling Switzerland – The Romantic Rhine.*

*These tours last for ten days each.

---

4 SUPERB NEW ANNUALS EVERY BOY WILL WANT!

EAGLE ANNUAL 1963

, bright and exciting as ever—176 s crowded with adventure, pictures, ting features . . . and all your LE favourites. 10/6d.

Dan Dare's SPACE ANNUAL 1963

New this year, this exciting addition to the EAGLE range of books is a must for every space-age boy. It's 112 pages of top value for 8/6d.

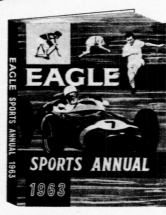

EAGLE SPORTS ANNUAL 1963

Favourite with the all-round sports enthusiast. Speed, spills and excitement from every sport. 128 pages. Only 9/6d.

EAGLE FOOTBALL ANNUAL 1963

This is the annual for every Soccer fan. With masses of action pictures player-profiles, coaching tips and features by top names in Soccer. 128 pages of super value for 9/6d.

ON SALE AT YOUR NEWSAGENT OR BOOKSELLER!

TONY BYGRAVES got Dad down to it!

"Now all our crowd go Raleigh-riding!"

"It didn't *really* take me long to convince Dad we needed two Raleigh bikes in the family!" says 15-year-old Tony, whose father is Film and T.V. star, Max Bygraves. "Maxine —that's my 10-year-old sister—and I told him all our crowd were Raleigh-riding these days. 'A Raleigh takes you out in the fresh air' we said. 'Gets you to all sorts of interesting places, away from the traffic, with no fares to pay. Good exercise, too. You can't be *with* it without a Raleigh, Dad!' He just grinned and said he was glad we were showing some sense at last! You ought to tell *you* folks the reasons for wanting a Raleigh".

RALEIGH EASY TERMS EVEN EASIER

Your Raleigh dealer has full details of the substantial reduced special Raleigh Easy Terms which include *insuranc* of the cycle against Accidental Damage, Fire or Theft, with the payments kept up for you in the event of accident, un employment* or sickness. (*Except in Northern Ireland.)

PRICES AND SPECIFICATIONS OF ALL MACHINES SUBJECT TO ALTERATION WITHOUT NOTICE

Gran Sport Model 74 Flamboyant colours: Venetian Blue, Firecracker Red, or Sunset Yellow with front fork ends chromium plated and the following Race Ace features: Frame: 21½″, 22½″, 23½″; fork crown forged and machined; wrap over seat stays; bottom bracket height 10¾″; Campagnolo gear and pump clips; G.B. alloy bend and stem; G.B. 'Coureur 66' centre pull brakes. Equipment: polished alloy inflator; feeding bottle. £28.17.11 (5 speed), £31.8.8 (10 speed) or on Easy Terms.

Explorer Model 80 (*Girl's 80L*) Wheels 20″. Frame: Boy's 14″ curved top tube, Girl's 14″. Finish: Royal Carmine or Electric Blue with Powder Blue mudguards. Two-tone saddle. White toolbag. £13.10.11 or on Easy Terms.

Trent Tourist Model 29 (*Girl's 29L*) Frame: 19½″, 21″, 23″. Finish: Carmine or Electric Blue, celluloid mudguards to match. Also 21″ and 23″ in black with red celluloid mudguards. Wheels: 26″ x 1⅜″. Calliper brakes: 'all-rounder' handlebar; two-tone saddle and kitbag. £20.15.7 or on Easy Terms.

Explorer Model 56 (*Girl's 56L*) Wheels 24″. Frame: 18″. Finish: Royal Carmine or Electric Blue with Powder Blue mudguards. Two-tone saddle. White kitbag. £17.14.9 or on Easy Terms.

FOR SUPER PERFORMANCE AND YEARS-AHEAD LOOKS YOU REALLY WANT A RALEIGH

THE LOST WORLD

by Sir Arthur Conan Doyle

The greatest adventure story of all time

Professor Challenger, famous zoologist, claimed he had found a Lost World where prehistoric monsters roamed, but no one believed him. The Editor of the *Daily Graphic*, however, saw a story here, and summoned his star reporter, Edward Malone . . .

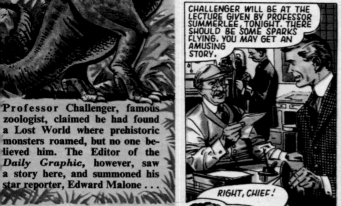

CHALLENGER WILL BE AT THE LECTURE GIVEN BY PROFESSOR SUMMERLEE, TONIGHT. THERE SHOULD BE SOME SPARKS FLYING. YOU MAY GET AN AMUSING STORY.

RIGHT, CHIEF!

When Malone got to the hall, it was in an uproar . . .

ORDER! I REPEAT THAT THE SAURIAN MONSTERS DIED OUT LONG BEFORE MAN APPEARED ON THIS PLANET!

AND I REPEAT THAT YOU ARE WRONG—THIS PHOTO WILL PROVE IT!

SIT DOWN! SIT DOWN!

WHAT PROOF IS THIS? OBVIOUSLY THIS PHOTOGRAPH IS A FAKE!

IMBECILES! IF ANYONE HAS THE COURAGE TO GO WITH ME, I'LL SHOW THEM THIS LOST WORLD!

'EGARD IT AS A WASTE TIME—BUT IN ORDER PUT AN END TO THIS NSENSE, I'LL GLADLY GO!

Malone tackled Professor Challenger after the lecture . . .

EXCUSE ME, PROFESSOR. I'M FROM THE 'GAZETTE'. WHY NOT TAKE ME ALONG TO DO A 'WRITE UP' ON THE TRIP?

AND I'LL GO TOO. I AM LORD JOHN ROXTON AND I KNOW THE AMAZON AREA!

WHY NOT? A PRESS MAN WILL COME IN USEFUL— IF ONLY TO GIVE PUBLICITY TO WHAT WE'RE GOING TO SEE!

Three weeks later, the adventurers embarked at Southampton . . .

WHEN WE RETURN TO THIS COUNTRY, GENTLEMEN, YOU WILL HAVE SEEN SIGHTS THAT WOULD SHAKE THE CIVILISED WORLD TO ITS FOUNDATIONS!

HMMMPH!

OW ABOUT LETTING US KNOW IST WHERE WE'RE GOING?

I'LL LET YOU KNOW SOON ENOUGH! TRUST ME!

Eventually, they reached the Amazon, and transferred to a steamer . . .

fter many more weeks in a small launch, navigated by two half breeds, hey left the main river to hire canoes . . .

I SPEAK THE LINGO—LEAVE IT TO ME!

But as Lord John pointed out the direction of their journey, terror gripped the natives.

Eagle covers don't get more beautiful than this. Turn the page!

CURUPURI! CURUPURI!

EAGLE

3 November 1962 Vol. 13 No. 44 · EVERY WEDNESDAY · 6d.

See page 7 for a
exciting new series
which you actual
help Sergeant Bru
in his fight agains
crime—if you're sma
enough.

PLUS

A whole host of features a
stories to entertain you!

EAGLE

20 October 1962 Vol. 13 No. 42

EVERY WEDNESDAY **5d.**

KINGS OF THE ROAD

Jean Hebert driving the world-record-breaking Renault Shooting Star, on the Bonneville Salt Flats in America. (See Page 13.)

EAGLE

10 FEBRUARY 1962
Vol. 13 No. 6
EVERY
WEDNESDAY

5d

MEN OF ACTION

No. 17— STANLEY MATTHEWS

A FEW days ago, Stanley Matthews celebrated his 47th birthday, and he is still playing professional football! Regarded as being the World's Most Famous Footballer, Stan Matthews, C.B.E., began his sporting career at the age of 13, when he played for England in the Schoolboys' International against Wales. At the age of 15, young Stan was taken on by the Stoke City Football Club, his first task being to sweep out the dressing-rooms!

Now, the maestro winger has played for 29 seasons as a professional footballer, and he has played for England on no less than 87 occasions. For his services to football, and English sport in general, Stan was awarded the C.B.E., (Commander of the Order of the British Empire), for he has spent much of his time overseas, coaching and giving demonstrations in South Africa, Canada and the United States of America.

After playing for Blackpool for over 14 years, the age-defying Stan has returned to Stoke City, the team which engaged him as a boy over 30 years ago.

MEN OF ACTION

No. 16 — DICK McTAGGART

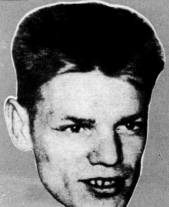

The world's most successful amateur boxer — that is the distinction of Dick McTaggart, the Scottish lightweight who astounded the boxing world in 1956 by winning an Olympic Gold Medal and the Val Barker Award for the most stylish boxer of the Games. In 1958, at the age of 22, Dick became the Empire and British Amateur Lightweight Champion, and he also gained the Scottish Amateur Lightweight title.

1960 saw Dick's third victory in the Amateur Boxing Association's lightweight contest. By this time, he had won no less than 285 of his 300 fights! Then, in the 1960 Olympics in Rome, came the young boxer's greatest honour, when he was chosen to carry the Union Jack at the head of the British contingent of athletes during the parade. Dick earned a Bronze Medal in the contests which followed.

Dick McTaggart's intelligent and extremely skilful boxing style has done a great deal to establish our reputation for clever ringmanship, and his refusal to turn professional illustrates this fine sportsman's genuine love for amateur boxing.

MEN OF ACTION

No. 14 — BRIAN PHELPS

Brian Phelps began diving seriously at the age of 9 – because his father gave him a shilling to keep him out of mischief! Brian spent the shilling going to the Baths and, remarkably soon after that, he was noticed as a promising diver. So rapid was Brian's progress that, by the age of 13, he was English Plain Diving Champion and English Junior Champion.

Since then, the amazing London schoolboy has won over 40 medals, has been winner of the Commonwealth Festival of Diving twice, and was European Highboard Diving Champion in 1958. Brian was the first British diver ever to win this title.

In 1959, Brian took to a new sport, the Trampoline, and he won both the Senior and the Junior English Trampoline Championships. Then, in 1960, at the age of 16, he gained his greatest honour when he won a Bronze Medal in the Olympic Games at Rome.

EAGLE

17 FEBRUARY 1962
Vol. 13 No. 7
EVERY WEDNESDAY

5d

MEN OF ACTION

No. 18 — MIKE SANGSTER

MIKE SANGSTER, Britain's greatest hope in tennis since the war, began playing at the age of 12 – because everyone at school said he was too fat and needed exercise! The rise to fame of this Torquay-born star began in 1959, when he defeated Drobny, a former Wimbledon Champion, shortly after winning the Junior Tennis Championships.

In 1960, Mike reached the semi-finals of the Covered Court Championships, while still only 19. After a tour of Australia, Mike's style greatly improved; as a result, he became the first Englishman to reach the semi-finals at Wimbledon since the war.

MODERNISING BRITISH RAILWAYS

Our Railway Planners look to the future

NOT since the great days of railway construction in this country has anything so vast as British Railways' modernisation programme been attempted.

The railway pioneers had the comparatively straightforward task of building railroads where none existed. Today, their successors have to replace tracks, stations, depots yards and signalling and telecommunications equipment while they are all in constant – and often congested – use. A railway system is a vital public service that cannot be halted while the changes are being made. That is why some schemes take a long time to complete. What it really amounts to is that virtually a new railway has to be built on top of one which must continue to serve the community for twenty-four hours a day. Some of the advantages and problems involved in this huge undertaking are described on this page.

DIESEL LOCOMOTIVES

The new Diesel locomotives are now widely used on main-line services. They are also extensively used for shunting, and a large shunting fleet has been steadily built up.

The biggest change has been in local and branch-line services, where Diesel multiple-unit trains are now in use on all Regions. They are cleaner, faster and cheaper to operate than steam trains, and have increased traffic by as much as 50 per cent – in some cases well over 100 per cent.

Modern signalling means speedier traffic. The colour-light signal is replacing the manual type. The Automatic Warning System is also being extensively developed (see page I). It is completed most of the way from King's Cross to Edinburgh, and on most of the newly-electrified lines.

The elaborate project of electrification is undertaken on very busy lines, where traffic must continue to pass throughout the operation. While overhead wires are being installed, bridges raised or the track lowered

ABOVE: An example of a modern signal box.
BELOW: In line with British Railways' modernisation programme, infinite skill is called for in a Diesel shed, where the electrical systems of a modern carriage must be thoroughly checked

to provide the necessary clearance, work must go on reconstructing the line itself – strengthening the track, installing the latest signalling equipment, rebuilding stations. All this work is carried on simultaneously, and phased so as to be completed at the same time.

Some idea of the complexity of an up-to-date marshalling yard can be gained from the picture below

PASSENGER STATIONS

On the newly-electrified lines, stations shared in the general improvement. The station at Harlow New Town is an exa of the modern architecture now b adopted for British Railways' passe stations. The materials used in its constru not only provide attractive contrast texture, but are lasting and need maintenance. At the Bank Station in Lon the famous Travolator – a 296-ft. mo pavement – daily carries 40,000 trave who used to walk up the long inclin the City streets.

A modern, fast freight train can be up to 50 wagons. The 'Tees-Tyne Freigh linking London and the Tees-Tyne indu area, provides next-morning deliveries consignments. A similar service is prov by the Diesel-hauled 'East Essex Enterp Door-to-door deliveries in containers special feature of this service.

CLOSED-CIRCUIT TELEVISION

British Railways are making use of the l techniques in many fields in the proce re-equipping themselves for the fu Some marshalling yards, for example, have closed-circuit television, transisto radio, electronic computers, and tape corders to note down wagon destination numbers. At Margram (South Wales), the operation of points is automatic – s a coded tape on a teletype machin computer works out how much pressure wagon 'retarders' have to apply as wagon rolls down the hump towards sorting sidings. The Diesel-shunting motives are linked with the control tow two-way radio, and there is telepr contact between the control tower various key points.

In other places on the railways, telev receivers are used for passing message train information for passengers, and dr less trucks snake round with parcels g only by a hidden wire buried in the road

A WORD OF WARNING

The purpose of the modernization our railways is to benefit the pub by providing faster, cleaner a safer services. British Railways c provide the speed, the cleanline and the best possible safety measur – but they cannot stop people fro endangering their lives, and oth people's, by acting foolishly carelessly. That is why it is necessa to point out the dangers that c result from doing something witho thinking. Study the colour chart the centre pages and remember t simple rules. It is better to be sa than sorry!

Danger!

On most lines nowadays, quiet-running trains can come upon you unawares. They can't stop quickly if you get in the way.

Danger!

Some lines have a THIRD RAIL which is LIVE.

Danger!

Where there are OVERHEAD WIRES, keep off all structures – there are dangerous things on them.

KEEP AWAY FROM THE LINE!

**Railway lines are well fenced in –
The main idea? To save your skin!
For near them lurk, as you should know,
DANGERS, as this chart will show.**

To young trespassers on railway property there is DANGER EVERYWHERE. Electricity powerful enough to drive a train can KILL anyone who comes near it. So –

➤ KEEP AWAY FROM IT – it strikes like lightning
➤ KEEP OFF THE TRACKS – modern trains are fast and quiet
➤ KEEP OFF BRIDGE PARAPETS
➤ KEEP OFF RAILWAY EMBANKMENTS
➤ KEEP WELL AWAY FROM PLATFORM EDGES

There's nothing clever about putting yourself in danger IT'S JUST PLAIN STUPID

You are very welcome to watch the trains – BUT WATCH THEM ALWAYS FROM A GOOD SAFE PLACE

KEEP AWAY FROM DANGER!

EAGLE

3 MARCH 1962
Vol. 13 No. 9
EVERY
WEDNESDAY

5d

MEN OF ACTION

No. 20 – Don Bragg

Twenty-three-year-old American Don Bragg earned a considerable reputation at an early age for pole-vaulting, and, in 1959, he set up a staggering new indoor world record height of 15 ft. 9½ ins.! The following year, this 6 ft. 3 in.-giant also set up an outdoor world record of 15 ft. 9¼ ins. Don Bragg then won a gold medal in the Olympics at Rome – a fitting climax to his career as a pole-vaulter. Now, however, Don has a rather unusual ambition – he wants to play 'Tarzan' on the screen! If Don gets his way, we think he will rise to even greater heights as the acrobatic film hero.

ARE YOU

THE ADAM FAITH TYPE

A FAITH—FULL—DAY

5.00	Alarm call, followed by quick breakfast before driving to film studio.
7.00	Make-up and costume department.
8.00	Report to film set for possibly only five minutes of actual filming.
9.15	Arrive at London office for conference with agent. (Views might be required on subjects ranging from details of contract to selecting covers for new L.P. disc cover.)
10.00	Meet stockbroker to discuss investments.
10.20	Return to office to meet delegation from fan club.
10.40	Photo session with GIRL magazine in Fleet Street.
11.15	Phone B.B.C. to arrange rehearsal times for the next day.
12.00	Catch plane from London to Manchester for afternoon live television engagement, followed by 20 minutes' drive by car to open new record shop. This would be followed by autograph signing until it was possible to get away. And fans MUST not be disappointed!
EVENING	Return by plane to London and have supper with an American film executive who is making a long-term contract offer.
10.00	Attend special showing of recent films and TV appearances for the benefit of American film executive.
11.00	Phone discussion with secretary about what has been arranged during his absence.
11.20	Check lines and rehearse on tape recorder for following day's filming and recording session. Try to remember to get some sleep!

CORRECT ANSWERS TO QUIZ

1. (A) 2. (A) 3. (C) 4. (A) 5. (C) 6. (A)

INDIVIDUAL PERSONALITY TEST

1. You are sitting on top of a high hill, with a pair of powerful binoculars:—
   A. Take a look at the whole countryside, bit by bit?
   B. Find something which interests you, look at it, and come back to it later?
   C. Keep steadily focused on one thing for a long time?

2. You are in a friend's house for a record-playing session. His elder brother comes into the room and suggests you should listen to HIS favourite music for half an hour. Would you:—
   A. Willingly agree and stay to listen?
   B. Reluctantly agree and stay to listen?
   C. Suggest that he borrows the record-player?

3. At a funfair you have thrown five wooden balls at the coconuts and haven't managed to knock down any. The man offers you another go – free! Would you:—
   A. Refuse, because you think he is trying to make you pay for an extra round later?
   B. Refuse, because you don't want to miss again?
   C. Accept his offer?

4. You have been told that you may be made a form prefect; but you know that, if you accept, you may lose some of your friends. Would you:—
   A. Accept the post?
   B. Refuse it?
   C. Ask to be given time to discuss things with your friends?

5. Would you rather:—
   A. Ride your own horse?
   B. Drive your own car?
   C. Fly your own plane?

6. Would you rather:—
   A. Run in a 100-yard race?
   B. Play football against a good team?
   C. Watch an international match from the grandstand?

Eagle gave readers the chance to test themselves and their psyche against a wide variety of world leaders and celebrities. The validity of these tests is somewhat dubious as they generally involved just a few questions, but they set down a marker of sorts. It was possible to see if you had what it took to be a Beatle, or maybe an astronaut and even, like JFK, perhaps you could be POTUS.

are you the KRUSCHEV type?

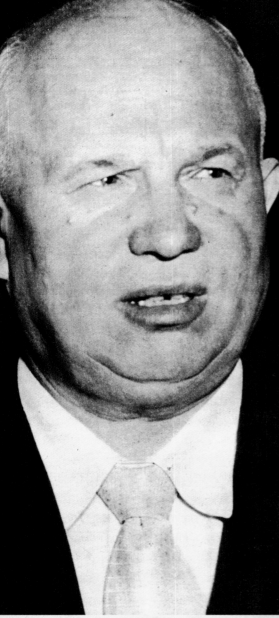

Check below to see whether you are the Kruschev † type:—

1. Are you:—
   (a) Lucky?
   (b) Unlucky?
   or (c) Do you not believe in luck, good or bad?

2. You are saving hard for a new sports bicycle. One day you see two advertisements. One reads: Good wages for newspaper delivery, bicycle essential; apply in person next Monday. The other: Old bicycle for sale, cheap. Must sell by Saturday! Do you:—
   (a) Risk your savings on the old bicycle, hoping to get the job and so save up all the quicker?
   (b) Consider the risk too great?
   (c) Find out more about both offers before deciding?

3. Have you:—
   (a) No real friends at all?
   (b) One good pal whom you have known a long time?
   (c) Several friends whom you keep changing?

4. Your class is going on an important educational sight-seeing tour by coach. Would you:—
   (a) Arrive half an hour early to get the best seat?
   (b) Wait for your pals and sit with them?
   (c) Take pot luck?

1.
2.
3.
4.

The pinnacle of power! Kruschev takes the salute from the Mausoleum

Kruschev was 18 when this photograph was taken of him playing football

ANSWERS:— 1-c; 2-c; 3-c; 4-a.

If you answered honestly and obtained four correct answers, then you may be a moderate Kruschev type, but if you studied the questions closely and gave what you thought were the right answers because you want to become a success, and totalled four all-correct answers — then you are well on the way to the top of whatever profession you choose to follow!

THE BEGINNING

This is the story of Bernard Law Montgomery – a man whose spectacular life has been dedicated to the service of his country. Bernard was born in London, in 1887, and spent his early childhood in Tasmania. He returned to London as a day boy at St Paul's School, Hammersmith, London. He was then fourteen years old . . .

MONTGOMERY OF ALAMEIN
THE DESERT WAR

THE BATTLE OF EL ALAMEIN

September, 1942. Within three weeks of his arrival in the Western Desert to command the Eighth Army, Lt. General Montgomery had fought the battle of Alam Halfa – Rommel's last bid to break Britain's hold on the Middle East. In this model defensive battle, Montgomery had repulsed the German Afrika Korps – and was now preparing to take the offensive himself.

MONTGOMERY OF ALAMEIN

TRAPPED BETWEEN EAST AND WEST

Christmas, 1944. The Allies had suffered their gravest setback since the invasion of Europe six months earlier. Without warning, the Germans launched a massive offensive in the Ardennes sector and punched a hole in the Allied front. At once, Supreme Commander Eisenhower ordered Field Marshal Montgomery to command all armies in the North. Meanwhile, the Americans took the brunt of the fighting.

MONTGOMERY OF ALAMEIN
THE YEARS BETWEEN

October, 1914. The British Expeditionary Force was fighting desperately alongside its allies in France to stem the German advance in the early stages of the First World War. In an action at the village of Meteren, Lt. Montgomery is wounded. A soldier is sent to help him, only to be shot down himself.

MONTGOMERY OF ALAMEIN
THE AIR ARMADA

21st August, 1944. The great battle of Normandy had ended in disaster for the German armies in France. Allied invasion troops were everywhere victorious. General Montgomery, persistently criticized for 'going slow', had justified his original plan of campaign. Now the Normandy battlefield was still . . .

THIS OFFICER HASN'T A CHANCE. HE'LL BE DEAD BY THE TIME WE LEAVE!

...ding to plan and casualties were slight . . .

Christmas Day, Bastogne. Heroic resistance by the besieged Americans frustrated all German assaults . .

WE'RE TOLD THESE AMERICANS HAD NO STOMACH FOR REAL FIGHTING — A VERY BAD MISTAKE!

ENGLISH CHANNEL

DUNKIRK
CALAIS
ANTWERP
BRUSSELS
LE HAVRE
BELGIUM
BRITISH 21st ARMY GROUP
AMERICAN 12th ARMY GROUP
FRANCE PARIS

AXIS TROOPS

LITTORIO
GERMAN UNITS
TRENTO
BOLOGNA
GERMAN PARA. BN.
PARA. BN.
PARA. BN.
21 PANZER DIV.
BRESCIA
ARIETE
PARA. BN.
FOLGORE

GREEK BDE.
TROOPS
50 DIV.
13 CORPS
44 DIV.
7 ARMD.

The German anti-tank screen held firm. The vicious fire from 88-mm. guns took a heavy toll of British armour . . .

. . . but the Luftwaffe, too, showed its old form with crippling raids on Allied airfields . . .

LE OF THE RHINELAND

Frank Bellamy had taken over Dan Dare for a while and whilst he performed the task admirably it is really away from the Hampson shadow that he shines. His series on Montgomery could be used as a textbook for future comic-strip artists. His use of colour, space, frames and shading are all stunning, original and always in service of the story. Much has been made of late about late 20th and early 21st century graphic novels but there is very little in such work that you won't find in this series. Space does not allow the whole to be displayed here and choosing what to omit was a thankless task, but we've done our best.

CAN YOU SPOT 'EM, MONTY?

YES. HERE THEY COME !

1908 NORTH-WEST FRONTIER

End of Episode One

THIS OFFICER HAS JUST MOVED! GET THE DOCTOR.

But near Arnhem . . .

AT THE DOUBLE, CHAPS! THE BRIDGE IS AT LEAST SIX MILES AWAY. EVERY MINUTE COUNTS.

ERATION ARKET GARD

worked hard, and, in the competitive examination for the Royal Military Albany,

FIRE !

RAGE OF 1,000 BRITISH GUNS

The BATTLE OF EL ALAMEIN !

LOOK! A NEW EAGLE NEXT WEEK

FREE INSIDE

EAGLE

10 MARCH 1962

Vol. 13 No. 10

THE TOP PAPER FOR BOYS EVERY WEDNESDAY **5d**

THIS SUPER ALBUM AND FOUR WONDERFUL COLOUR CARDS

MARVELS OF THIS MODERN AGE

PRESENTED WITH

EAGLE

GREAT SCOTT! THOSE GIGANTIC THINGS — THEY'RE GROWING AND TEARING THE EARTH APART UNDER OUR EYES!

MONTGOMERY OF ALAMEIN

The epic story of Britain's great soldier!

DAN DARE OPERATION EARTH-SAVER

Dan Dare knew that every minute counted in this Mission if the Earth was to be saved from destruction. The Question was – could it be saved?

ALSO INSIDE

The greatest adventure story of all time
THE LOST WORLD
by
Sir Arthur Conan Doyle
PLUS Many more new picture stories and features!

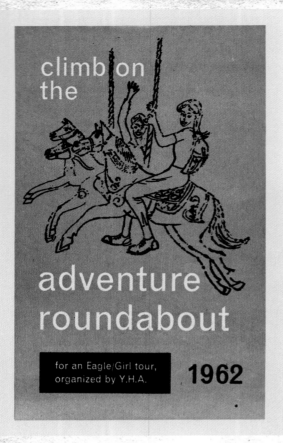

climb on the

adventure roundabout

for an Eagle/Girl tour, organized by Y.H.A.

1962

When The Road of Courage ended on the 8 April 1961 most people thought that was the last they would see of Frank Hampson's art in the comic. Eagle-eyed readers though would have picked out his distinctive style in this Bovril advert.

SPOTTING GAME

The fellows in our class at school hav devised a new game. We each take EAGLE' back-page diagram and, after covering u the numbers on the drawing, try to iden tify the different features from the 'Ke to Numbered Parts'. The boy who gets th most correct is the winner.

Tom Jones, Newcastle

The Man From EAGLE
Visits THE ROYAL NAVAL
SUBMARINE ESCAPE SCHOOL

HAND SIGNALS by INSTRUCTOR
TAPS ON CHEST.... BREATHE OUT MORE RAPIDLY
FINGERS ON LIPS.... SLOW DOWN the RATE of VENTING THROUGH MOUTH
HAND OVER MOUTH... STOP VENTING THROUGH MOUTH

BREATHE OUT the WHOLE TIME WHEN MAKING A FREE ASCENT WITH BUOYANCY

THIS may sound a strange thing to say: although I have never been under water in a submarine, I now know how to escape from one and reach the surface alive!

Don't think this is just a simple matter of letting yourself out of a submarine from the sea bed and floating up to the surface. The startling fact is that if you were to keep your mouth tightly closed as you floated up, you would be dead when you reached the top!

If you are scientifically minded, you already know why this is the greatest danger you would have to face when trying to escape.

THE STARTLING PROBLEM

The deeper you go in water, the greater the pressure becomes. Normally, atmospheric pressure at sea level is 14.7 lb. per square inch – called an 'atmosphere'.

Thirty feet under water, the pressure is two atmospheres; at 100 feet down, the pressure is four atmospheres.

What has this got to do with escaping from submarines? Just this: a man escaping at a hundred-foot depth starts out with four times as much air in his lungs than they can hold at the surface.

This means that something terrible will happen to his lungs if he doesn't breathe out air ALL THE TIME HE IS RISING.

It's no good waiting for some kind of natural warning. Nature doesn't provide

Men awaiting their turn to escape, use temporary breathing equipment

any. So you see, an escaper's lungs could actually be responsible for his death without his ever knowing that, simply by blowing out the air, he would be saved!

Now this isn't merely a lot of text-book theory. I tried this out myself at the R.N. Submarine Escape School at Portsmouth.

C.O. IN A DRESSING GOWN

Most of us have a fairly stereotyped idea of what a commanding officer looks like in his office. In my job I'm used to surprises – but even I blinked when I was shown into the office of Commander Hamlyn.

He sat at his desk wearing the official naval instructor's yellow trunks with a towel dressing-gown on top.

He is a C.O. who believes in doing at least as much as his instructors and often more. If there is a particularly hazardous test, then Commander Hamlyn is the man to do it first.

SPECIAL TEST

Less than twenty minutes after I had arrived, I found myself undergoing pressure tests before being allowed into the 100 ft.-deep circular tank of water.

I had gone to Portsmouth armed with a certificate to prove to the Commander that

The end of a 100-ft. 'Free Ascent'

I had undergone a thorough medical examination, including chest X-rays.

He took me into a re-compression chamber, looking from the outside like a huge, metal boiler covered in gauges and dials. We sat perfectly still inside the chamber while, outside, a petty officer pressed the necessary buttons to subject us to a pressure of a hundred feet under water. Commander Hamlyn taught me how to clear the pressure on my eardrums by holding my nose, keeping my mouth tightly closed, and breathing hard to equalize the pressure.

My final test was to see how buoyant I was. In the water at the side of the tank, an instructor gently pushed me under – and I popped straight up again. He announced I was very 'positive'. They told me that many people are 'negative' – which means they sink even when their lungs are full of air.

I was now ready to make my first ascent. But, before I could come up, I would obviously have to get down. To do this I went down in a diving-bell to a depth of 30 feet, wearing goggles and nose-clip. Standing inside the diving-bell with water up to my shoulders, I could hear an officer at the top of the tank giving me instructions over the intercom. Through the glass window of the diving-bell I saw the depth we were going to marked on the side of the tank . . . 15 feet . . . 20 feet . . . 25 feet . . . 30 feet . . .

The diving bell stopped.

"Prepare to ascend!"

I took a good, deep breath, ducked under the water and under the bottom of the bell.

Knowing now how vital it was to breathe out, I opened my mouth and huge bubbles of air rose to the surface as I ascended slowly. I say 'slowly' because you must remember I wasn't at this stage wearing any sort of life-jacket. I was depending on my buoyancy to take me up. Although instinct told me to keep my mouth closed and hold on to my

breath, I now knew what would happen if I did this.

So I did what the instructors had told me, and still had plenty of air in my lungs when I broke surface.

After these early practice runs I was then allowed to make more ascents from increasing depths. For the final ascent, I wore a life-jacket. As you can guess, this increased my speed enormously and, as the photograph on this page clearly shows, the effect on breaking surface is like a rocket being shot from an under-water gun.

OPERATION SUB. SUNK

As I made my way down to the changing room, Lieutenant Commander Andrews told me something of the methods of training at the school.

They are extremely proud of their 'no-fatal-accident' record, since well over 100,000 people have trained there.

The course is usually a two-day one, and trainees have included civilian divers, as well as the submariners for whom it is primarily intended. The school is responsible for submarine escape throughout the British Navy, and always stands ready for Operation Sub. Sunk, which rushes help to a submarine in distress anywhere in the world.

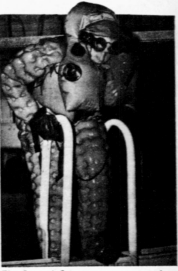
The Survival Suit protects escapers from exposure after they reach the surface

---

COLLEGE OF KNOWLEDGE

SPACE RACE

The distance to the nearest star is 25,000,000,000 miles. To express such distances more simply, another unit of measurement – the light year – was used. A light year is the distance light travels in one year (the speed of light being 186,000 miles per second), roughly 6,000,000,000,000 miles. As knowledge of space increased, so did the distances measured, and a new unit was introduced – the PARSEC (which is the distance the radius of the Earth's orbit would subtend at 1 second of arc, about 3¼ light years).

VITAL STATISTIC

The surface area of the inside of the lungs is about fifty times as great as the surface of the whole body. Through this very thin membrane surface, the blood is able to absorb oxygen and also exude carbon dioxide.

IT'S LIFE & DEATH

The virus is the smallest and simplest of all living things. Each virus unit consists of a single molecule of chemical substance resembling a crystal – showing no signs of life. Yet, if these are introduced into living tissue, they thrive and multiply. As they feed on living creatures, they produce poisonous waste products that may cause serious illness.

THE LONG AND THE SHORT OF IT

Short waves were thought to be of little use in the early days of broadcasting. Large wireless stations took over all the long and medium wave-bands. Amateur enthusiasts were allowed only the short wave-lengths for their use. They grumbled, but carried on, with amazing results. Soon amateurs with two-valve sets were communicating across the Atlantic. One such amateur made contact with New Zealand, the greatest distance possible. He was a schoolboy in Mill Hill.

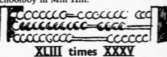

XLIII times XXXV

Have you ever wondered how the Romans with their strange numerals managed to do arithmetic? The answer is they used an Abacus (like a baby's bead board). This instrument, which has been in use for over 3,000 years, is still used today in Russia, China, Japan, and many other parts of the world. Experts use it like a slide rule, and can calculate rapidly.

NEXT WEEK: 'THE MAN FROM EAGLE' meets the Brave Men of the Sea!

HEROS

the SPARTAN

The new Caesar, a ruthless and tyrannical man who sought Heros's death, had given the young Spartan command of the Fifth Legion, the worst unit in the armies of Rome. Accompanied by Caesar's courier, Crassus, the Legion marched north to Gaul, with orders to stamp out an evil Druid cult. Soon, Heros and his men were attacked!

Fear and panic broke out among Heros's legionnaires . . .

NO, YOU FOOLS! HOLD YOUR RANK! FORM BATTLE ECHELON!

WE ARE AMBUSHED! RUN—MAKE FOR THE ROCKS!

Suddenly, a thousand bow-strings twanged . . .

CLOSE UP! USE YOUR SHIELDS TO FORM A PROTECTIVE ROOF!

But many of the descending barbs found a target. The treacherous Crassus cowered amid a chaos of slaughter . . .

THEY SCREAM LIKE MEN WITHOUT HOPE! THE LEGION IS DOOMED! I MUST FLEE THIS PLACE OF SLAUGHTER!

Unnoticed in the confusion, he slid up behind Heros, and . . .

BUT FIRST—I STRIKE A BLOW FOR CAESAR!

THERE IS NO ESCAPE!

As Heros's senses faded, the Barbarians massacred his legionnaires . . .

BY MITHRAS! THE GAULS ATTACK IN UTTE SILENCE!

SIL THE

Through the pain of Crassus's sword-thrust, Heros saw the flaxen-haired giants attacking . . .

IT IS THE END FOR THESE WRETCHES I COMMAND! WITHOUT THIS WOUND, I MIGHT HAVE LED THEM TO SAFETY! BUT I—I . . .

Barbarian hands lifted the standard of the legion . . .

WE WILL CARRY IT THROUGHOUT THE LAND AS A TOKEN OF OUR VICTORY! IT WILL INSPIRE THE TRIBES OF GAUL TO UNITE, AND MARCH IN A CRUSHING TIDE ON THE EMPIRE OF ROME!

The eyes of Heros the Spartan slowly opened . . .

UUUHHH! THE—THE BARBARIANS HAVE—GONE! BUT WHAT OF MY MEN— THE LEGION . . . ?

LEFT OTHE DEAD! FIFTH IS D

FRANK BELLAMY

But Heros's cowardly army scattered like sheep. And, up above . . .

Next moment, the rocks above Heros swarmed with the advancing foe . . .

MORE OF THE BARBARIANS— AND ON OUR FLANKS, TOO! WE ARE TRAPPED!

NOW, MEN OF THE BRIGANTES! IT IS TIME TO STRIKE!

LET HIM GO! LET HIM RETURN TO ROME AND TELL HIS EMPEROR OF THE FATE WHICH AWAITS ALL THOSE FOOLISH ENOUGH TO TEST THE MIGHT OF THE BRIGANTES!

As Heros fell, his horse was seized by Crassus, and urged from the battlefield . . .

AS CAESAR ORDERED, I HAVE ENSURED THAT HEROS WILL NEVER RETURN FROM THIS MISSION! BUT MY OWN LIFE IS STILL IN DANGER!

A cry from their leader stayed the Barbarians' bows . . .

BUT THE OTHERS MUST DIE! SLAY THEM! LET NO ROMAN ESCAPE!

In vain, a handful of battle-hardened veterans tried to rally their comrades . . .

FORM A RING AROUND THE EAGLE! FIGHT, YOU SPINELESS CUR—AAAGH!

THE STANDARD-BEARER FALLS! IT IS THE END!

The grim carnage continued. And, as the last Roman fell . . .

ENOUGH! IF ANY ROMAN STILL BREATHES, LEAVE HIM TO THE BUZZARDS! BUT BRING THE RED CRESTS' EAGLE-GOD!

Racked with shame and remorse, Heros stumbled from the silent battlefield . . .

I LED MY COMMAND—INTO DISHONOUR AND DISGRACE! I AM NOT—WORTHY— TO LIVE . . .!

As Heros once more collapsed beneath the blazing sun, harsh, hate-filled eyes glared angrily down at him . . .

End of Episode 5

Letter from the Editor

I suppose quite a number of you will have been abroad for your holidays this year, grappling with the intricacies of a foreign tongue. Those phrases you painfully mastered at school can come in very handy, but the trouble is, when you ask a Frenchman the way to the station, he will rattle off instructions to you in French. Then where are you? Uncomprehendingly, but trying to look as though you know what he's talking about, you mutter a confused "Merci, monsieur" and hurry off to find someone who can speak English!

Of course the problem wouldn't arise if you could speak French fluently, and this prompts me to ask whether enough attention is given in schools to learning a foreign language, especially in view of the closer links that are being forged between Britain and the Continent. If our Continental visitors take the trouble to learn English, why shouldn't we learn theirs?

Let me have your opinion by Friday, 1st November, and I will pay a guinea for the best letter. All other letters published will win 5s.

Now for your letters on 'pop' singing . . .

It's your opinion

This week's guinea letter

Dear Editor,

It is my opinion that 'pop' singing is generally a good thing. The careful vocal arrangements, the backing that swings and the tricky guitar playing all help to create a feeling of light-heartedness in the listener. However, I feel that 'pop' singing can monopolize some young people's minds. They become so obsessed with the catchy melodies that they cannot concentrate on things such as homework. I am a victim myself.

To become a 'pop' singer, I think that one must be blessed with an individuality which appeals to most people. This asset will enable any singer to make a success of most songs. As for gimmicks, I think they are dying out. Style of singing is the deciding factor. This is shown by the way that Mr Harris and Mr Presley have given up their wild singing and dressing for a more specialized singing.

J. O'Dell, West Drayton, Middlesex.

Dear Editor,

I do not think that 'pop' singing is ridiculous. It's groups like the Beatles, Gerry and the Pacemakers and Billy J. Kramer and the Dakotas that people like to hear. I think that I am right in saying that there are more 'pop' records sold than classical records. I think that anyone can draw their own conclusions from that.

J. Fox, West Bromwich, Staffs.

Dear Editor,

On the whole, I like 'pop' music – to listen to, that is. But I always tend to laugh at most of the artists I see on TV. They wriggle and writhe and jump about as though they have just eaten a few pounds of apples. I also think that some artists get far too much money. For example, my teenage brother tells me that the 'Beatles' get £5,000 a week. That is ridiculous! All that money would be better spent on some charity!

J. M. O'Donnell (12), Kirkby-in-Furness, Lancs.

Dear Editor,

In my opinion, 'pop' singing has its own place in the music world.

Just think what would happen if there was none of it. "Shall we dance the minuet?" one teenager would say to another. No, thanks!

P. Harris, Whitby, Yorks.

Dear Editor,

It is impossible to give an answer which is as generalized as your question, because there are so many singers (some employing 'gimmicks', others not).

Second, it depends what is covered by the term 'pop' singer. Although people who are ignorant of the subject often do not realize it, 'pop' music does not include Rock 'n' Roll, Country and Western, Rhythm and Blues or Folk Music (all of which are closely related to Modern Jazz and stem from Blues).

Speaking generally, however, I like guitars, rock, etc., and modern jazz, but I dislike many 'pop' singers.

C. L. Taylor (17), Orpington, Kent.

Dear Editor,

I think 'pop' singing is ridiculous, and I cannot understand how anyone could enjoy it.

If people listened to classical music, they would soon begin to think it was much nicer, and realize that 'pop' music is just an unpleasant noise.

J. J. Fabricius, Woldingham, Surrey.

Dear Editor,

I like 'pop' singing because it is lively and keeps me happy.

I think that a really good 'pop' singer should feel the same way when he or she is singing.

As the late 'pop' singer Eddie Cochran once said: "This kind of music comes from the heart." So I think it should be sung that way if a 'pop' singer wants to be a success.

Lastly, 'pop' singing certainly is not as gimmick-ridden as it was in the days of 'rock 'n' roll. You very seldom see a 'pop' singer these days who shakes his body all over the place.

R. Payn (15), Orpington, Kent.

Mozart

Dear Editor,

In my opinion, 'pop' music as a whole is underrated by people who have lived and are living in the world of Mozart and such. My father is an example of this, and is always making fun of modern singers, groups and dances.

In his day, he admits, he enjoyed 'pop' music, but he just does not bother with the hits of today.

M. Baldock, Maidstone, Kent.

Dear Editor,

Being a 13-year-old myself, I am very interested in 'pop' singing. Some 'squares' call it a lot of noise and rubbish which anyone could write, but this is not so. There is a strict technique in the writing of 'pop' songs, and the majority that are issued are good recordings. This type of singing is the up-and-coming generation's favourite. I see no reason why people should condemn it. My personal favourites are guitar instrumentals and group records, but I like all 'pop' music. 'Pop' is modern and exciting, so let's enjoy it.

A. Permier, Gravesend, Kent.

Send your letters to :– The Editor, EAGLE SWIFT, 161 Fleet Street, LONDON, E.C.4.

Dear Editor,

I have been a reader of EAGLE for close on ten years — and the best thing that ever appeared on the front page was the Dan Dare feature. The futuristic scenes were never displayed better, and I would laud any attempt to return him to the front page in colour.

Douglas Marden, Hoboken, New Jersey, U.S.A.

I hope to make an announcement about Dan Dare in next week's issue. — Editor.

Are the Beatles worth it?

LETTER FROM THE EDITOR

It used to be said that every private soldier had a Field Marshal's baton in his knapsack. Nowadays, it seems as though every schoolboy has a guitar in his satchel. For 'pop' singing is the current craze, and the guitar has become a symbol to thousands of youngsters of a way to fame and fortune.

What is your opinion about 'pop' singing? Do you feel that it gives freedom to the singer to interpret the song in his own individual way, with whatever actions he thinks are necessary to help him in his performance, or is the whole business becoming gimmick-ridden and ridiculous?

Let me have your views by Friday, 20th September, and I'll pay a guinea for the best letter. All other letters published will win 5s.

Now for your opinions on school uniforms, which are printed below . .

IT'S YOUR OPINION . .

Gold Rush!

Thousands of prospectors stampeded out of Kanowna in Western Australia one August afternoon in 1898. They knew where the 100 lb. solid gold 'sacred nugget' had been found. The only man to see it—a young priest called Father Long—had at last revealed the exact spot. The diggers moved tons of rock and earth, but none struck gold. And the two men who had painted a piece of iron with gold paint to fool the priest had to run for their lives from the murderous mob.

Today gold mining in Australia is highly organised, along with other industry, but Australia is still a country of golden opportunity. A land of modern cities, verdant pastures, open country, glorious beaches, and above all the sun.

AUSTRALIA—A BIG YOUNG COUNTRY WITH A BIG FUTURE

Ask your father if he knows how much gold is mined annually in Australia. And if you would like the free booklet Facts about Australia write to this address:—

Chief Migration Officer, Dept. 655/63, Australia House, Strand, London, WC2

R.A.F. BELVEDERE

The Westland Belvedere, of which R.A.F. Transport Command has several squadrons, is the largest and most capable helicopter in the Service. Some of the squadrons will be stationed in the Middle and Far East.

The Belvedere will perform lifting operations in tactical support of the Army. A load of 2½ tons can be carried internally or slung underneath. Typical loads are 19 troops or 12 stretcher cases, or a Land-Rover and trailer, or a light-weight bridge slung underneath.

The powerplant is composed of two 1,650 h.p. Napier Gazelle free-turbine jet engines. These engines are mounted at either end of the main cabin. An intermediate shaft running along the top of the fuselage enables one engine to drive both rotors if necessary.

Forward cruising speed, 120 knots; range, about 450 miles; vertical rate of climb, 440 ft. per minute.

KEY TO NUMBERED PARTS

(1) Rear rotor head. (2) Rotor reduction gearbox. (3) Cooling-air intake to gearbox and rotor head. (4) Rear rotor controls. (5) Rudder. (6) Stabilizer. (7) Rear engine air intake. (8) Napier Gazelle free-turbine jet engine. (9) Jet exhausts (each side). (10) Rear fuel tank – 116 gallons' capacity. (11) Engine oil tank. (12) Intermediate fuel tank – 164 gallons' capacity. (13) Generators. (14) Oil cooler. (15) Electrical panel and radio racks. (16) Accommodation for 12 stretcher cases. (17) Alternative accommodation for 19 fully-equipped troops. (18) Escape hatch and window. (19) Intermediate shaft drive and rear rotor controls. (20) Sliding door. (21) Electric haulage winch. (22) Front fuel tanks – 280 gallons' capacity. (23) Swivelling front undercarriage wheels. (24) Front engine air intake to compressors. (25) Air compressors of Napier Gazelle free-turbine jet engine. (26) Combustion chambers. (27) Firewall. (28) Jet exhausts (each side). (29) Rotor reduction gearbox. (30) Intermediate shaft drive between engines; this allows one engine to drive both rotors, if necessary. (31) Front rotor head with collective and cyclic pitch control spider. (32) Flying control ducts. (33) Pilot, co-pilot, and radio operator on left-hand side. (34) Collective pitch lever: this controls the pitch of the rotor blades for vertical flight. (35) Cyclic pitch lever: this controls the pitch of the rotor heads for forward, backward and sideways flight (see insets below). (36) Rudder pedals. (37) Powered flying-control apparatus. (38) Slung load of up to 2½ tons. The Belvedere is shown here bringing supplies to a forward Army post.

COLLECTIVE PITCH – Control of Rotor Blades

Forward Flight

Vertical Flight or Hovering

CYCLIC PITCH – Tilt of Rotor Head

Backward Flight

Left or Right Flight

COMBINED PITCHES

The application of the above flying controls, which are shown in simplified form, gives the helicopter its great powers of manoeuvring. With combined pitches, it can swing or turn on its own axis while in vertical flight or hovering, turn left or right in forward flight. An experienced pilot can make it do amazing

I. ASHWELL

A great little sports car

Latest in the line of sports cars from Lotus is the Elan 1500, a smart little two-seater designed by a team headed by racing-car designer Colin Chapman, for high-performance touring and occasional racing. Built on an immensely strong light-weight welded steel 'backbone' chassis and fitted with a glass fibre body, the Elan embodies a number of Ford parts, including the basis of the engine which is a derated form of the racing engine fitted to a Lotus 23 and raced successfully in the 1,000 Kilometre Race at Nürburgring last year. All-round independent suspension and disc brakes fitted to all four wheels contribute to the ease of handling and high safety factor required to match the performance of the Elan.

Acclaimed the most advanced sports car in the world, the Elan is available either as a completed car or, as most owners prefer, a ready-to-assemble kit of parts for home construction, which provides the builder with a potent and individual sports car at a much reduced cost.

KEY TO NUMBERED PARTS

(1) Glass fibre reinforced moulded plastic body shell. (2) and (3) Foam-filled front and rear glass fibre bumpers. (4) Fabricated welded-steel 'backbone' chassis. (5) Four-cylinder 1,498 c.c. Ford Classic-based engine (developing 100 b.h.p. at 5,700 r.p.m.) fitted with a Lotus-designed head with two chain-driven camshafts (6). (7) Short-stroke piston, 72.75 mm. stroke x 80.96 mm. bore. (8) Balanced five-bearing crankshaft. (9) Radiator. (10) Cooling-air inlet for radiator. (11) Two twin-choke 40 DCOE Weber carburetors. (12) Air cleaner fitted with replaceable element. (13) Four-branch exhaust manifold. (14) Ford four-speed all-synchromesh gearbox. (15) Propeller shaft. (16) Final drive with Lotus-designed aluminium casing containing Ford Classic differential unit. (17) Drive shafts to wheels, fitted with rubber couplings to allow for independent suspension movement. (18) Rear-wheel independent suspension coil spring and telescopic shock absorber. (19) Rear 10 in.-diameter Girling disc brakes. (20) Front 9¼ in.-diameter Girling disc brakes. (21) Front independent suspension by wishbones and coil springs with telescopic dampers. (22) 15 in.-diameter wood-rimmed dished steering wheel. (23) Inset showing teak-veneered facia panel fitted with fuel gauge, speedometer, rev-counter and combined oil-pressure and water-temperature gauge. (24) Fully retractable head-lamps. (25) Wide-opening glass fibre doors, fitted with sliding windows, map pockets and arm-rests. (26) Spare wheel. (27) 10-gallon fuel tank. (28) Side view showing the weatherproof P.V.C. fabric hood in position. (29) Luggage compartment. (30) Rear view of the Elan.

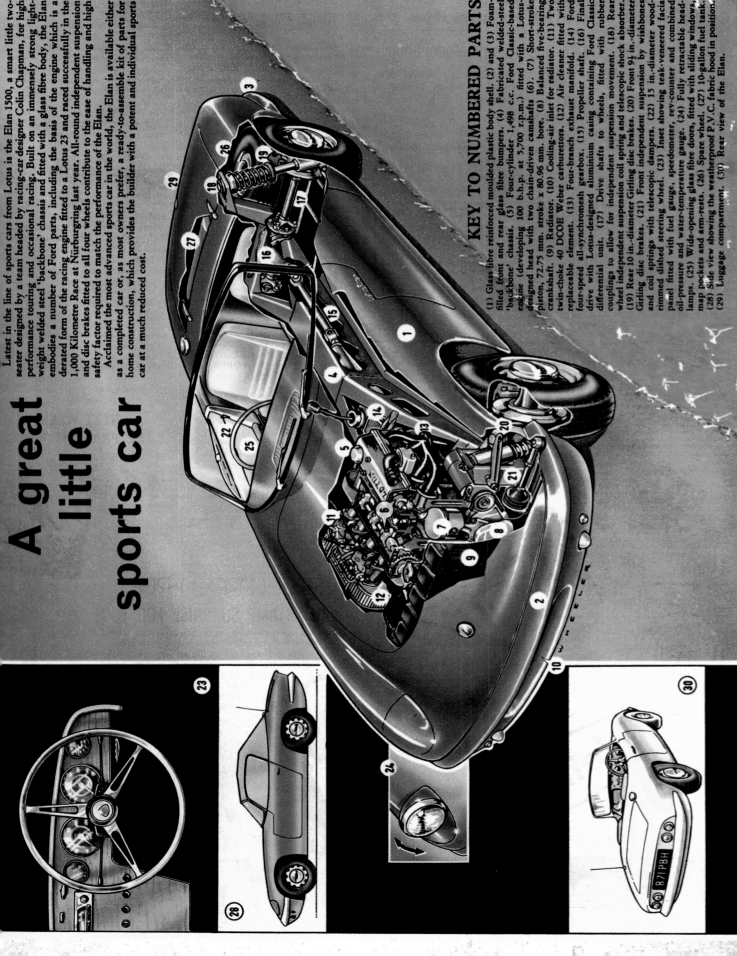

HOME OF THE WANDERERS

Dave Corbin was an early example of a footballer crossing over into the music world. For him it proved rather unsuccessful as his team mates resented the attention he got from fans, and his antics in playing up to them. He was dropped from the team because of his swinging ways. When he finally got back in he realised his guitar had got him into too much trouble and had it locked away for good.

...WHEN OTHER FELLERS TAKE A HEADLONG FA-ALL ...THAT'S WHEN YOU'LL FIN I'M REALLY ON THE BALL.

HOME OF THE WANDERERS

'Pop' singing soccer star Dave Corbin had attracted a big crowd of youngsters from his own Fan Club to Wanderers' League match against Barling United. Trying to show off to them, Dave played so indifferently that centre-half Geoff Coggan decided to keep feeding the ball out to the opposite wing...

DAVE'S FANS, MANY OF WHOM KNEW LITTLE ABOUT FOOTBALL, WERE BECOMING IMPATIENT...

DON'T LET THEM KEEP THE BALL AWAY FROM YOU, DAVE!

GO IN AND GET IT YOURSELF!

MAYBE THEY'VE GOT SOMETHING THERE! NEXT TIME JIM GETS THE BALL, I'LL GIVE HIM THE SIGNAL TO DO OUR CROSS-OVER MOVE...

AS DAVE WORKED THE BALL INTO THE PENALTY AREA, THE DEFENCE MOVED TO COVER HIM...

NOW! BACK TO ME!

INSTEAD OF FLICKING IT BACK TO THE UNMARKED JIM, DAVE TRIED TO SHOW HIS FANS HOW HE COULD SHOOT!

OH, NO! THAT BACK'S HAD TIME TO MOVE ACROSS.

BLOCKED BY THE BACK, THE BALL LOFTED HIGH INTO THE AIR...

SOME MINUTES LATER, RIGHT-WINGER JIMMY HALLIDAY RECEIVED A PASS AND LOOKED ACROSS THE PITCH...

IT'S DAVE! HE'S GIVING ME THE SIGNAL FOR THE 'X' PLAN. I SUPPOSE IT'S O.K. TO GIVE IT A TRY...

IT WAS A MOVE THEY'D WORKED OUT BEFORE. JIM SLICED DIAGONALLY ACROSS TO THE LEFT— SLIPPING IT TO DAVE AS THEY CROSSED IN THE CENTRE...

NOW, DAVE! YOURS!

THAT'S A CLEVER PIECE OF FOOTBALL! IT'S GOT UNITED GUESSING!

DAVE TURNED TO TAKE ANOTHER SHOT, BUT GEOFF COGGAN HURLED HIMSELF HEADLONG!

IT'S THERE! GOAL!

WHAT A HEADER! A SHOT IN A MILLION!

WANDERERS 1. BARLING UNITED 1.

MOST WANDERERS FANS WENT WILD WITH DELIGHT— BUT SOME OF DAVE'S FANS WENT WILD WITH RAGE!

THAT OUGHT TO HAVE BEEN DAVE'S GOAL!

DOWN WITH COGGAN! HE STARVES DAVE OF PASSES AND THEN POACHES HIS SHOTS AT GOAL!

AND WHEN GEOFF TROTTED TOWARDS THE TUNNEL AT HALF TIME...

BOOOH! HERE COMES A ROTTEN SPORT!

WHAT'S THE IDEA, COGGAN—KEEPING THE BALL FROM OUR DAVE?

LET'S ROUGH HIM UP!

SKIPPER STEVE BRADY PAUSED IN THE TUNNEL AND LOOKED BACK IN DISMAY...

MY STARS! THEY'RE GOING OVER ON TO THE PITCH — OUT FOR GEOFF'S BLOOD! THIS CAN MEAN BAD TROUBLE FOR WANDERERS!

MORE THRILLS NEXT WEEK!

XYZ CARS — CALLING 'U' FOR USELESS!

Registered at the G.P.O. for transmission by Magazine Post to Canada (including Newfoundland) Eagle and Swift Magazine with which is incorporated the Merry-Go-Round, printed in Great Britain by Eric Bemrose Ltd., Long Lane, Liverpool, 9, and published by Odhams Press Ltd., Long Acre, London, W.C.2. Sole Agents for Australia and New Zealand, Gordon & Gotch (A/sia) Ltd., South Africa, Central News Agency Ltd. Subscription Rates: Inland – 12 months, 43/4; abroad, including Canada – 12 months, 36/10. Dollar rate for U.S.A., $5.50; Canada, $6.00. Please send your order to Subscription Dept., 1/3 Pemberton Row, London, E.C.4.

LETTER FROM THE EDITOR

Naturally enough, your views on pocket money varied according to your age. But I must admit I was surprised by such a large variation – the sums mentioned ranging from ninepence to ten shillings. Generally speaking, two shillings and sixpence a week seemed the average demand, although many of you made the point that extra money should be worked for.

Now for this week's topic. Many of you send jokes for illustration in the paper and say which features you like best in EAGLE/SWIFT. But of course many of you don't send in jokes.

So what about writing to me and letting me know which stories or features you like best – or dislike most – and giving me the reason. After all, this is your paper, and your letters can enable me to give you what you want.

IT'S YOUR OPINION...

Dear Editor,
I get 9d. pocket money a week and I agree that boys ought to have a penny increase every birthday. Would any readers like to dispute that?
S. B. Pattison, Sunderland, Co. Durham.

I'm sure they would. After all, when you ... fourteen, you would be getting only ... 2d. – and I don't think you'd consider ... enough. – Editor.

Dear Editor,
I get 9d. and I think it is enough because ... save it. I am quite lucky because I do not ... ave to use my pocket money on sweets ... d comics – my parents buy them.
My brother, who is nearly nine, gets a ... illing. I have another brother who gets ... (he's four). My sister, who is two, gets ... penny. The last brother gets no pocket ... oney, and he's one.
Benjamin Hyde (7), Birkenhead, Cheshire.

Dear Editor,
I think that boys should not be given more than 2s. 6d. pocket money per week. If they want anything which costs more than this, they can save up for it. If they get too much money, they expect everything to be given to them.
John Abramson (11), Ayr, Ayrshire.

Dear Editor,
I get 2s. 6d. for my pocket money, which is enough. Once I heard of a boy who got a rise from 5s. to 10s. If the father gave 10s. to the other three brothers, they would have to live in a tent!
N. Byrne, Manchester, 23.

Dear Editor,
I think boys should get a shilling a week pocket money, because, later on, when they are older, they will appreciate the value of money. It also teaches them not to waste

it on things not worth buying.
Bruce Malcolm, Cheltenham, Glos.

Dear Editor,
I think that children should not have more than 1s. 6d. a week pocket money. If we had more, we would only spend it on sweets and our teeth would decay. Also I think that we should save 6d. of it to buy presents for relations and friends.
Peter Bennett (9), Southgate, London, N.14.

Dear Editor,
I think children should have 1s. 6d. pocket money; one shilling to save and sixpence to spend. This enables them to have enough money for going on school outings, holidays and going out for the day. I think that 6d. is enough for spending.
Peter H. Martin (9), Coventry, Warks.

Dear Editor,
I think 2s. is a good sum for a week's pocket money. At school, when the others learn I have 2s., they goggle at me like fish and say: "That all? Not much is it?" They are accustomed to 2s. 6d., 3s., even 4s. How some parents can give 2s. 6d. when

they can barely buy a loaf of bread beats me!
R. Renold (11), Bradford, 9.

Dear Editor,
I think that boys should not be allowed more than 2s. a week, otherwise, in later life, they will be encouraged to spend more money than is necessary.
David Hall, Malvern Link, Worcs.

Dear Editor,
I think that a boy under 11 should get 2s. a week. Why? Well, I think it's sufficient and should buy most of the things a boy would want. If, however, his mother or father worked at a shop and got sweets and comics cheap, then his pocket money should be reduced.
When a boy reaches his teens, he has the disadvantage of having to pay for two if he gets a girl friend. If possible, pocket money should be raised for this, but the best answer then is that the boy should try and earn a few shillings himself.
Jimmy Wiseman (11), Westcliff-on-Sea, Essex.

Dear Editor,
I think boys should have 3d. for every year. At the age of 13, however, mothers should make a rise to 6d. a year. I myself am nine, and get 2s. 3d. a week, out of which I have to pay for Church, Cubs and EAGLE/SWIFT!
Raymond Foster, East Cowes, Isle-of-Wight.

Dear Editor,
Every Friday I receive 2s. spending money, with which I supply a family of six Abyssinian guinea pigs with food. This takes about a shilling to 1s. 6d. a week, depending on their appetites. I also pay a weekly visit to the local swimming club,

costing another 6d. Owing to the fluctuating amount needed to support my cavies, I can usually afford to go on fairly regular fishing sprees. These cost 1s. 9d. and, the odd penny or two I save, I buy fishing tackle, spares and replacements for my bike. If by any chance I should need a shilling or so, my father usually helps.
Geoffrey Brown, Nelson, Lancs.

Dear Editor,
I think 2s. a week is a good average for pocket money. Not much more, because then the person receiving it might think he could get away with 5s., going up to 10s., and finally to a point where the poor parents would start being annoyed by their child's greediness. There would then be rows, and a happy family might turn into a very unhappy one – all because of some pocket money.
William Derraugh, Belfast, 6.

The following letter wins our guinea prize.
Dear Editor,
I think that boys ought to work for their pocket money. This is how my brothers and I get our pocket money. This also means that if you work hard and often, you get more. We start with a basic sum of a shilling. I used to get 2s. 6d. every week without fail, but now I can get more.
Thomas Ashe (14), Maidstone, Kent.

Dear Editor,
I say boys under ten should have no more than 2s. 6d. If they want any more, it should be earned by gardening, running errands, golf caddying and other jobs.
Hugh Lomas, Wythall, Nr. Birmingham.

Dear Editor,
I think that boys over the age of 12 should work for their pocket money, whether they help in the house or get a paper-job. As for the younger boys, I think that they should get 2s. 6d. until they are nine years old, and 5s. until they are 12 or 13.
The reason for this is that I think boys nowadays do not appreciate their 5s. and 10s., that they take it for granted and think they are entitled to it.
As for myself, I get 5s. a week – but that includes bus fares to school.
J. Hubbard (13), Gateshead, 9, Co. Durham.

Dear Editor,
The amount of pocket money a boy receives each week depends to a great extent on his age. Two shillings should be quite sufficient for anyone up to the age of five, and from five to ten years, 5s. sho be adequate. From the age of ten to 15, 10s. would suffice.
Boys should get a regular fixed amount, never too much – for boys must learn to 'budget' their spending in preparation for when they go to work.
Michael Edwards, Godalming, Surrey.

Dear Editor,
I think that boys between 13 and 16 years should have at least 6s. pocket money. I am 15 and have 6s. per week with everything found.
Pocket money of 6s. a week can teach me the value of money. If one wants to buy an article and has to save up to buy it, the article is appreciated all the more.
Wealthy parents are able to give their children a large amount of pocket money. Through having too much pocket money the child becomes spoilt, because he can buy almost anything he wants.
M. M. Ash, Sheldon, Birmingham, 26.

Z Cars first appeared on the BBC on 2 January 1962 and it was not too long afterwards that *Eagle* took a comic swipe at the cult cop show. Whilst Z Cars is no longer on television the theme tune can still be heard in one small corner of the country. At Goodison Park, home of Everton, it is played to accompany the team on to the pitch. The programme was set in the fictitious new town of 'Newtown' which was situated in a never actually identified area somewhere in the North-West.

CONCORDE

THE SUPERSONIC JETLINER OF TOMORROW

The supersonic airliner is going to come for certain. The British and French Governments have signed an agreement for the joint production of the Concorde Mach 2.2 airliner.

Work is to begin immediately. It is planned that the aircraft's first flight will be in 1966, and it will be ready for airline service in 1970.

The Concorde will be built mainly in aluminium alloy, with stainless steel in vital parts. It will be powered by four British Siddeley Olympus 593 turbo-jets mounted in pairs in two underslung nacelles beneath the wing. The cruising speed of Mach 2.2 is in the region of 1,450 m.p.h. – over twice the speed of sound at 40,000 feet.

The form of the wing will be 'ogee' – a term meaning 'of double curvature', applying mainly to the shape across the wingspan.

Britain is all keyed up for her part in this tremendous venture to build the first supersonic airliner in the world.

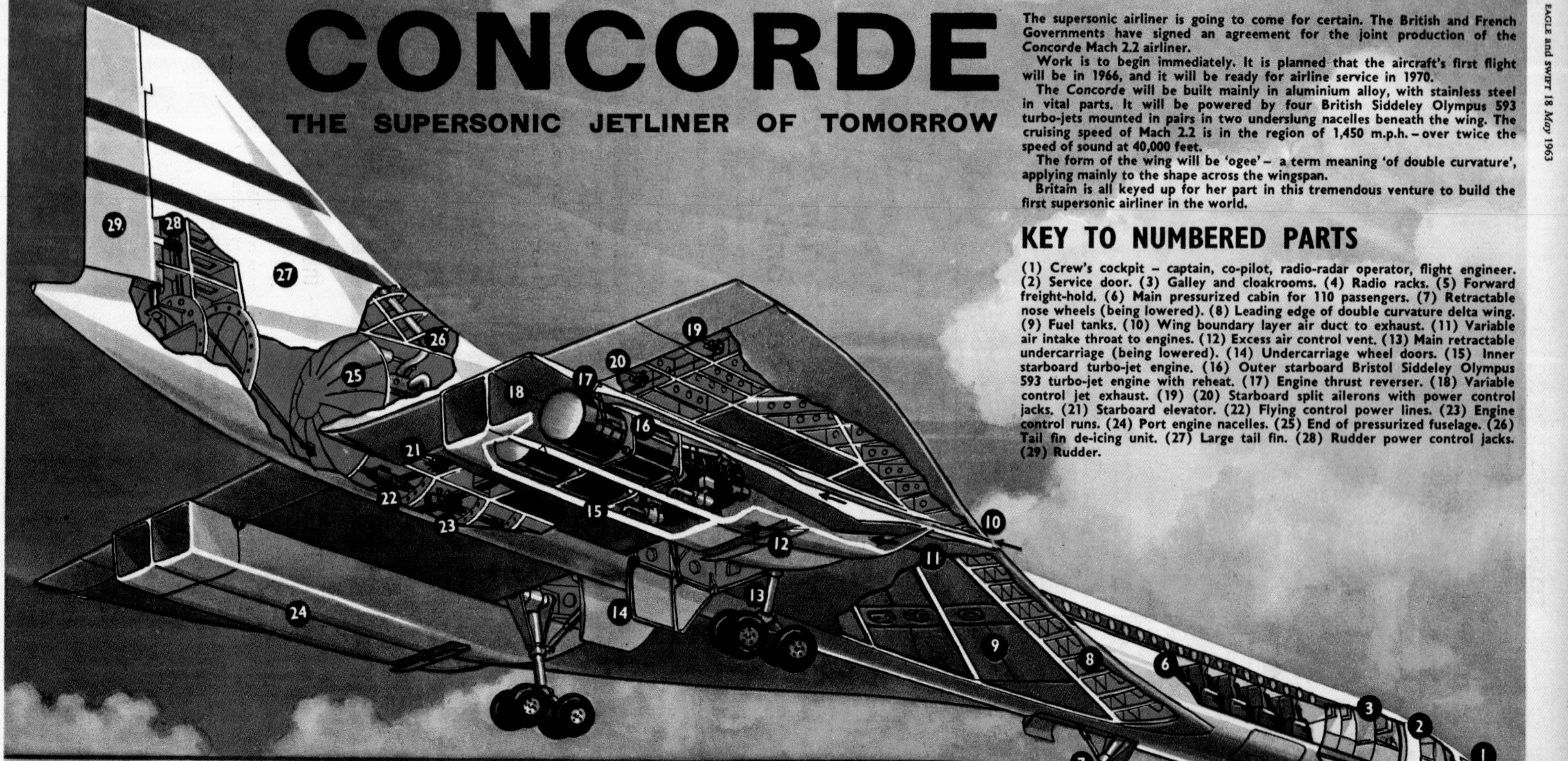

KEY TO NUMBERED PARTS

(1) Crew's cockpit – captain, co-pilot, radio-radar operator, flight engineer. (2) Service door. (3) Galley and cloakrooms. (4) Radio racks. (5) Forward freight-hold. (6) Main pressurized cabin for 110 passengers. (7) Retractable nose wheels (being lowered). (8) Leading edge of double curvature delta wing. (9) Fuel tanks. (10) Wing boundary layer air duct to exhaust. (11) Variable air intake throat to engines. (12) Excess air control vent. (13) Main retractable undercarriage (being lowered). (14) Undercarriage wheel doors. (15) Inner starboard turbo-jet engine. (16) Outer starboard Bristol Siddeley Olympus 593 turbo-jet engine with reheat. (17) Engine thrust reverser. (18) Variable control jet exhaust. (19) (20) Starboard split ailerons with power control jacks. (21) Starboard elevator. (22) Flying control power lines. (23) Engine control runs. (24) Port engine nacelles. (25) End of pressurized fuselage. (26) Tail fin de-icing unit. (27) Large tail fin. (28) Rudder power control jacks. (29) Rudder.

ASHWELL WOOD

TRANSATLANTIC COMPARISONS

The Atlantic crossing has always been one of great importance. The chosen cruising speed of 1,450 m.p.h. will enable the Concorde to make a transatlantic flight in under three hours instead of the seven required by current large jet aircraft. (The Boeing 707 and Concorde are drawn to the same scale.)

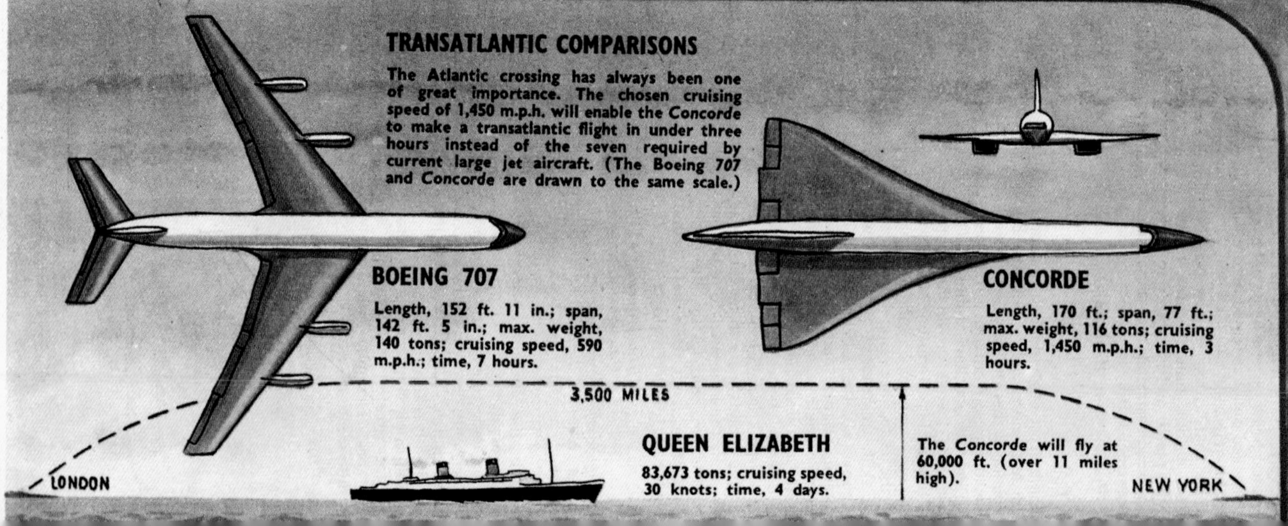

BOEING 707

Length, 152 ft. 11 in.; span, 142 ft. 5 in.; max. weight, 140 tons; cruising speed, 590 m.p.h.; time, 7 hours.

CONCORDE

Length, 170 ft.; span, 77 ft.; max. weight, 116 tons; cruising speed, 1,450 m.p.h.; time, 3 hours.

The Concorde will fly at 60,000 ft. (over 11 miles high).

3,500 MILES

NEW YORK

LONDON

QUEEN ELIZABETH

83,673 tons; cruising speed, 30 knots; time, 4 days.

GOING FISHING...
with
OLD FRED and JOHNNY

NEXT WEEK: **FISHING FOR CARP**

The animal which has changed hardly at all from its ancestors of prehistoric times is – the Tapir. It is related to the horse family and the rhinoceros, and four species are found in Central and South America. The Tapir's snout is drawn out into a short trunk and it has four toes on the front feet and three on the hind.

IT'S A FACT

Spanish bullfighters will never fight a cow – it's too dangerous and much more deadly than a bull when roused. This is because a bull will make a straight rush at his enemy, while the cow will fence from side to side with her horns, and she is so quick that a man's chance of escape is slight.

The greatest air ace of World War I was Rittmeister Manfred von Richthofen. Nicknamed the 'Red Knight', because of his all-red machine, he shot down over eighty Allied planes before being killed during the last months of the war.

The camel is the hardiest and longest-working animal. It can carry as much as 1,000 lb. over a distance of 25 miles per day for three days without eating or drinking. And its strength and endurance increases year-by-year until it is 50 years old.

Thomas Fuller was only twelve years old when he entered Queen's College, Cambridge, in 1620. He took his B.A. degree when he was 16, and his M.A. at 20.

GREAT GUNS
The COLT LIGHTNING

When William Bonney was twelve, he [kill]ed his first man. He became an out[law] – a man on the run. He was still [run]ning ten years later, when Pat Garrett [shot] him dead in New Mexico.

What was it that turned William Bon[ney], a mere boy, into Billy the Kid – the [mos]t dangerous gunfighter in the Wild [We]st?

[Bi]lly's widowed mother was too busy [look]ing after her boarding house to worry [abo]ut her young son and, as there were [no] schools in Silver City, he got his ['edu]cation' from o t h e r sources. He [wat]ched the drunken cow-hands fighting, [and] the gun duels in [the] streets. In the [sal]oons, he listened to [the] stories o f t h e [gam]blers, the profes[sion]al killers and the [catt]le rustlers.

[Bi]lly admired these [men]. T h e y seemed [stro]ng; they were re[spec]ted – or perhaps [mere]ly feared. H i s [chan]ce to be one of [them] came when a [bull]y, who had insulted his mother, came [into] the saloon. Billy attacked him with [a kn]ife, and fled from town.

[By] the time he was 17, Billy was [repu]ted to carry no fewer than fifteen [notc]hes on the barrel of his Colt! [H]e teamed up with English cattle[rais]er John Tunstall, but the partnership was abruptly halted with the killing of Tunstall by a Sheriff's posse. Billy swore revenge. Two of the posse, Morton and Baker, were dead within the month. The blood-letting ended with Sheriff Brady and his deputy, George Hindman, lying dead in Lincoln City.

Billy the Kid was indicted as a murderer and was brought back for trial. However, he managed to get hold of a gun and fought his way out of jail, leaving two deputies dying.

But the Kid's days were numbered. The new Sheriff of Lincoln City, Pat Garrett, was hot on his trail and Billy seemed to be permanently on the run. The end came as something of an anti - climax. Garrett and two deputies surrounded t h e N e w Mexican ranch house in which Billy was hiding. Garrett crept up to the house and banged on the door.

"Quien es?" Billy inquired from within.

Garrett didn't reply. As Billy opened the door, Garrett's Colts barked, and Billy the Kid was to kill no more!

So Billy the Kid died at the age of 22. But what sort of person was he? Experts disagree. Some describe him as an avenging angel seeking only revenge for his comrade. Others call him a cowardly killer.

HOW IT WORKS

The Colt Lightning .41-calibre revolver favoured by Billy the Kid was lighter than the normal Colt 'Peacemaker' and of double-action design. This meant that it could be fired either by cocking the hammer between shots or by pulling on the trigger which, as it moved back, cocked the hammer and released it. In each case, the cylinder moved round automatically.

NEXT WEEK: WILD BILL HICKOK'S COLT DRAGOON!

GREAT GUNS

THE DEVIL'S BARREL-ORGAN

FROM an early age, Richard J. Gatling had been obsessed with the idea that guns could be made to fire more than one shot without having to reload.

In 1862, he took out patents on a 'machine-gun', a revolutionary weapon which even startled the makers of the first model.

Disaster struck from the beginning. Fire broke out in the factory in Cincinnati and destroyed the partly-finished models and all the drawings.

Various types of ammunition were used in the newly-built guns until they worked perfectly but, no matter how hard he tried, Richard Gatling could not get the army interested.

During this time, the Civil War was raging and a new development like the Gatling would have made a lot of difference to the Union forces. However, the generals would not entertain the thought until General Benjamin Butler ordered 12 guns. Only Butler used the guns in this terrible war and, at the battle of Petersburg, he used them to good effect.

The war came to an end and, when the guns had been improved, the army began tests and ordered 100 of the New Gatlings.

By this time, other countries had heard of the weapon and production was moved to the Colt factory. The Germans, whose tests had been severe, ordered 300. They matched one Gatling gun against 100 men using needle-fire muskets – and the Gatling would have beaten them even if there had been 300 riflemen, judging by results!

In the war between Russia and Turkey, in 1877, both sides used Gatlings with devastating effect. They were used against the Mexicans and Cubans by the Americans. All over the world, armies had units mounting Gatlings. But there was one man in particular in the U.S. Army who did not think much of them. He was General Custer and, when he set out with his command in 1876, he left his four Gatlings behind. There might have been a very different result to the battle of the Little Big Horn had he taken along Richard Gatling's machine-gun!

HOW IT WORKS

Produced from 1862-1911, the Gatling gun was, in the true sense, a ten-barrelled revolver. The barrel 'unit' turned and, as it came to the top central position, the cartridge was slipped in, fired and ejected in 3 quick movements. The ammunition was held in long clips similar to the modern Thompson sub-machine-gun and, with a lot of these prepared, the Gatling would fire 800 rounds per minute. A handle on the side worked a gear which turned the barrel unit. This in turn operated the simple firing mechanism. Built in various calibres such as .50, .65, .75, .85 and one inch, the gun was carried on mules or its own carriage, according to the type of country using it.

Russian soldiers using the Gatling machine-gun in their war against the Turks

NEXT WEEK: GUN ODDITIES

LETTER FROM THE EDITOR

Last week I published the letter from an American reader who said how much he missed Dan Dare in colour on the front page. His was not the only letter I have had expressing the same opinion. In fact, I have had scores.

Well, my aim is to give you what you want, and although with new features and stories I have to *guess* whether or not you will like them, here is a case where I *know* what you like.

So, when Dan Dare and Digby step out on to the planet of Meit next week, their adventures will be recorded on the front page in colour. I'm sure this will mean double enjoyment for you.

Meanwhile, don't forget to let me have your views, in not more than 150 words, on whether or not schoolboys should do newspaper rounds. I will pay a guinea for the best letter and five shillings for each letter published – and that applies to all other letters printed, too.

LETTERS TO THE EDITOR

Dear Editor,

If people saw a 'flying saucer' land on Earth, they would surely call the police and the army. But why? Because they fear our universal visitors? Obviously, such people haven't examined all the facts about the subject. There is one obvious theory why these visitors should not be feared.

If these people have come across many millions of miles of 'space', surely they must be much more intelligent than we are – as we haven't yet visited our own Moon, which is less than 250,000 miles away. People as intelligent as they must be, would surely know better than to fight wars! You will agree, I'm sure, that it is not at all intelligent to settle arguments by fighting, and, intelligent as they must be, they have no reason to come to Earth to invade it! So why be afraid of them?

R. W. Passey, Tamworth, Staffs.

Dear Editor,

When I went to school in Stevenage, Hertfordshire, I read EAGLE in the playground – and sometimes during prep.

Now I read it between scenes on a film set.

I am a pupil at the Italia Conti School in London, where Noel Coward, Jack Hawkins and many other famous stars attended.

At the stage school, we have ordinary lessons in the morning and spend the afternoon learning voice production, mime, dancing, singing and different acting techniques for stage, screen and radio.

My biggest thrill happened in May last year when I was asked to play Judy Garland and Dirk Bogarde's son in a film called 'I Could Go On Singing'.

Coming to this kind of school, the things you miss most are football and cricket. There just isn't time for them.

Gregory Phillips, London, S.W.9.

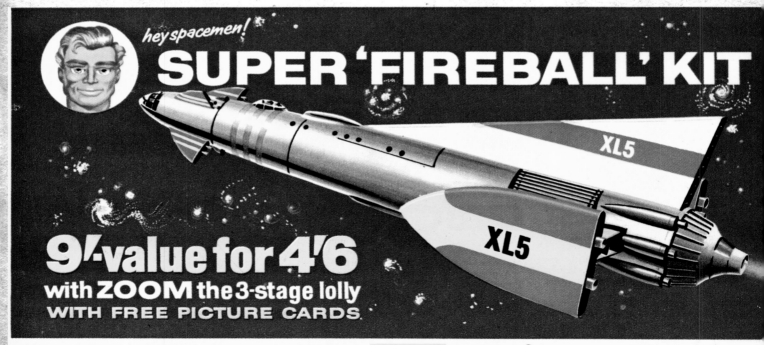

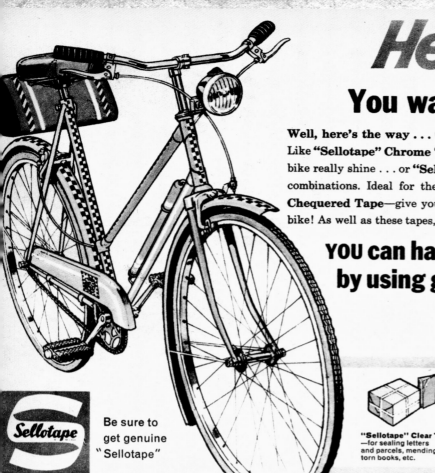

JOHN PULMAN

Glasses to the rescue

SPORTING TALK
By Ex-Pro, the man who knows everyone in the game

YURI VLASOV

WEIGHTLIFTER Yuri Vlasov, the 'strongest man in the world', wears them; the referee I saw last Saturday OUGHT to wear them; top sprinter Livio Berruti would be positively lost without them.

So if you are forced to wear glasses, don't think that it rules out any chance you have of taking part in sport's biggest spectacles.

Scots fall over themselves to make passes at one footballer who used to wear glasses – Denis Law. But an operation at the age of 15 cured Denis's squint, and he hasn't needed his specs since.

Contact lenses are the modern answer to this problem, of course, though they take a bit of getting used to. Another dodge favoured by tennis players, cricketers and athletes is to use a special elastic holder, worn round the back of the head and fastened to each temple end. This prevents slipping or knocking off while in action.

Though he wears thick, rimless specs when opening the batting for Hampshire, West Indian-born Roy Marshall never suffers what cricketers call 'a pair of spectacles' – that is a 'duck' in both innings. On the contrary, he is known as one of the hardest hitters in the game, and his reaction to fast bowling is lightning quick.

As for the fast bowlers, glasses were never a handicap to Bill Bowes, whose deliveries found the middle stump for Yorkshire and England with devastating regularity.

I can still conjure up the picture of Jaroslav Drobny pausing to wipe the perspiration from his dark glasses when winning the men's singles at Wimbledon in 1954.

Olympic sprint champion Livio Berruti, of Italy, wears sun glasses on the track even on the dullest days. "They help me to concentrate on what lies ahead," he says.

The wearing of spectacles does not appear to curb the hurricane hitting of the world champion Chinese table tennis players, nor that of our own Lesley Bell.

But snooker now – that's a game where accurate eyesight and keen judgment are absolutely essential. Nevertheless, Fred Davis and reigning world champion John Pulman both wear spectacles in play. These have been specially constructed with an extra hinge so that the lenses swivel upwards when the player makes a stroke.

SWIVELLING LENSES FOR SNOOKER

"Once I forgot my specs when I was due to play an exhibition match in a boys' club," John told me. "Without them, the snooker balls seemed to form a dull blur in the far distance, so I had to play strictly from memory."

But because his stance, stroke, bridge and cue action are so perfect, John was able to pot those balls without anyone realizing that he was playing 'from memory'.

To every sportsman, a 'good eye' is indispensable. But for most games there is absolutely no reason why you should not call on the artificial aid of spectacles or, when you are older, contact lenses. Indeed, there is plenty of evidence to suggest that they improve the concentration, and that, too, is an essential quality.

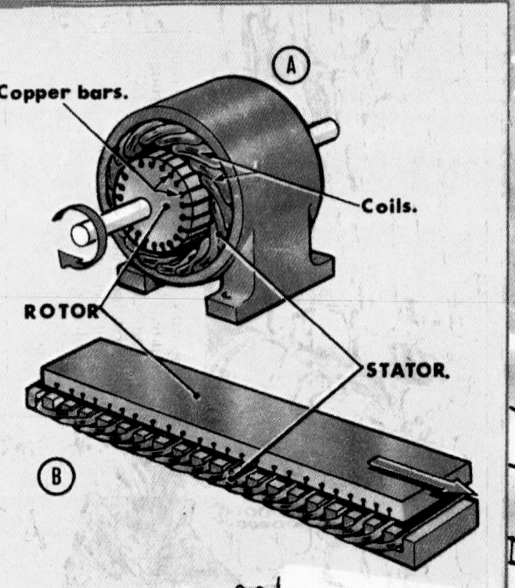

The Railway of Tomorrow

Trains that travel at 300 miles an hour! London to Edinburgh in ninety minutes, to Plymouth in under an hour, Birmingham in half an hour! Such speeds on railways, however, are not quite as fantastic as they would appear. Already, an electric train in France has exceeded 200 m.p.h. and now a new British development may well put Britain way ahead in rail travel. This new development is an electrical device known as a Linear Motor – a relatively simple machine that

has no rotating parts like the normal electric motor, hence no gears or wheels are required to use it for propelling a vehicle. Instead, the Linear Motor draws itself along a rail, the rail actually forming part of the motor.

Shown here is a possible application of a Linear Motor to a lightweight rail vehicle. Completely unmanned, these vehicles would be controlled by radio.

HOW THE LINEAR MOTOR WORKS

Figure 'A' shows a conventional induction motor with its rotor (made up of copper bars), which is made to revolve by the influence of magnetic fields caused by passing an alternating current through the fixed coils which form the stator.

Figure 'B' shows the same motor as if its rotor and stator were opened up and laid out flat with an air gap between them. Now, instead of revolving, the rotor will tend to travel as indicated by the arrow until it is out of range of the influence of the magnetism of the stator, when it will come to rest. But if the rotor were fixed and the stator free to travel, the stator would move in the same way. Both arrangements could be used to propel a vehicle by attaching the vehicle to the moving part.

Figure 'C'. Worked by using a plain aluminium or copper-plate rotor instead of that made up of copper bars. Two sets of coils are used to form the stator, to which the vehicle is attached.

KEY TO NUMBERED PARTS

(1) Aircraft-type body built of aluminium. (2) Support nacelles. (3) and (4) First-class luxury saloons at each end of vehicle, each having a seating capacity of 36 passengers. (5) 80-seat tourist-class centre saloon. These air-conditioned saloons are fitted with reclining seats and safety belts. (6) Stewardess's galley. (7) Air conditioning unit. (8) and (9) Access doors with automatic compressed-air operation. (10) Retractable steps. (11) An inflatable emergency escape-chute. (12) Cushion-forming air trunks. (13) Trunk extending along full length of the vehicle. The cushion trunks are pressurized by electrically-driven, two-stage rotary air compressors (14), which receive air from the intakes (15) and (16). When running in the reverse direction, air is taken in through the rearward-facing intakes (17) and (18), and an electrically-operated flap-valve (19) closes off the intake not in use. (20) Air filter. Compressed air from the compressors is stored in the pressure cylinders (21) and (22), and distributed to the cushion trunks through the manifolds (23) and (24). A drop in air pressure in the system is compensated by air held in low-pressure tanks (25), thus adding to remaining pressure in the high-pressure container to ensure that the vehicle is lowered gently. (26) Surfaces shaped to provide extra lift while vehicle is in motion. (27) Retractable undercarriage, held up while vehicle is in motion. When pressure in the cushion trunk drops, a pressure-sensitive valve (28) releases the undercarriage. (29) Buffers, used mainly for manoeuvring the vehicle at the end of its run, etc. (30) and (31) Linear motors at each end of vehicle. (32) Aluminium plate rotor rail. (33) Plate-centering wheels. (34) Compartment containing radio and elec-

tronic control equipment. (35) Radio control aerials in contact with control signal aerials along the route, as well as maintaining contact with vehicle's destination. (36) Low-voltage turbo-generator, charging miniature batteries (37) used for supplying radio equipment. (38) Switch room. (39) Overhead electric pick-up equipment. (40) Overhead cable-carrying cantilever pantographs. (41) Radio control signal aerials. (42) Signal box – a fully automatic control box containing radio equipment. (43) Reinforced concrete pillars bearing the running rails (44). These are also concrete, having steel faces on which the air cushions of the vehicle act. (45) Head-on view of vehicle and rails.

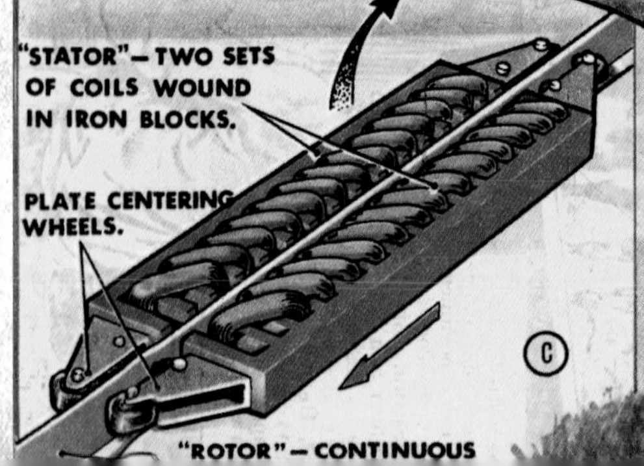

Copper bars.

Coils.

ROTOR

STATOR.

"STATOR" – TWO SETS OF COILS WOUND IN IRON BLOCKS.

PLATE CENTERING WHEELS.

"ROTOR" – CONTINUOUS

AN EAGLE cutaway DRAWING

LETTER FROM THE EDITOR

Have you read any good books lately? Sooner or later, that question is bound to crop up when you are talking to people. They may be genuinely interested – or just stumped for topics to discuss. Anyway, it's a good old stand-by, and if I spring it on you this week, it isn't because I have been staring blankly out of the window for the last half-hour – I really would like to know if you have read a book recently that particularly inspired you or fired your imagination. Tell me all about it and what most interested you in the book, and I will pay a guinea for the best letter on the subject. All other letters published, which must reach me by Friday, 21st February, will win 5s.

Now for your views on 1963 . . .

This week's GUINEA LETTER

Dear Editor,

In my opinion, the assassination of President Kennedy must surely be regarded as the lowlight of the year. He was a brilliant statesman, and a great leader. He was liked the world over, and his death was mourned by everyone. Many people eagerly followed his great fight against racial discrimination, which he carried on against all opposition. He had a pleasant nature and made many friends with his cheerfulness. His death caused a great shock throughout the world, and came at a time when the world could least afford to lose him. For three days, his death overshadowed all other events, and everyone followed, on television, the events of that tragic week-end.

D. J. McDiarmid (13), Hyde, Cheshire.

Dear Editor,

I think to pick one event from 1963 as a highlight or lowlight is a very hard thing to do, but after some thought on the matter, I picked on a flight in an Auster aircraft from Staventon Airport to Coventry, to see the air show which is held there each year. This flight proved to be very eventful as, on the return trip, we came across very low cloud and, as we were flying without a radio transmitter, we had to fly at 150-200 ft! Having become late, we eventually found a railway track which we recognized on our map, and hence we followed the track all the way back to Cheltenham. Three cheers for British Railways!

Shelagh Cartwright, Cheltenham, Glos.

IT'S YOUR OPINION . . .

Dear Editor,

I think that in sport the highlight of the year was when Tottenham Hotspur defeated Atletico Madrid 5-1 in the European Cup Winners' Cup. It was a proud event for England and Spurs, being the first British side to win a European competition as well.

Stephen Greenaway, Ewelme, Oxford.

Dear Editor,

I have not had to look back very far for my story. The day was New Year's Eve (1963). My mother and father were at a New Year's Eve party, Dinner and Dance, and I was baby-sitting! I had persuaded my mother to let me stay up and see the New Year in.

I was on my own and almost falling asleep in the chair when I decided to try reading my new edition of EAGLE to keep me awake, so I began reading. When I had read each story three times, the advertisements twice each, and all the conditions of sale, it was twelve o'clock.

I then switched on the television and celebrated on a bottle of lemonade!

Anthony Turner (13), Bolton, Lancs.

Dear Editor,

The highlight of the year for me was when our school recorder group went to Blackpool musical festival and won the coveted Well's trophy. As I am a member of the group it was quite an experience. To end this happy day, we had a trip round the illuminations. This certainly was my highlight of 1963.

David Reveley, Bredbury, Cheshire.

Dear Editor,

Looking over the past year, I find things which are very pleasant and also things which are sad.

I consider the highlight of the year was the terrific appearance of none other than the Beatles.

Many people, including myself, like these four hairy figures from Liverpool.

Sometimes I wonder why they don't take up a more civil job.

Whatsoever anyone says about this big bang in the 'pop' world, I will still be inclined to think it's the 'greatest' thing that has happened to us teenagers in 1963.

But that's only my opinion.

Jennifer Copper, Birmingham 23.

Dear Editor,

To sort out the most important event of the year is a difficult task. The most important, politically, was the assassination of President Kennedy; the most tragic was the earthquake in Agadir.

The highlight of the year, for me, was the final of the Master and Miss Therm competition, which was held in London last January. During the competition I stayed at a large hotel for two nights, and on the evening after the competition I went to see the musical 'Blitz', all at the Gas Council's expense. In the competition I came third, which I didn't mind as I do very little cooking at home. I returned home the next day with the memory of two days which I will never forget.

David I. Boniface, Bromley, Kent.

Dear Editor,

The best highlight of the year was the cold winter. It was great fun sledging and making many snowmen. But the worst side of it was for the birds who could not get any food, and many died. The old people will wish they will never see the snow again, because they cannot get out and about very easily.

J. Crossley, Harrogate, Yorks.

Dear Editor,

I think that the highlight of this year was my stay in Poland. There, I had the time of my life. I visited Warsaw, Cracow and, towards the end of my stay, I went on an excursion to the Tatra Mountains (the range at the south of Poland) and saw the beautiful scenery. A voyage on the river Dunajec brought the end to my story. I enjoyed mostly the trip to the Tatra Mountains. Although some of the visits were very trying, quite a lot were very interesting, such as the visit to Wieliczka, with its wonderful salt mine.

P. Kieniewicz, Nr. Perth, Scotland.

Dear Editor,

As far as I can remember, the winter was the lowlight of the year for me. I had an appointment with a dentist in Wimborne but, because of the snow, I could not get there – a great joy for me, as I don't like going to dentists. But that joy turned into toothache, so I had to go to our village dentist to have fillings and that tooth had to be taken out. Not much fun for me!

Shaun Gallagher (11), Dorset

Dear Editor,

My most exciting adventure in 1963 was when we moved our floating home from Wakefield (in Yorkshire) to Thorne (near Doncaster).

Our boat is a large one (50 ft. in length) and my family is a large one (5 of us and a big dog).

When the television people heard about us moving to Thorne, they wanted to film us just starting off from Wakefield. (The programme was called North at Six). This we saw on a friend's television set a few days later.

If anyone thinks this journey was easy they would be wrong, for we ran aground once and got blown on to a lock wall when we were just coming through the gate. The damage was quite bad and it caused us to leak slightly and this made the journey slower and rather dangerous.

John Vaughan (13), Thorne, Yorks

Dear Editor,

The thing I recall most is when I put a pin on a teacher's chair.

I found a pin and flicked it on to the teacher's desk. Unfortunately it missed and landed on his chair, point upwards. Before I could pick it up the teacher came in. A pupil then shouted: 'Don't sit on your chair, sir – there is a pin on it.' Of course nobody owned up.

At the end of the lesson he inquired again, then I owned up. The teacher gave me a hundred lines.

M. Talbot, Elson, Gosport, Hants

LETTER FROM THE EDITOR

Ring out the old year – ring in the new. As we step into 1964, it is timely to pause and look back on 1963. What do *you* recall as being the highlight – or lowlight – of that year? Was it the terrible winter, when we all went around muffled up like Eskimoes? Was it some exciting sporting event, a holiday abroad, a meeting with someone you particularly admire, an exam passed? Whatever it was, write and tell me about it and I will pay a guinea for the best letter. Runners-up will receive 5s.

While you're casting your minds back, the writers of the following letters on Shakespeare as a humorist have got something to look *forward* to – a postal order!

it's your OPINION

William Shakespeare

this week's GUINEA LETTER

Dear Editor,

I think that it is impossible to deny William Shakespeare the great talent which is attributed to him. Sometimes, however, his plays seem to be a trifle boring if not comprehensively understood. As a comedian, his comedies excel all other playwrights' efforts. Nobody can fail to laugh at his, to my mind, most comical character, Sir John Falstaff in 'Henry IV' or, for example, the stupid but hilariously funny Bottom the Weaver in 'A Midsummer Night's Dream'. All his famous comedies must have had the audience in his Globe theatre 'rolling in the aisles'. Yes, William Shakespeare was the greatest playwright who ever lived and long live still his hilarious comedies.

C. Turner, Banbury, Oxon.

Bottom and Titania, from 'A Midsummer Night's Dream'

Dear Editor,

William Shakespeare, in my true opinion, has a great sense of humour, and if all his plays are performed in the correct manner, they can have great effect on the audience.

Anthony Kelton, Lincoln.

Dear Editor,

From my own experience of Shakespeare's works at school, I have found that his jokes are very subtle and not easily understood. He does, however, bring his wit into his plays in order to suit the characters. We must remember, however, that Shakespeare wrote his plays a long time ago and his wit is different from ours. But, nevertheless, Shakespeare's wit can be enjoyed only if the play has been thoroughly read.

Ron Challinor, Wigan, Lancs.

Dear Editor,

I personally think that Shakespeare is very boring.

I know that a collection of his plays is classed 'Tales From The Comedies of Shakespeare', but I really think that this is a lot of nonsense.

Noel Gilmartin, Buckhurst Hill, Essex.

Dear Editor,

William Shakespeare's jokes were funny in the age he lived in but are not really regarded as amusing to the young people of today. As not much comedy had been written before William Shakespeare's time, these comedy plays were highly thought of.

William Chantler, Tenterden, Kent.

Dear Editor,

Some of his plays, like 'A Midsummer Night's Dream' and the 'Taming of the Shrew' are quite funny.

Dear Editor,

I have been to see 'The Merchant of Venice' in London. It wasn't exactly funny, but it had a sense of humour. Some people call Shakespeare dull and boring, but if they just stop to think, he can be very amusing, as I have found out.

John Barley (12), Haslemere, Surrey.

Dear Editor,

In my opinion Shakespeare was not a comedian. I think people laugh because the actors have tight pants on and jump about the stage in a serious manner.

Robert Eye, Lincoln.

Dear Editor,

I consider that Shakespeare had a very good sense of humour. To prove this, in the play 'Henry IV' he created a fat and cheerful man called Falstaff who always got into trouble in many ways and was described as a 'mass of tallow'. Our sense of humour is not of the same kind as Shakespeare, because we all have our likes and dislikes, so even the most overcast person has to at least smile when he reads any of his plays. In every one of his plays he always creates a comic such as Falstaff in 'Henry IV' and Puck in 'A Midsummer Night's Dream'.

Christopher Birchall (12), Hyde, Cheshire.

Dear Editor,

I went to see William Shakespeare's 'A Midsummer Night's Dream'. Some parts were amusing, especially when Puck (the elf) seemed to pop up through the ground. Everyone roared with laughter. I think he has an extremely rich sense of humour, because only a person with this gift could have seen the troubles that occur when Titania waking up from her love potion saw Bottom with an ass's head, and fell in love with him.

Andrew Long, North Harrow, Middlesex.

Dear Editor,

I went to see 'The Tempest' and I found parts of it very funny.

Sometimes it is difficult to see the comedy at first. For instance, in 'A Midsummer Night's Dream' the parts of the Athenian workmen are very amusing when they are studied closely. Also, when Puck is leading Demetrius and Lysander away from each other, it is comical the way that they become angry and threaten each other.

Miss M. McIlwraith, Penn, Wolverhampton.

SEND YOUR LETTERS TO: THE EDITOR (Readers' Letters), EAGLE/SWIFT, 64 LONG ACRE, LONDON, W.C.2.

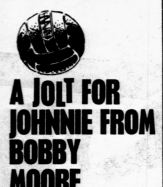

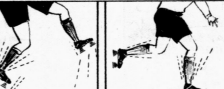

Anti-smoking campaign with Bobby Moore: over two years before lifting the World Cup Bobby Moore was taking part in an even more important campaign. Using the West Ham and England captain, amongst other sports stars of the day, was an attempt to convince youngsters of the harm of tobacco. Perhaps Bobby should also have been used to discourage the purchase of Spring-heel Jacks. Whilst no statistics are available it seems quite obvious how dangerous this 'sensational toy' was. At 22 shillings and sixpence it must have been a cheap way to get a trip to the hospital.

IT'S A FACT!

ok out! It's Mr Marples's latest brainchild – the n bin'. Aimed at stopping jams at busy cross-ads, it is being tried out in London's West-end. torists who enter the big, yellow-striped square st first make sure they can get across it without pping – and causing a hold-up. If you *do* stop – ur 'sin' will cost you a £20 fine.

GIRLS IN EAGLE

Lancelot Bokay's letter asking readers if they would like to see girls in EAGLE certainly made you boys see red! By an overwhelming majority, you rejected the idea. So relax, readers – there'll be no 'cissy' stuff in EAGLE. Here is a selection of your opinions on the subject:–

Dear Editor,
I feel girls would completely spoil EAGLE. Instead of my sister taking only a few minutes to glance through it, she would take nearly an hour and read every word!
Paul Grellier (12), Somerset.

Dear Editor,
Even if I am a girl myself, I think that cowboy or space films are too often spoiled by soppy girls. Please, I beg of you, don't put girls in your paper.
Denise Gould, Emsworth, Hants.

Dear Editor,
I agree with Lancelot Bokay; girls should appear in EAGLE. For a start, you could bring back Professor Peabody into the Dan Dare stories, but please don't overdo this. I would hate to see stories starring girls in EAGLE (like Diane Dare, Marjory Dimworthy or Jenny Frog).
John Sullivan, Slough, Bucks.
Professor Peabody is now married and living in a Martian colony. – Ed.

Dear Editor,
I think what Lancelot said is just plain *nonsense*. EAGLE is a very good paper just as it is. Anyway, what would a woman be doing in Dan Dare? We wouldn't want Dan going sloppy over women – would we?
Paul Wolley (12), Wolverhampton, Staffs.

Dear Editor,
I think that it would be a bad idea to have girls in a boys' magazine. I think EAGLE is very good as it is, and I think that girls would make it 'cissy' and 'soppy'.
Charles Platt, Bromley, Kent.

Dear Editor,
EAGLE is a boys' paper and is very good as it is. If Lancelot Bokay wishes to read about girls, there are plenty of girls' comics available.
Thomas Clarence-Smith, Limpsfield, Surrey.

Dear Editor,
I quite agree with Lancelot Bokay when he says we should see more females. Even though it is a boys' paper, one or two girls drifting around in the background would be much more natural than BOYS! BOYS! BOYS! However, I would hate EAGLE to turn into a soppy, romantic paper, as there are enough, if not too many, on the market already.
Diana Brueton (12), Bristol.

Dear Editor,
Having seen my sister all day long, I would like to forget girls for a while and enjoy reading in comfort without the sight of screaming girls, and, besides, the girls have their own paper, one of which my sister reads, and it never has a boy mentioned in it.
Timothy Davies (12), Wirral, Cheshire.

Dear Editor,
The introduction of female characters in any section of EAGLE will, I think, totally ruin the aim of the paper.
It's the only paper of its kind that caters especially for the younger male generation – which has grown out of the comic-paper stage, and is looking for the ideal exciting series-paper.
If any youngster wants a paper that includes girls, he only has to go out to a paper-shop and buy one.
D. Townley (15), Wilmslow, Cheshire.

Letter from the Editor

Boys, you won't want to miss the fascinating supplement in next week's great issue. You'll be astonished at your powers when you've mastered the amazing secrets in HOW TO BE A SUPERBOY!

But in the meantime, you'll be the envy of your pals when you show them the terrific Lightning jet plane given away free in this week's issue. It's simple to operate. Just attach the elastic band to the slot on the plane, draw back – and the sky's the limit! But don't forget, it 'goes like a bomb', so get out into open spaces before you fly it.

On the subject of Cassius Clay, your letters were almost equally divided, with a slight edge to those who thought Clay was marvellous. A blow-by-blow summary is given below.

This week sees the start of the Test series between England and Australia. Will England win back the Ashes? What do *you* think our chances are? Let me have your opinion by Friday, 12th June, and I'll pay a guinea for the best letter. All others published will win 5s.

Now seconds out for Cassius Clay . . .

In EAGLE next week!
HOW TO BE A Superboy!

IT'S YOUR OPINION . . .

This week's guinea letter

Dear Editor,

In my opinion Cassius Clay is the most controversial World Heavyweight Champion of all time. There is no denying, however, despite clowning and incredibly bad poetry, that he is a very competent and skilful boxer who displayed his talent in defeating the formidable Sonny Liston. His predictions are almost always fulfilled. His lines of poetry are an extremely successful publicity campaign and, had it not been for his irrepressible 'gift of the gab', he admitted that he would be working at a lowly-paid job in his home town.

I think that he ranks among the most famous former World Heavyweight Champions, and deservedly so.

Richard Guest, Edinburgh.

Dear Editor,

When most people see headlines in newspapers concerning Cassius Clay, they immediately think to themselves: "What has the old parrot to say this time?" "How's his mouth today?" But now, we can hardly blame him for what he has said (sorry, shouted), because he has proved his point – he is the greatest and will continue to be until somebody defeats him.

E. S. Weinberger, Peterborough.

Dear Editor,

I think Cassius Clay is THE greatest. He has done more for boxing than any other boxer of modern times.

Clay completely outboxed Sonny Liston, and, in the 5th round, made him look like a sparring partner.

Philip Robertson, West Lothian.

Dear Editor,

In my opinion Cassius Clay is a loudmouth. Take, for instance, the 'weigh in' before the great fight on February 25th.

Clay was fined a large sum of money for shooting off his mouth.

Myself, I think Clay's win was a fluke and, if he has a return fight with Liston, I think Liston will come out on top.

Graham Lougher, Wonastow, Monmouth.

Dear Editor,

As a girl I find boxing a bore usually, but when Cassius Clay is fighting or being interviewed, I quite enjoy watching it. He may be extremely boastful and big-headed, but at least he makes a change from ordinary boxing.

Judith Lloyd-Jones, Sevenoaks.

Dear Editor,

Personally I think Cassius Clay is slightly mentally ill. When he was young he was not very bright, and lately this has become obvious when he was turned down by the U.S. Army because he failed the Intelligence Exam.

Regarding his 'loud mouth,' I think this stems from his mentality. This is the only way he can think of getting into the limelight, but one must admit he has been very successful with the combination of his mouth and his fists.

Jan Souter, Buckie, Banffs.

Dear Editor,

Cassius Clay's methods are very unorthodox, but behind the outward appearance, there must be a very shrewd brain. I don't think he is really such a 'bragger' as he pretends. I believe he boasts because the constant 'needling' and bragging makes his opponent nervous, or because of a gimmick. His outburst before the fight with Liston was to bring more people to the hall. In my opinion Cassius Clay is one of the cleverest world champions ever.

Christopher Missen, Cambridge.

Dear Editor,

I think Cassius Clay is a good boxer, but he should not boast as much as he does.

It is possibly good publicity for him and is probably a psychological help, prophesying in which round he will defeat his opponent, but he should not broadcast his boasts.

J. D. Cowan Ibstone, High Wycombe.

Here's a curious sign. An 'ancient light' is a window which has let in light for twenty years or more. It is against the law for anyone on adjoining property to build so as to cut off the light.

The London district of Maida Vale is named after Sir John Stuart's victory at Maida on 6th July, 1806, when 5,000 British troops won against the combined forces of French and Italian troops numbering 7,500.

The name 'Currant' is derived from 'Corinth', the name of the Greek town from which this fruit was first distributed to Western Europe.

Tortoise-shell, as used for decorative purposes, is made from the marine tortoise, or turtle called the Hawk's Bill. The ancient Romans often inlaid their furniture with it.

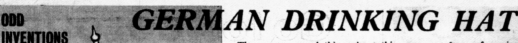

ODD INVENTIONS
GERMAN DRINKING HAT

The most unusual thing about this expensive form of service headgear was that it was completely useless!

It was a certain Herr Peter, of Germany, that managed to get the German military leaders interested in this unusual helmet to be used in East Africa.

In the 1880s, German expeditions protected by troops were plagued by malaria and similar diseases – caused by drinking water from ponds, streams and rivers. To combat this, Herr Peter thought up this amazing rain-storing helmet. The idea was as follows. While marching through rain, the helmets would catch rain in the trough round the rim. It would run to the back and pour down the small drain-hole provided. The thick, broad brim of the helmet was hollow and acted as a storage tank with a capacity of approximately three pints. When given the opportunity to refresh with a drink of water, the soldier took off his helmet and used the small tap provided. The steel dome and spike on the top of the helmet could be unscrewed and used as a cup or dish.

What the inventor and military chiefs did not think of was that after a few days, the helmets would come into contact with insects and undergrowth, harbouring malaria germs, etc., and would make even rain water deadly to drink! Another fault was the causing of fatigue through carrying 3 pints of water on the head. Further, within the tropics, most places only have rain in certain seasons.

N DARE CARTWHEELED HELPLESSLY TO A FUNNEL OF SWIRLING POUR...

THE STRANDS OF THE 'RAINBOW MIST' TUGGED AT HIS LIMBS, RESTRAINING THEM AS THEY FLAILED VIOLENTLY BACK AND FORTH!

THE STUFF FILLED HIS EYES AND THE ODOUR FROM IT SWIRLED INTO HIS BRAIN AND STRANGE PATTERNS WHIRLED AROUND HIM...

THEN, IN A DREAM-LIKE WAY, HE FELT STRANGE SENSATIONS FROM BOYHOOD DAYS...

...HE SAW HIS SMILING FRIENDS OF LATER YEARS — HIS LEERING ENEMIES, TOO...

AND WHEN HIS STORE OF MEMORIES WAS FINISHED — HE WAS TOSSED ASIDE LIKE A 'SECOND-HAND BOOK'!

IT WAS AS THOUGH HE HAD BEEN MADE TO RELIVE HIS WHOLE LIFE IN ONE INSTANT OF TIME!

...e panels shown here depict, ...erally, a trip down memory ...e for Dan. Fans of the Pilot ...the Future can have much ...n trying to identify all the ...ures from his past. There are ...prizes on offer but it is still ...orth the effort.

WHAT IS THIS PLACE?

DAN DARE, YOU ARE LIVING THE LAST HOUR OF YOUR LIFE!

GREAT SCOTT!

EAGLE AND BOYS' WORLD 26 *December* 1964

POP PICK OF THE WEEK

George Harrison

Paul McCartney

A Very Merry Krimble to all seagull readers and a gear New Year, too

John Lennon

Ringo Starr

Don't forget, Eaglers, every week, we award an E.P. voucher for the best rhyme about your favourite pop star or group. Send it on a postcard to Pop Pick of the Week, EAGLE, 96 Long Acre, London, W.C.2.

We have had so many verses from you on the Beatles, it has been decided that, as a Christmas gift 'From Me To You', three extra E.P. vouchers will be awarded this week. Here are the winning verses:—

The Beatles are gorgeous,
The Beatles are gear,
Their sound will go on
For year after year.
John is so manly,
Paul is so cute,
Ringo's my favourite,
And George is a beaut.
To dislike them must mean
That you're surely a square,
Or secretly envy their
Shiny, long hair.

    Terry Lenchan, Highgate, London.

If I could be a Beatle,
I think I would be John;
Or else I'd be like Ringo
If my hair were only long.
If I had George's talent
I know I'd be a star,
Even Paul would be ideal
If I could play guitar.
    Michael Rose, Leeds, 8.

The Beatles are a craze rage,
The lasses scream when they're on stage.
Twist and Shout – 'She loves you, too',
'Please me', Yeah – they always do.
Ringo plays his drums with speed,
George is great – he plays the lead.
John plays rhythm, keeps the pace,
Paul is FAB – he plays the bass.
Think their music is real cool?
'Course! They come from Liverpool.
    Mairwen Shorney, Anglesey, North Wales.

Beatles are Active,
Beatles are Big,
Beatles are Candid,
Beatles, we Dig.
Beatles are Everywhere,
Beatles 'cross Foam,
Beatles are Gearest when
Beatles at Home.
Beatles Indelible,
Beatles not Junk,
Beatles are 'Karefree',
Like it or Lump.
Beatles are Marvellous,
Beatles are Nice,
To Ogle the Beatles
I'd pay any Price.
Beatles are Questioned
Till Ready to drop,
Beatles are Super
Beatles are Tops.
Beatles – Unique, man!
Beatles not Vain,
Beatles round World,
Win 'X-ceptional' fame.
Whenever they leave us
It's always the same,
We Yearn for our Beatles
To Zoom home again!
    R. Ayers, Luton, Beds.

Christmas GREETINGS from the STARS

I wish all the readers of EAGLE a very happy Christmas, and hope you will all spend it as I will, with my family in front of a big log fire. **Adam Faith.**

Happy holiday to all EAGLE readers. **Cliff Richard.**

All our best wishes to EAGLE readers for Christmas, and stay happy in 1965. **Barron Knights.**

A Merry Christmas to all EAGLE readers! **The Manfreds.**

Merry Christmas to you all. **The Shadows.**

Wishing all EAGLE readers a very happy Christmas. **Rolling Stones.**

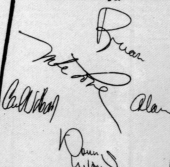

Happy Christmas and a surfing New Year to all EAGLE readers. **The Beach Boys.**

POP PICK of the WEEK • POP PICK of the WEEK • POP PICK of the WEEK •

MIKE JAGGER

BRIAN JONES

CHARLIE WATTS

KEITH RICHARDS

BILL WYMAN

THE ROLLING STONES

The page where you can win an E.P. VOUCHER EVERY WEEK

SECOND only to the Beatles in popularity are the Rolling Stones. Everywhere they go, Mike, Brian, Charlie, Bill and Keith, play to packed audiences, often causing riots among the thousands of fans who witness their wild stage act.

Their success story started in the June of last year when they recorded an old Chuck Berry song called "Come On", which climbed to No. 18 in the charts and earned TV and radio appearances for the shaggy-haired five. Soon R & B fans were shouting the praises of the Stones – and Britain's parents were stating their revulsion of them. Using such titles as "Cave Men", "The Ugliest Group in the World" and "Hairy Monsters", adults united to hurl insults at the Stones. But this had absolutely no effect in preventing them from rapidly gaining in popularity.

As a follow-up to "Come On" the Stones recorded a song written by Beatles John and Paul called "I wanna be your man", which climbed steadily up the charts to the No. 8 spot. Still their popularity went on increasing and their next disc "Not Fade Away" reached the No. 3 spot in the Top Twenty, proving beyond doubt that the Rolling Stones were here to stay.

PERSONAL

Mike Jagger lead vocalist. Mike is 5 ft. 10 ins. tall, was born July 26th, 1944, and was educated at Dartford Grammar School.
Brian Jones guitar, harmonica and vocals. Brian was born in Cheltenham, Gloucestershire, on Feb. 28th, 1944. He likes sitting on mountains.
Charlie Watts drums. 5 ft. 8 ins. tall and weighing 10 stones, Charlie was born in Wembley, Middlesex, on June 2nd, 1941.
Keith Richards lead guitar. Educated at Dartford Technical School and Sidcup Art School. Keith, whose real name is Keith Richard, enjoys sketching.
Bill Wyman bass guitar. The quiet Rolling Stone, Bill was born in Lewisham, London, on October 24th, 1941, and educated at Beckenham Grammar School. Likes casual clothes and dislikes marmalade and arguments.

Below is the rhyme from a reader which wins him an E.P. record voucher!

Their hair is never tidy,
Their clothes are seldom neat,
But when it comes to rhythm,
They'll get you on your feet.
They may be unconventional,
But that will break no bones,
They are idols to the young ones,
They're the swinging "Rolling Stones".

David Lee, Whitley Bay, Northumberland.

Yes, every week EAGLE will give away an E.P. Voucher. All you have to do to win the E.P. of your choice is to write on a postcard a short rhyme about your favourite pop star or group and send it to: Pop Pick Of The Week, EAGLE, 64 Long Acre, W.C.2.

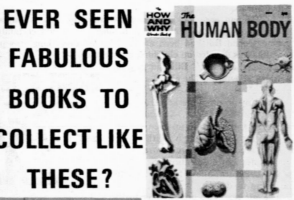

ROGER MOORE

TELLS YOU | ***HOW TO BE A DETECTIVE***

"This is the book you've been asking me for ever since I started playing the part of the best-known crime-buster in the (TV) business. Your questions have poured in by the hundred. And in this book I'm going to give you some of the answers.

"One thing's certain – there's going to be plenty of crime to fight for a long time to come. So you can't start learning how to be a detective too soon! Good hunting!"

Rogan Moore

Are YOU a DETECTIVE type?

HOW TO SUP...

LEARN HOW TO...

★ *Improve your cricket*
★ *Tame that bully*
★ *Improve your school...*
★ *Develop real strength...*

Every now and then to boost sales and expand the comic's girth for a week or so *Eagle* would include special inserted supplements. Readers were encouraged to cut these out and keep them. A few shown in these pages include How to be a Superboy, an Olympics Special, a detailed look at the European Community and Roger Moore explaining how to be a detective.

OLYMPICS SPECIAL

PRESENTED WITH **EAGLE** AND *Boys' World*

Bobbie Brightwell, captain of the British Olympic Games team and one of our main hopes for a gold medal in the 400 metres.

The first European School, founded in Luxembourg in 1953, celebrated its twelfth anniversary on April 4th.
Young Nicholas Prag tells you how he and his friends are learning to become citizens of the New Europe.

Take a look at my school — it's DIFFERENT!

Sport is voluntary at our school, but 60% of the boys took part in a recent athletic meeting

A section of our school orchestra

My name is Nicholas Prag. I am twelve years old and I come from England...

My school was founded by the parents of the first pupils, just twelve years ago. They had come to Luxembourg as staff for the headquarters of the Coal and Steel Community. But they had come from six different countries – and wondered how all the pupils would begin to understand each other, not to mention the teachers!

★ ★ ★

So they founded our school and made three rules: –

1. That we pupils would still go on learning our own language, and about the countries where we were born.

2. That we must carry on with the same subjects we had studied before in our own countries.

3. That we should all of us, from many different coun-

tries, study together and help to make the New Europe our parents were working for.

To begin with, the school was very small – just a nursery kindergarten and a primary school. As the pupils grew older, new teachers were appointed to teach them – and so began our secondary school.

I almost forgot to tell you – our school is co-educational. That is, boys and girls are taught in the same classes. It also teaches all religions – not just one, as many of our old schools used to. Teaching is in four languages – Dutch, French, German and Italian.

We even have our own special leaving exam. It is called the European Leaving Certificate (or the Baccalauréat Européen), which is now recognized in all parts of Europe, including Great Britain.

Of course, with so many friends

from other countries, we soon manage to pick up each other's languages. In fact, we even start learning other languages officially in the classroom from Primary School onwards. I don't know if that happens anywhere else in the world.

From the third year at the secondary school, everyone learns English. It's not at all unusual for boys and girls learning at our school to speak three languages – fluently – and I know some who can speak FOUR.

★ ★ ★

Our school was thought to be so successful that others have now been set up, at Brussels in Belgium, Mol in Belgium, Ispra in Italy, Karlsruhe in Germany and Petten in Holland. But, as I know you'll understand, I'm very proud indeed to be at the First European School.

The photographs will show you what our school is like. It's not as puzzling as it may sound – and it's tremendous fun having so many friends from different countries.

Our school language laboratory. Here, the mo up-to-date methods are used to give us practi in foreign tongues. Many of us are fluent in fo languages when we leave school

6 NATIONS BECOME ONE!

The European Parliament in session at Strasbourg

The European Community
INSTITUTIONS

ECSC
EUROPEAN COAL AND STEEL COMMUNITY
HIGH AUTHORITY

COMMON MARKET
EUROPEAN ECONOMIC COMMUNITY
COMMISSION

EURATOM
EUROPEAN ATOMIC ENERGY COMMUNITY
COMMISSION

THE EXECUTIVES

COUNCIL OF MINISTERS

LEGISLATION

EUROPEAN PARLIAMENT

DEMOCRATIC CONTROL

COURT OF JUSTICE

JUDICIAL CONTROL

ONLY by making new rules, which apply to every country in the community, and by setting up institutions, can this unity be made to work.

The institutions work out, put into force and supervise the common rules and common policy of the Common Market.

The main institutions are:—

THE COMMON MARKET COMMISSION
THE COAL AND STEEL COMMUNITY HIGH AUTHORITY
THE EURATOM COMMISSION
THE COUNCIL OF MINISTERS
THE EUROPEAN PARLIAMENT
THE COURT OF JUSTICE

and this diagram shows how they work with each other. It will all become much simpler after next January, when the High Authority and the two Commissions will be merged in a single European Commission.

The date which European schoolboys know, as well as you know 1066, is May 9, 1950. This was the day when the French Foreign Minister, Robert Schuman, called a meeting of the world's Press in Paris. He read to them a Declaration, prepared with the help of another Frenchman, Jean Monnet, on behalf of his Government.

People at that meeting on May 9 were present at one of the great moments of modern history. What the Declaration suggested was that:—

1. France and Germany should share steel and coal resources and production, thus ending hundreds of years of rivalry and making future war between the two countries impossible.
2. That the countries of Europe should work towards a United States of Europe.

As soon as the meeting was over, talks between other European governments began. Their aim was to produce a treaty based on the suggestions in the Declaration.

Soon, agreement with France was reached by Germany, Italy, Belgium, the Netherlands, and Luxembourg. These countries have been known since as 'The Six'.

This Trans-European Express (TEE) is a luxurious train linking the European capitals

CONTINENTAL QUIZ

Perhaps this year you will be paying your first visit to the Continent. But how much do you know about the countries of Europe NOW? Try the quiz below and see what sort of 'armchair traveller' you make!

1 What are the Continental equivalents for

a Miles,
b Feet,
c Pints, and
d Pounds.

★ ★ ★

2 How is time measured for official purposes and for railway time-tables?

★ ★ ★

3 We measure temperature by Fahrenheit. What do they use?

4 Which country is divided into 'Cantons'?

★ ★ ★

5 In which countries would you spend the following currencies:

a Kroner, b Lire,
c Escudos, d Pesetas,
e Drachmae f Marrka.

★ ★ ★

6 In which capital cities would you find the following:

a The Tivoli Gardens,
b The Fountain of Trevi,
c Notre-Dame,
d The Prado.

7 Which Continental National Anthem has the same tune as God Save The Queen?

★ ★ ★

8 Which are the Benelux Countries?

★ ★ ★

9 In which country do the Flemings and Walloons live?

Answers

Score one point for EACH correct answer. If you get (a), (b), (c), (d), etc., right in an answer, that will score four or more marks.

(1) (a) Kilometres, (b) Metres, (c) Litres, (d) Kilos. (2) By the twenty-four hour clock. (3) Centigrade. (4) Switzerland. (5) (a) Norway, Sweden or Denmark, (b) Italy, (c) Portugal, (d) Spain, (e) Greece, (f) Finland. (6) (a) Copenhagen, (b) Rome, (c) Paris, (d) Madrid. (7) Switzerland. (8) Belgium, Holland, Luxembourg. (9) Belgium.

How do you rate?

Between 16-20. Excellent. You hardly need to go to the Continent – you know it already! Between 10-15. A very good average. You're just the type to really enjoy such a holiday. Between 5-9. I'll bet neither Geography nor General knowledge is your best subject! Still, you do take an interest in other countries, and you'll do a lot better at both these subjects after your holiday. Under 5. You really NEED this holiday, don't you! Never mind – you'll soon learn, and a happy holiday anyway.

ROVING REPORTER

AT LAST THERE IS TO BE A CHUNNEL— A TUNNEL BENEATH THE CHANNEL.

It will be a twin-tunnel affair, carrying an electric railway, stretching 32 miles from Westenhanger, near Folkestone, to Sangatte, near Calais, and should be in use by 1972.

Passengers will travel in the normal way and cars will be loaded on to trucks. Trains are expected to average 70 miles an hour and should make the crossing in less than 20 minutes. Fares are expected to be about 32s. for passengers and £7 16s. for cars. Travellers may remain in their cars.

The idea has been talked about since 1802, when someone suggested to Napoleon the idea of two tunnels with an island in the middle to allow the horses to come up for air.

Eric Kincaid

PEOPLE ON BOTH SIDES OF THE CHANNEL LIKED THE IDEA, BUT BRITAIN AND FRANCE—WHO WERE ENJOYING A TEMPORARY TRUCE—WENT TO WAR AGAIN LATER THAT YEAR AND THE PROJECT WAS PUT TO ONE SIDE.

It was revived many times, and even got to the stage of being started. That was in Queen Victoria's day. The French made tests and soundings 150 feet below sea level.

And the British sank two shafts near Dover. One was over a mile long. Prime Minister Gladstone had a champagne lunch in it to celebrate, but then everything was stopped. Our army said it might lead to an invasion.

The cost of the new project is estimated at more than £110,000,000, but it is cheaper than other plans put forward for a road tunnel, which would have had to be very much wider - and of a road and rail bridge. Suggested cost for that: £300,000,000.

AT THE MOMENT, THERE ARE STILL MANY PROBLEMS BEFORE THE TUNNEL EXPERTS. FOR INSTANCE, IT HAS STILL NOT YET BEEN DECIDED WHETHER TO DRILL BELOW THE CHANNEL OR TO SIMPLY LAY LARGE TUBES ON THE SEA BED. BUT AT LEAST WE ARE GOING TO HAVE A TUNNEL!

NEXT WEEK: THE FASTEST ANIMAL ON LAND!

LAUNCH VEHICLE LINE-UP

The history of the rocket is long – and somewhat slender. Exactly when rockets were first invented, no one knows. History tells us, however, that the Chinese armies were using 'arrows of fire' in the early 13th century, and the use of war rockets reached a fine art during the Napoleonic wars. The Congreve rocket, developed in the early part of the 19th century by Sir William Congreve, had put Britain well to the fore in rocketry, both in warfare and as a means of projecting life-saving equipment at sea.

Congreve had developed the solid-fuel 'black powder' rocket to its maximum, so attention was turned at the beginning of the present century to improving rockets. The world's first liquid-fuelled rocket was launched in the U.S.A. in 1926, and development went ahead in Germany, resulting in the devastating V.2 weapons of World War II.

In the past 20 years, tremendous strides have been made in rocketry, and, keeping pace with progress, EAGLE has from time to time presented the inside story of the launch vehicles as they became news. From information supplied by the National Aeronautical and Space Administration, EAGLE this week takes a look at a family gathering of the launch vehicles in use, or being developed, by the U.S.A.

Each has a peaceful mission, and each is destined to play its part in probing new frontiers of Science and Space.

Simple Rocketry

(a) In a firework rocket, a slow-burning explosive powder ignites, the resulting hot gases being allowed to escape at the bottom end of the container. The force of this downward surge of gases causes the rocket to react with an upward motion. In science, this is known as 'Newton's Third Law of Motion'.

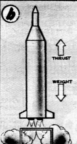

(b) The same thing happens in a launch vehicle, only on a much grander scale. The upward reaction, or 'thrust', is measured in pounds, and in order to lift itself, the vehicle must produce a thrust greater than its own weight. If thrust and weight were the same, the vehicle would merely hover, and if thrust were smaller there would be no lift-off at all.

THRUST

WEIGHT

(c) Most (but not all) launch vehicles use a liquid fuel, such as kerosene or liquid hydrogen, mixed with an 'oxydizer' – 'lox' for short – which are brought together and burned in the rocket's engines. There is no oxygen out in space, and without it the fuel would not burn. Oxygen, too, increases the burning rate of the fuel to give greatest thrust.

FUEL

OXYDIZER

PUMPS

ENGINE

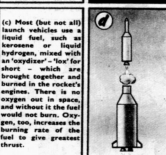

(d) Launch vehicles are usually built in 'stages' – separate rockets mounted on top of each other, the biggest and most powerful (sometimes called a 'booster') being used to lift the vehicle off the ground when the greatest thrust is needed. As one stage burns out, the next ignites and takes over to thrust farther out into space.

★ 1. SCOUT

The smallest (72 feet high) and only all-solid-propelled launch vehicle used by the U.S.A. A four-stage vehicle, it weighs 38,500 lb. and can place a 240 lb. payload in orbit 300 n.m. (nautical miles) above the earth.

★ 2. THOR-AGENA D

'Thor' rocket topped by an 'Agena D' second stage. Both are liquid-propelled and their combined efforts can place a payload of 1,150 lb. in a 100 n.m. orbit. 'Thor-Agena D' is 76 feet high and is mainly used for launching scientific and weather-observing satellites.

★ 3. DELTA

'Delta' has three stages – two are liquid-propelled, topped by the third which uses solid propellant. Overall height, 90 feet. 'Delta' can place 500 lb. in a 300 n.m. orbit, or rocket a 60 lb. probe to the moon. 'Delta' is shown here with a cluster of three 'Castor' rockets around the base to increase thrust at lift-off.

★ 4. ATLAS-AGENA D

An 'Atlas' topped by an 'Agena D' – 104 feet overall with payload. Liquid propelled, the 'Atlas D' has a main 'sustainer' engine, assisted by two booster engines like fins. These assist in lift-off and are jettisoned in flight. The 'Atlas-Agena D' has been used successfully for launching the unmanned interplanetary and moon probes 'Mariner' and 'Ranger'. Also used in the 'Gemini' two-man capsule programme.

★ 5. ATLAS-CENTAUR

113 feet high, a modified 'Atlas D' topped by a liquid hydrogen/oxygen propelled 'Centaur' second stage. A high-performance, general-purpose vehicle, it is designed to send advanced types of satellites to explore Venus and Mars, as well as soft-landing probes on the moon.

★ 6. GEMINI-TITAN II

Very much in the news just lately as the vehicle responsible for placing the two-man 'Gemini' capsules in orbit. A two-stage vehicle 109 feet high, it weighs 300,000 lb. and has a lift-off thrust of 430,000 lb.

★ 7. SATURN I

First of the moon rockets, it is 190 feet high with payload – taller than Nelson's Column! Weighing over a million pounds, its lift-off thrust is in excess of 1½ million pounds. Two stages, liquid-propelled – the first using kerosene and lox (liquid oxygen) and the second liquid hydrogen and lox. Used for testing in earth-orbit the mock-up of the 'Apollo' spacecraft that will eventually land on the moon.

★ 8. SATURN IB

Similar to the 'Saturn I' but taller (225 feet overall) and with a more highly-powered second stage, this vehicle will be used to launch manned 'Apollo' mooncraft in earth orbit. It will also be used for orbital 'rendezvous' test flights with 'Apollo' spacecraft.

★ 9. SATURN V

Destination Moon! The biggest and mightiest of them all, the gigantic 'Saturn V' launch vehicle, 362 feet tall (3 feet short of the tip of the cross of St Paul's Cathedral), and requiring a 7½ million lb. thrust to lift this 6 million lb. tower of energy on its journey. Initial thrust is provided by kerosene and lox, and with two further stages propelled by liquid hydrogen and lox, 'Saturn V' will send its three-man 'Apollo' spacecraft to the moon.

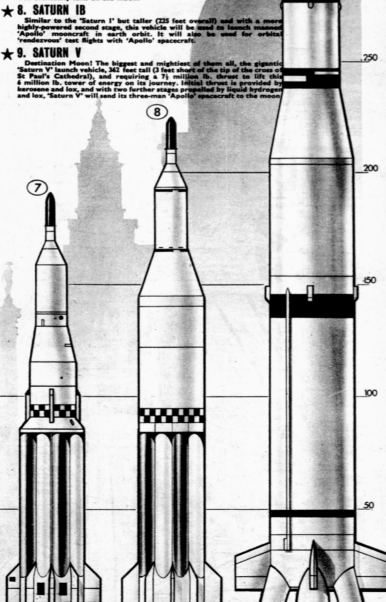

Feet
360
350
300
250
200
150
100
50

SHALL WE HAVE PICTURES ON OUR POSTAGE STAMPS?

DESIGNED BY JOCK KINNEIR, F.S.I.A., FOR STANLEY GIBBONS LTD., AND PRINTED BY HARRISON & SONS LTD.

BRITAIN is the only country in the world which has no pictures on its ordinary postage stamps (with the exception of the high values of 2s. 6d., 5s., 10s. and £1), only the portrait of our Queen. It is true that, from time to time, pictorial commemorative stamps are issued on special occasions; for instance, stamps with flower designs for a Botanical Congress, or with the pictures from Shakespeare's plays and so on.

But these commemorative stamps are in use for a few weeks only and are printed in comparatively small quantities.

Our everyday, ordinary stamps, however, have an extremely dull design.

For a long time suggestions were made that Britain, too, like all foreign countries, should show on her stamps, designs which would tell about our national heritage, our history, our technical achievements and our countryside. Some years ago this was discussed in Parliament, but nothing came of it.

Now the famous firm of Stanley Gibbons has commissioned an artist to design a set of British stamps bearing such designs which would tell the world something about our country. Twelve of these 'pictorial' stamps were designed and printed and we show them in our illustration. They have, of course, no validity for use on letters and are quite 'unofficial', but they may very well serve as an example of what could be done.

The present Postmaster-General recently expressed the view that Britain should use her postage stamps for informing the world about us, and it may well be that he will accept the suggestion for pictorial stamps, though they might have different designs from those proposed.

BACK GARDEN SAFARI

No. 10 EARWIGS

By Christopher Reynolds

EARWIGS become fully grown in August. From then until the onset of winter they roam widely and often appear in houses.

Out of doors earwigs rest, during the day, under stones or logs, in cracks and crevices of walls, under loose bark, in holes, burrows, or nests made by other small creatures, under moss and the matted parts of plants, beneath crinkled and folded leaves, or among the petals of flowers.

Adult earwigs live through the winter and early spring. Male and female earwigs are easily distinguished. The pincers at the back of the male are very curved, while those at the back of the female are only slightly curved.

I have seen earwigs use their pincers to help themselves over when they have

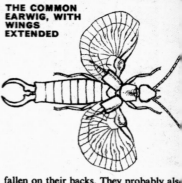

THE COMMON EARWIG, WITH WINGS EXTENDED

MALE EARWIG, SHOWING CURVED PINCERS

fallen on their backs. They probably als[o] serve a protective purpose and are said t[o] be used for folding the wings on the ver[y] rare occasions when these are used.

Very few people have ever seen [a] common earwig in flight, but I am prou[d] to be one of them. I was walking down [a] country lane in August, and I noticed a[n] unfamiliar-looking insect fluttering alon[g] on broad, filmy wings that flickered in th[e] sunlight. It landed on a tuft of grass, but [I] wasn't in time to see it in the act of foldin[g] its wings. I could then have found ou[t] whether it really used its pincers to tuc[k] them under its short wing covers.

The folding of these delicate wings i[s] very complicated. They are closed rathe[r] like a fan, which is then doubled over i[n] two or three places, leaving many thick[-] nesses of wing beneath the short covers[.]

This article is adapted from 'Smal[l] Creatures in my Back Garden', publishe[d] by Andre Deutsch at 13s. 6d.

ODD INVENTIONS

MOBILE TUNNEL

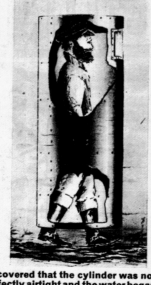

WHEN Peter Svensen settled in Montana in 1899, he decided to 'stake his claim' near a slow-moving river where the lush vegetation showed promise of good crops for his farm-to-be. He built his house, and then set about laying out amenities. After two years' hard work he was able to allow himself some leisure time, and always spent it inventing something. Some things worked, some did not. One of his strangest inventions was a method of crossing the river without getting his clothes wet, and without resorting to a boat.

If you hold a tumbler upside-down over water, and then lower it into the water, you will see that the water will not go up inside the glass because of air pressure, and, provided the glass is not tilted to allow the captive air to escape, the water will never enter the glass. Svensen soon got to work on this idea, and the illustration shows, in a cutaway form, the cylinder he produced. It was six feet high and two feet six inches in diameter. A piece of glass near the sealed end enabled him to see where he was going and a pair of handles riveted on the inside allowed him to carry the cylinder into the water and guide it along its watery journey.

Peter's troubles started when he

discovered that the cylinder was not perfectly airtight and the water began to creep up inside. Also, although heavy on land, once in the water, the air made it so buoyant that it was difficult to keep it down! The only answer was to make the cylinder heavy enough to counteract the natural buoyancy, but by doing this, it would have been impossible for the user to lift the cylinder out of water. It is not surprising that this strange contrivance never went into production. It needed nothing but the very smallest current to send the user to the bottom – inside a cylinder full of water!

In Victorian times, [it] was fashionable [to] use these curv[ed] knives. The advanta[ge] was that the rais[ed] edge of the pla[te] didn't stop you fr[om] cutting the food.

A species of Crick[et] frogs found in Sou[th] America carry the[ir] eggs in pouches [on] either side of the[ir] mouths, and t[he] embryos stay he[re] until they are pe[r]fectly formed ba[by] frogs.

FREE! FREE! FREE!

HE DAY OF YOUR LIFE— T··· *Butlin's*

OUTDOOR POOL, FILEY

YES, it's true! The best day of your holidays is waiting for you at *any one* of Butlin's fabulous holiday camps. And it's FREE to EAGLE readers!

Each week during the summer we will publish a pecial voucher coupon, like the one below. All you ave to do is collect *six* of these coupons and send nem to us. In return we will send you a Butlin's atrance ticket for you *and* your father or mother!

This ticket usually costs 15/-, but because of a pecial arrangement with Butlin's Holiday Camps, *will cost you nothing*! You can use this ticket any ay up to the end of the season, but the last date for pplication for entrance tickets is August 31.

A MILLION PEOPLE will go to a Butlin's Holiday Camp this year – *YOU* could be one of them! here are camps at Ayr, Scotland; Bognor Regis, ussex; Clacton, Essex; Filey Bay, Yorkshire; wllheli, North Wales; Minehead, Somerset; kegness, Lincolnshire.

THE FUN NEVER STOPS AT BUTLIN'S!

nd no wonder! There are over 1,000 acres of gardens, heated swimming pools, 52 different free amusement ark rides, 23 different outdoor sports with free equip- ent on loan, 50 acres of boating lakes and more than 0,000 prizes to be won by children every summer!

INDOOR POOL, AYR

E AND BOYS' WORLD 20 January 1968

What a neck!

ear Editor,
I am sending you a photograph of y brother in one of his rare oods.
John Davey, Sedgefield, Co. Durham.

Funny photos are always wel- ome, so snap to it, readers! — Ed.

* * *

NEXT PAGE

Whereas in the 1950s the cover of *Eagle* had been the exclusive home of Dan Dare it underwent many changes during the 1960s. As the publishers attempted to compete in an ever more crowded market the cover became a battleground in more ways than one. Some of the attempts to attract the 5d of the discerning young boy were more successful than others and here is a small selection showing both ends of the spectrum.

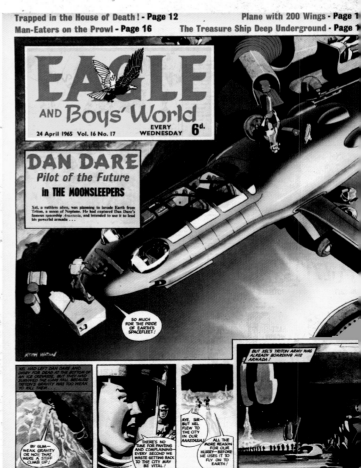

FABULOUS STINGRAY OFFER FROM GOLDEN WONDER

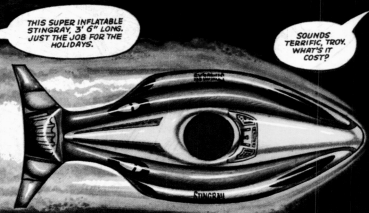

A Steamer Lives On. The level of detail in the cutaways never deteriorated. Through everything, starting with reduction to a single page, being moved around the comic and, the final cut, the loss of colour, the detail was immense. Here though we see how it came close to being death by a thousand cuts, as a typically intricate drawing of a train loses all clarity due to a lack of hues.

A STEAMER LIVES ON

THE 'Golden Shuttle' was one of the powerful Gresley A4 Pacific locomotives built to work the 'West Riding Limited' – a crack high-speed luxury train between King's Cross and Leeds in the halcyon days of the streamlined fliers just before the outbreak of World War II.

War came, and the 'Golden Shuttle' was allocated the more serious task of hauling the special train of the Supreme Headquarters of Allied Forces in Europe and, as a tribute, 'Golden Shuttle' was renamed after the Supreme Commander, General Dwight D. Eisenhower.

Now, as a further tribute on her retirement from active service, 'Dwight D. Eisenhower' has been shipped across the Atlantic to become part of the National Railroad Museum in the U.S.A. There she stands as a worthy example of one of the most advanced designs of steam locomotives from Britain – the cradle of railways.

A sister locomotive, 'Mallard', the world steam speed record holder, is preserved in the Museum of Transport at Clapham, London.

KEY TO NUMBERED PARTS

(1) Rigid main-frames, extending the whole length of the engine – from the buffer beam (2) to the cab steps (3). (4) Streamlined shell. (5) Boiler. (6) Firebox. (7) Rigid stays separating boiler casing and firebox. (8) Crown stays, allowing expansion between firebox crown and boiler casing. (9) Rocking firebars. (10) Ashpan. (11) Firehole door. (12) Brick arch. (13) Small firetubes. (14) Large firetubes. (15) Smoke-box. (16) Banjo-shaped steam-collecting dome. (17) Perforated steam-collecting plate. (18) Owens-type regulator valve. (19) Main steam pipe. (20) Superheater header. (21) Superheater tubes inside the large firetubes. (22) Steam pipe feeding outside cylinder. (23) Steam pipe to inside cylinder. (24) Outside cylinders (each side of engine). (25) Piston. (26) Crosshead and slide bar motion. (27) Connecting rod. (28) 6 ft. 8 in.-diameter coupled driving wheels. (29) Driving wheel axlebox. (30) Springs. (31) Coupling rod. (32) Piston valves for outside cylinder. (33) Walschaerts valve gear (shown set for forward motion at full cut-off). (34) Reversing screw. (35) Reversing rod, linking screw to valve gear. (36) Inside cylinder. (37) Inside connecting rod. (38) Crankshaft for inside drive. (39) Piston valves for inside cylinder. (40) 'Two-to-one' linkage transferring the motion of the outside valves' travel to the inside valve. (41) Exhaust steam blast pipe. (42) Twin 'petticoat' arrangement of exhaust uptakes to chimney. (43) Double-blast chimney. (44) Blower rings. (45) Anti-vacuum valve. (46) Three-note chime whistle. (47) Ejector vacuum pipe. (48) Ejector, controlling brakes. (49) Twin Ross safety valves. (50) Regulator handle. (51) Steam and vacuum gauges. (52) Turret-mounted steam valves. (53) Smoke-box door. (54) Access door in streamlined casing. (55) Screw jacks for opening doors. (56) 3 ft. 2 in.-diameter bogie wheels. (57) Bogie frame and springs. (58) 3 ft. 8 in.-diameter trailing wheels under firebox. (59) Catazzi axle boxes allowing radial movement on trailing wheel axle. (60) Steam-assisted sanding gear. (61) Brake gear. (62) Wheel splashers. (63) Crew's seats. (64) Corridor, providing passage for changing crews while on the move. (65) Corridor opening on footplate. (66) Vestibule for connecting corridor to first coach of train. (67) Water tank. (68) Water well-tank between frames (total capacity – 5,000 gallons). (69) Water filler. (70) Water pick-up scoop. (71) Trunking from scoop to tank. (72) Handle-operating pick-up scoop. (73) Sloping coal space (9 tons). (74) Tender brake handle. (75) Brake gear for tender. (76) Flexible weather protection canopy between loco and tender.

EAGLE is 15 ...and still flying high!

1950

EAGLE – THE NEW NATIONAL STRIP CARTOON WEEKLY

DAN DARE
PILOT OF THE FUTURE

EAGLE

DAN DARE, the most famous name in space fiction, set out into the unknown in the very first issue and is still going strong. Today his story is told by David Motton (left) and drawn by Keith Watson.

BUCK OF THE LEGION

SERGEANT Luck was one of the most popular characters ever devised. Beginning in 1952, he continued right up to 1961, shortly before the Foreign Legion moved its headquarters to Corsica.

1952

FRIDAY the thirteenth! Unlucky for some – but lucky for the hundreds of thousands of boys who, on Friday the thirteenth just 15 years ago, received the first copy of EAGLE.

And what a reception it had! Launched in a blaze of publicity, it was greeted with acclaim all over the country, and indeed, all over the world.

It led the field then; it leads the field now. No other boys' paper can match it in terms of colour, printing, artwork, or sheer varied entertainment.

On this page I have shown just a few of the highlights of the past 15 years. Space does not permit them all, but many of you will remember the painting competition with a first prize of a trip to Russia; the Sportsman of the Year Trophy; the Carol Services; the Boys and Girls exhibition at Olympia; The Road of Courage; Storm Nelson; Jack O' Lantern; and so on.

All things must change. Today's EAGLE is different from yesterday's EAGLE; and tomorrow's paper will be different again. But of one thing you may be certain: it will be the very best that my staff and I can produce.

The Editor

1954

SUPERSONIC JET BOMBER OF TOMORROW

ALL things must change – except the quality of Ashwell Wood's drawings. His work appeared in the first issue and, 470 drawings later, also in the current issue. In 1954 he gave his impression of what tomorrow's six-engined jet bomber would look like. On page 15 is his cutaway of a Boeing B-70, and you can see how accurate he was.

1954 also saw the start of the EAGLE/GIRL Table Tennis championships, later to be recognized as the British Junior Championships. Among the winners were Mary Shannon (1957) and Chester Barnes (1961), Britain's senior champions of 1965.

Little Mary Shannon with chief coach Johnny Leach

Chester Barnes

HOW YOUR *EAGLE* REACHES YOU

The paper begins with a conference to decide the contents of next week's issue. Here we see Editor Robert Bartholomew making a point to Alfred Wallace, the Managing Editor, at the weekly get-together with the staff.

After the artists and script-writers have been briefed by the Editor, the art work and features are returned to the office for lettering and checking. Here we see Chief Sub-Editor Dan Lloyd discussing an alteration with a lettering artist.

The finished artwork and copy is collected by van and rushed to the printers. The artwork is immediately photographed down to reproduction size with this huge camera mounted on rollers.

1955

THE year of the EAGLE/Y.H.A. holiday tours. Since then well over 100,000 boys and girls have taken part in these great adventure holidays.

1957

BEGINNING TODAY!

The HAPPY WARRIOR

The new life story of SIR WINSTON CHURCHILL

WINSTON CHURCHILL WAS BORN AT BLENHEIM PALACE ON THE 30th NOVEMBER, 1874.

1962

IN 1957 we published the life story of that wonderful Englishman Sir Winston Churchill. We presented the Great Old Man with a specially bound copy – and he was delighted! In 1962 we began the saga of Heros the Spartan, another classic EAGLE story. And the link? Both stories were illustrated by the fabulous Frank Bellamy (left).

HEROS the SPARTAN

1963

AN ADVENTURE BEGINS TODAY!

BLACKBOW THE CHEYENNE

FROM Riders of the Range (which he took over in 1952) to Blackbow was an easy step for artist Frank Humphris. Frank is an acknowledged expert on the West, has a wonderful collection of guns and Red Indian clothes, and is an honorary Deputy Sheriff of Bexar County, Texas.

RIDERS OF THE RANGE

1964

EAGLE's companion paper BOYS' WORLD was merged into the paper – and right to the top of the popularity charts went the amazing Iron Man, one of the great characters in boys' fiction.

Captain L. D. Empson, commanding officer of H.M.S. Eagle.

WHEN H.M.S. *Eagle* was re-commissioned last year, this biggest ship in the Royal Navy was adopted by EAGLE. Twenty lucky readers were taken over the ship, and the Editor presented the crew with two canoes on your behalf. We hope to have more news of H.M.S. *Eagle* soon.

1965

WHAT of the next 15 years? We can't say – there is so much activity in our crystal ball that we cannot make out anything definite. But we do know we shall be packing into the next 15 years as many good things as went into the past 15.

1980

...illed retouchers then remove any faults revealed by the ...ra. Their work is not unlike that of the artist except that ...work on the photographs. ...ile the artwork is being handled, the compositor is

setting the stories and features in type. A printed page is then produced and is sent to the editorial offices for final checking. Then back to the giant press which prints your EAGLEs at the rate of 20,000 copies an hour.

The thousands of copies are then packed and distributed to newsagents throughout the country—and into the hands of avid readers like these two pictured here!

GET EAGLE TODAY

DON'T MISS YOUR COPY!

DRY-LAND SURFING IS ALL THE RAGE!

How to turn

REMEMBER the yo-yo and the hula-hoop? They were play-crazes from America which caught on in this country about ten years ago. It looks as though craze number three is on its way now.

To be a top-teenager in America, you've got to be able to handle a surfboard. 'Riding the waves' is so popular that they even make pop records about it!

But surfing will never catch on here, because only a few resorts have waves large enough to be 'ridden'. Only in Cornwall, the Channel Islands and Ireland do surfers abound.

THRILLS AND SPILLS

But the invention of the dry-land *Skateboard* means that *everyone*, whether they live in town or country, city or sea-side, can enjoy the thrills and spills of surfing!

They were developed by Californian surfers who wanted to keep in trim when the sea was too rough to train. Basically, a Skateboard is a piece of hardwood about two to three feet in length and eight inches wide, with two pairs of roller-skate wheels fixed underneath.

Riding instructions couldn't be simpler. Just find a well-surfaced, empty road, give the Skateboard a gentle push, and jump on. Naturally, if you can find a sloping surface, you've got the ideal 'Skateboarding pitch'! Turning the Skateboard is easy. If you want to turn, just put as much weight as possible on the side in which you want to go. You can make the board perform complicated manoeuvres by pressing on different sides of the platform.

This new sport is a boon to skiers for summer practice, because the majority of

You can reach high speeds on the Skateboard

Skateboard movements are the same as those of the skier.

In America, the sport is so popular that inter-State championships are now held. In fact, if the Skateboarders had their way, there would be a Skateboard championship at the next Olympic Games!

DRY-LAND SURFING

WHO READS THE *EAGLE?* THE WHO DO—THAT'S WHO!

THE WHO

POP PICK

ROGER   PETE   KEITH   JOHN

This week's prize-winning poem was sent in by Graham Hawkins of North London. If you can make up a poem, send it to us. It could win you an E.P. record!

**'The Who' are great – with 'I Can't Explain',
I wish I could hear it again and again.
Their style is great – and they are, too;
I wish that I was one of 'The Who'.**

IT all began in January. By February they were rapidly increasing – and by March they were everywhere in and around London's West End. Throughout the maze of narrow back streets around Soho they appeared in their hundreds, hanging on walls and hoardings, and still more in shop windows.

To those outside the pop world, these black and white posters boldly announcing 'Maximum R&B – The WHO' seemed very weird – but to the with-it beat fraternity, it was enough to arouse interest and curiosity.

Attendance figures began shooting up at clubs like 'The Scene', where The WHO were appearing, and, in a matter of weeks, this way-out foursome were winning a reputation as a group with a big future.

Having built up a large following in the London area, The Who set out to capture the remainder of Britain's pop fans with their first record, 'I Can't Explain', a number written by their lead-guitarist Pete Townsend.

Appearances on TV shows like 'Top Of The Pops' and 'Ready Steady Go!' helped to plug the disc, which soon began rocketing up the charts and into the top ten. The Who had made it!

At the time of going to press, Keith, Roger, John and Pete were busy recording an L.P. for the 'States, an E.P. for France, and a follow-up single to 'I Can't Explain'.

When they paid us a recent visit, prior to these recording sessions, they told us that although it had not been decided what their follow-up single would be, it would definitely be a joint composition. If it's as good as their first, then they can be sure of another big hit.

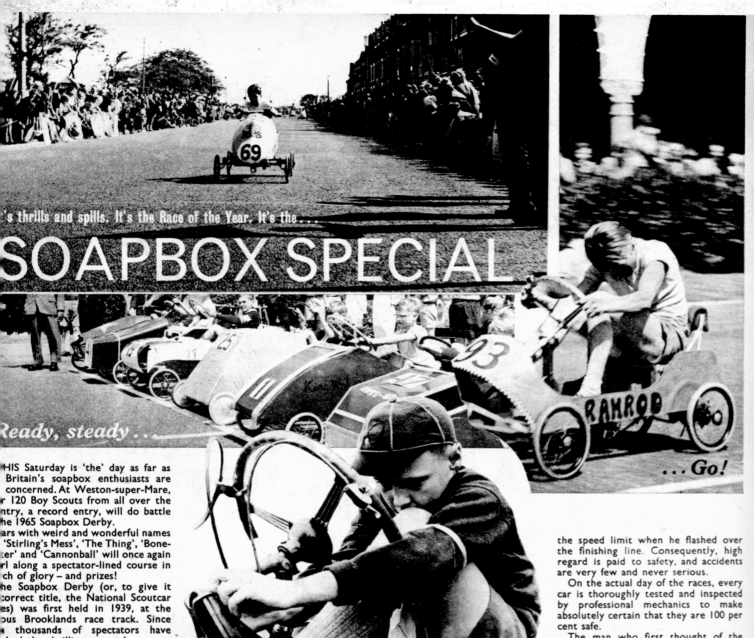

's thrills and spills. It's the Race of the Year. It's the . . .

SOAPBOX SPECIAL

Ready, steady . . .

...Go!

THIS Saturday is 'the' day as far as Britain's soapbox enthusiasts are concerned. At Weston-super-Mare, [or] 120 Boy Scouts from all over the [cou]ntry, a record entry, will do battle [in t]he 1965 Soapbox Derby.

[C]ars with weird and wonderful names ['Stirling's Mess', 'The Thing', 'Bone-[sha]ker' and 'Cannonball' will once again [hu]rl along a spectator-lined course in [sear]ch of glory – and prizes!

[T]he Soapbox Derby (or, to give it [its c]orrect title, the National Scoutcar [Rac]es) was first held in 1939, at the [fam]ous Brooklands race track. Since [then] thousands of spectators have [wat]ched the thrilling spectacle.

[T]he races have become an important [eve]nt in the Boy Scout calendar and

several times have been covered by both B.B.C. and I.T.V. television, as well as being featured in documentary films.

Unlike the famous American competition, the British Derby is for pedal-driven machines – not streamlined shells that just roll down a gradient to the winning post. For this reason, the races are a test not only of the owners' driving ability, but also of their skill in design, construction and mechanical know-how. (Cars have been produced with as many as nine gear changes.)

Trophies and prizes are awarded to the owner of the car with the best mechanical design and construction, for the most ingenious construction, and for the machines recording the fastest time in the various classes.

SPEED RECORD

Amazing speeds have been attained at these meetings. At present, the record over the 440-yard course is 26.87 m.p.h. That's from a standing start – so the driver was easily breaking

the speed limit when he flashed over the finishing line. Consequently, high regard is paid to safety, and accidents are very few and never serious.

On the actual day of the races, every car is thoroughly tested and inspected by professional mechanics to make absolutely certain that they are 100 per cent safe.

The man who first thought of the British Soapbox Derby was the late Hadyn Dimmock, who for 36 years was the editor of 'The Scout' magazine. He knew of the American 'Derby', but felt that the British version should be a test of the boys' mechanical skill as well as their driving ability.

PEDAL-DRIVEN

He recommended that the cars should be pedal-driven along a flat course from a standing start. The machines should be built unaided by the boys, although they could seek adult advice. He also stated that materials used in construction should not cost more than a certain figure (£8 at present), thereby encouraging boys to use odd scraps from bicycles, prams and the like. These rules have remained unchanged.

The British Motor Corporation agreed to sponsor the event as well as supply the prizes and trophies. They also offer free advice and the use and facilities of their workshops for the soapbox builders.

Who knows – among them could be another racing driver Stirling Moss or Mini-car designer Alec Issigonis.

last-minute check-over before the big race

GET GOING WITH EAGLE

AND

No. 1 This picture shows Jim Clark winning this year's French Grand Prix. What car is he driving?

A. B.R.M.
B. Ferrari
C. Lotus

No. 2 Sir Frank Whittle (above) invented something which brought about a major development in aviation. What was the invention?

A. The jet engine
B. Radar
C. The Spitfire

No. 3 This display has thrilled many at the Royal Tournament. From which branch of the Army do the riders come?

A. Royal Army Ordnance Corps
B. Royal Engineers
C. Royal Signals

No. 4 This blue and white flag, known as the Blue Peter, is hoisted to indicate – what?

A. Ship is about to sail
B. Ship is entering port
C. Ship has a Customs Officer aboard

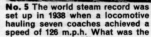
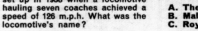

No. 5 The world steam record was set up in 1938 when a locomotive hauling seven coaches achieved a speed of 126 m.p.h. What was the locomotive's name?

A. The Comet
B. Mallard
C. Royal Scot

No. 6 Below are listed three well-known ships of the Royal Navy. Which one is shown in our picture?

A. Duke of York
B. Eagle
C. Vanguard

No. 7 One of the difficulties in planning a successful invasion is in maintaining a supply line. For the Allies' invasion of Europe, during the last war, they laid a pipe-line under the ocean through which to pump fuel for vehicles at the front. What was the code name for this operation?

A. Fido   B. Leo   C. Pluto

No. 8 This is the Snowdon Mountain Railway which rises to 3,493 ft. – the highest reached by rail in Gt. Britain. The highest point reached by standard track railway in the world is 15,848 ft. . . . in which country?

A. Peru
B. Switzerland
C. Tibet

No. 9 Nine times, between 1924 and 1935, Sir Malcolm Campbell broke the existing land speed record. In July of last year, his son – Donald – raised it to 403.1 m.p.h. Then, on New Year's Eve, he made it a double by breaking the water world speed record in Bluebird. What was his record-breaking water speed?

A. 276.33 m.p.h.
B. 301.01 m.p.h.
C. 375.31 m.p.h.

No. 10 To test your aircraft recognition, what is the aircraft shown in our picture?

A. Concorde
B. VC 10
C. Viscount

No. 11 Here is America's Kennedy Airport. What was its previous name?

A. Cape Canaveral
B. Idlewild Airport
C. New York Airport

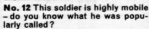

No. 12 This soldier is highly mobile – do you know what he was popularly called?

A. Chindit
B. Desert Rat
C. Red Devil

No. 13 What is this famous liner?

A. Queen Elizabeth
B. Queen Mary
C. United States

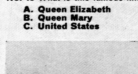

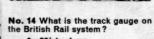

No. 14 What is the track gauge on the British Rail system?

A. 56½ inches
B. 63 inches
C. 71¾ inches

No. 15 Whether or not there's a tiger in the tank, this motor cycle is named after another big cat – which?

A. Cheetah
B. Lynx
C. Panther

TURN TO THE NEXT PAGE FO

★ FLIGHT IN A GLIDER
★ TRIP IN A HOVERCRAFT
★ DAY AT SEA WITH THE ROYAL NAVY
★ RIDE IN A TANK WITH THE ROYAL ARMOURED CORPS
★ TRIP ON A LOCOMOTIVE SIMULATOR
★ VISIT TO THE ROYAL AIRCRAFT ESTABLISHMENT
★ SCALEXTRIC MOTOR-RACING SET

WIN A FABULOUS PRIZE

No. 16 Here is a modern tank . . . in which war did tanks first take part?

A. Boer War
B. First World War
C. Second World War

No. 17 The 'Golden Arrow' is one of our crack Continental expresses linking London with Paris and Brussels. Another, of which the carriages are ferried across the Channel, is the . . . what?

A. Night Ferry
B. Paris Express
C. Silver Arrow

No. 18 What is the maximum speed allowed on this Motorway?

A. 30 m.p.h.
B. 50 m.p.h.
C. No limit

No. 19 This war-time aircraft certainly packed a sting! After what was it named?

A. Gnat
B. Mosquito
C. Scorpion

No. 20 Here's the British Rail *s.s. Sarnia* taking holidaymakers to a popular resort . . . where?

A. Channel Isles
B. Isle of Man
C. Isle of Wight

No. 21 This train, often seen in Westerns, may have been bound for Dodge City. In which State is 'Dodge'?

A. Arizona
B. Kansas
C. Texas

No. 22 What type of bridge is this, built by Army sappers?

A. Platoon
B. Poltroon
C. Pontoon

No. 23 Where did Nelson lose his right eye?

A. Copenhagen
B. Corsica
C. Trafalgar

No. 24 Bicycling was a bone-shaking business before the invention of the pneumatic tyre. Who first registered his pneumatic tyre invention—in 1845?

A. Dunlop
B. Thompson
C. Goodyear

No. 25 After what bird of prey is the new vertical take-off aircraft named?

A. Eagle
B. Falcon
C. Kestrel

- - - - - - - - CUT ROUND BROKEN RULE - - - - - - - -

'GET GOING WITH EAGLE'
COMPETITION FREE ENTRY COUPON

AGE.......... NAME.......................................
(Block letters)
ADDRESS.......................................
(Block letters)

Write the key letters (A, B or C) of your chosen answers in the blank spaces below – each under its question number

1	2	3	4	5	6	7	8	9	10	11	12	13	14	15	16	17	18	19	20	21	22	23	24	25

My last line for the incomplete verse is :...

Post your entry to 'GET GOING WITH EAGLE' COMPETITION, 96 LONG ACR

Work out your answers. Fill out your form, and send to 'Get Going with *Eagle* competition' c/o Orion Publishing, 5 Upper St Martin's Lane, London, WC2H 9EA by 1 June 2010. Sadly no day at sea with the Royal Navy, or a trip on a locomotive simulator, but a 2011 *Eagle Diary* for the first FIVE correct entries out of the hat.

See www.orionbooks.co.uk for terms and conditions.

DETAILS OF HOW TO ENTER

TARTING THIS WEEK!

BACK GARDEN SAFARI

. 1 WOODLICE

There's no need to go on a safari to study the natural ways of wild life. Your own back garden is a teeming jungle of hundreds of different creatures – from bees and butterflies to slugs and spiders. You'll find them in the trees, bushes and hedges, among the weeds and grass blades and under stones and logs. Bright flowers have their own community and even more live underground.

It's fun to stalk across your garden on the trail of these tiny creatures. If you're careful and don't allow your shadow to fall across them, they will let you get really close. Take a notebook, pencil and magnifying glass on your 'expedition' – simple sketches will give you something of lasting value.

In this series, Christopher Reynolds will show you the most fascinating

Woodlice

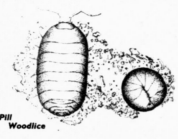

Pill Woodlice

This is adapted from *Small Creatures in my Back Garden* by Christopher Reynolds to be published at 13s. 6d. by Andre Deutsch.

creatures to look for and where and how to find them.

There are enormous numbers of woodlice in my garden. I can find them by turning over stones and bricks – they cling upside-down to the undersurfaces. There are two main types of woodlice – the *Pill* woodlice, which roll up into a tight ball when disturbed; and the *Flat* woodlice, which cannot roll up.

Although woodlice are the only *crustaceans* that have become complete land-dwellers, they cannot live long in dry air, and have to find a damp retreat in order to survive. (That is why we do not see them in the open during the day.)

AN EXPERIMENT TO TRY

You can prove this by a little experiment. I covered one half of the bottom of an oblong tin with dry blotting paper and the other half with damp blotting paper. Then I placed a dozen flat woodlice in the tin.

At first they wandered all over the tin, but within a quarter of an hour all the

woodlice were resting in the half containing the damp paper.

I noticed that the woodlice always came to rest against the *sides* of the tin. They seemed unable to rest comfortably unless they made contact with an upright surface. So I leant glass slides against the inside of the tin with just enough room for them to crawl between. In a short time the woodlice had all settled behind the glass slides, making contact with both sides of their bodies.

I also noticed that woodlice only enter crevices where there is room to go without squeezing. I proved this was so by placing my glass slide on the floor of the tin and raised one side with Plasticine. The woodlice started walking under the glass, but as soon as they felt the pressure of the glass on their backs, they came out again.

The reason is that woodlice have a soft underside. Their legs are not very powerful and they could easily become trapped and damaged in tight crevices. You can easily try these little experiments yourselves.

OP PICK of the WEEK BURT BACHARACH

IT is over five years since Britain had its first taste of the 'Bacharach sound', with two songs called *Magic Moments* and *The Story of My Life*.

Since then, with several more hit compositions, a hit record of his own, and a TV programme devoted to him and his music, Burt Bacharach has become one of the world's leading songwriters.

Together with his musical collaborator, Hal David, who writes the lyrics, he has found the perfect formula for a hit pop song. The results of their work are some of the most outstanding songs of the beat era.

Listen to Burt talking about his music and Hal David, and you will get some idea of his dedication and the tremendous thought that goes into each arrangement.

"We have worked out a pattern over the years in which the words and music become virtually inseparable. To make sure that the words are given maximum display, I often use lyric breaks in the choruses."

On learning that EAGLE was doing a feature on Burt, world-famous pop stars Gene Pitney and Dusty Springfield immediately came forward with their own tributes.

Dusty: "It's hard for me to find words sufficient to do him justice – to me he's the end!"

Gene: "I have worked with many creators of songs and fresh concepts, but few, if any, have the dynamic talents of Burt Bacharach."

Just before going to press, Dionne Warwick phoned through her tribute. "The charm, personality and talent of this man speaks for itself. To me he is talent in every respect of the word."

Burt Bacharach was born 35 years ago in Kansas City, the son of a journalist father and an artist mother.

His love of music grew during his time at High School and at McGill University. A highly intelligent and very thoughtful young man, Burt moved on to the Music Academy of the West to study serious music.

His first contact with the show-biz world came when he was signed up by American singing star Vic Damone as musical director.

In the last six years, in addition to his song writing activities, he has toured all over the world as pianist and musical arranger to Marlene Dietrich.

Besides *Trains And Boats And Planes*, which recently took him high up the charts, Burt has been responsible for such hits as *24 Hours From Tulsa; Anyone Who Had A Heart; There's Always Something There To Remind Me;* and *Walk On By*, and many others.

All of these are featured on Burt's recently-released L.P., aptly entitled 'Hit Maker'.

On the album, Burt displays not only his talent as a songwriter, but as a pianist and a leader of an orchestra, too.

M. Rolf, of Woodford, Essex, wins an E.P. record of his choice for his rhyme, right. Send us a short poem about your favourite – and you could be next week's prizewinner! (But remember not to write about a group we have already featured.)

His songs first established Burt Bacharach's name;
As a pianist-composer he's travelled to fame.
Now with 'Trains and Boats and Planes' in the charts fans declare,
There's more 'Magic Moments' that they all can share.

POP PICK

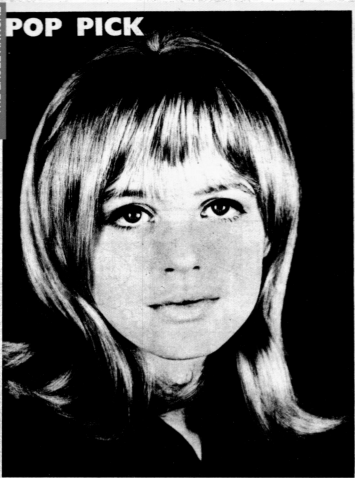

MARIANNE FAITHFUL

★ ★

SHE looks as pretty as she sounds – two good reasons for the tremendous impact that the 18-year-old Marianne Faithfull has had. Her sound, which is best described as folksy-pop, rests on the border line where pop and folk music meet.

But how does Marianne see herself – as a pop or folk singer?

Recently, she visited EAGLE offices and so we put this question to her.

"I'm a pop singer, although I do sing folk music in a commercial form – and I love to sing folk songs," she answered, gazing at the multitude of pictures of pop stars round the office wall, many of whom had themselves glanced around the same office at the very same pictures.

Her eyes came to rest on a picture of Bob Dylan.

"Now there's a folk singer! I don't think he cares if he's a commercial success or not – he certainly doesn't intend yielding to commercialism!"

It soon became very obvious that here was a blonde who was anything but dumb.

During the length of her all-too-short v Marianne spoke with confidence authority, although very quietly, abov wide range of matters within the pop fiel

"I was born in Hampstead, and educa at St. Joseph's Convent, which is in Read My favourite subject was English Litera – I have always enjoyed reading and sti when I get the chance.

"I enjoy singing very much – also rea poetry and meeting people – not just s biz people, but from all walks of life. musical tastes are very varied. I like Sa Shaw, both her voice and as a person, the Beatles, Bob Dylan, Segovia, M Callas and Chopin."

Besides her two hit singles 'Come With Me' and 'This Little Bird', Maria has recorded two L.P.s.

One of these, entitled 'Come My Way aimed entirely at the folk market and se as proof of her talent in this realm. standing among the 14 tracks are 'Fare Well', 'Bells Of Freedom', and the title 'Come My Way'.

Stuart Goode of Cardiff wins an E.P. record of his own choice for this rhyme. Compose a short verse about your favourite – and you could win one, too!

What took the youngsters by surprise?
The blonde-haired singer with bright blue eyes.
'As tears go by' was the song she sang,
Who is the singer? – our Marianne.
And then her disc 'Come stay with me',
Went right up in the top twenty.

POP PICK OF THE WEEK
SANDIE SHAW

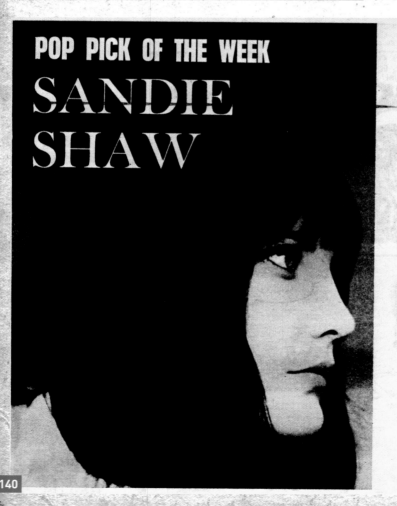

IT was a cold and windy night in March last year when a 17-year-old Dagenham girl, Sandra Goodrich, began her rapid and fairy-tale-like climb from a pop-crazy teenager into Britain's most popular female vocalist, Miss Sandie Shaw.

Sandie's story is a publicity agent's dream, and would do credit even to Hans Christian Andersen.

After meeting the Roulettes, Adam Faith's backing group, at a party, she called to see them back-stage after a show at the Commodore Theatre, Hammersmith.

A few minutes later, who should come strolling down the corridor but Adam Faith, just as Sandie was half-way through singing 'Everybody Loves A Lover', "Just for a giggle," she says.

Adam listened, looked and liked! A few days later, Sandie was signing a contract with Adam's manager, Miss Evelyn Taylor.

Six weeks later, Sandie Shaw was at No. 1 in the hit parade with a Burt Bacharach song 'There's Always Something There To Remind Me'.

A fantastic breakthrough – even by pop standards!

Shortly afterwards, Adam Faith stated firmly to the cynics: "Don't worry, Sandie won't be a 'one-hit wonder' – there's plenty more where that one came from!"

Some 16 months later, we all know just how right he was.

Next record, and next big hit, was Don't Come', followed by the equ popular 'I'll Stop At Nothing', recently by her 2nd No. 1 – 'Long Love'.

Sandie was voted 'Best New Singer of 1964' to climax a great yea

With Sandie away in America on first visit, Adam spoke to EAGLE ab his barefoot discovery.

"Now that she's at last got her problem sorted out, I don't see anyth stopping her from being the biggest singer ever to come out of this count America will go crazy about her.

"Why? Well, musically, she's got s a great sound and it's her own soun not like anyone else's."

Adam then turned from Sandie singer to Sandie the person.

"Without a doubt, she's the m straightforward girl I've known. S a very frank and open person wit great sense of humour and her suc has had little, if any, affect on her."

A good example of Sandie's mus talents is her L.P. simply called 'San

It features a selection of 12 tra varying from the rocking 'Everyb Loves A Lover' to the soft ballad put Ketty Lester in the British cha 'Love Letters'.

Other attractive numbers included the album – the folksy 'Lemon Tr 'Always', Pet Clark's hit, 'Downtov and 'It's In His Kiss'.

N. Osgood of Portsmouth, Hants, wins an E.P. record of his choice for his rhyme. Send us a short poem about your favourite – and you could be next week's prize-winner! (But remember to write about a group we haven't already featured.)

What a wonderful girl Sandie is,
The one and only, in show-biz.
Just listen to the tremendous roar,
As she appears bare-footed on the floor.
Then she sings with such great feeling,
Causing her fans to raise the ceiling.
She's definitely here to stay,
And that is all I've got to say.

COMPUTERS

World knowledge at your fingertips.

A fantastic dream — OR IS IT?

Computers could give you this and

lots more — as early as the 1990s.

for EVERYONE

HOW would you like to be able to solve any mathematical problem in a fraction of a second: summon any page of any book or newspaper instantly before your eyes: have all factual information known to man at your fingertips—and without leaving your own living-room? This fantastic dream of scientific achievement may come true by the 1990s if a plan now being worked on by top scientists in this country and the U.S.A. is successful. These scientists are now beginning to realize that the wonder-invention of our age, the computer, has so far been used in only a tiny, highly-specialised field and the time has come to think about putting it where it may be of most benefit—right into the homes of ordinary citizens.

When your first domestic computer is carried in by the delivery men in the 1990s, you can ask them to take away with them your TV set, your telephone, your electricity and gas meters, and your typewriter, tape-recorder and record player. All these things will be as out of date as the gas-lamp is today, for the computer will control all power supplies to your house, your videophone link and multi-channel TV signal.

The problems the scientists are wrestling with to bring this dream closer to reality are, of course, fantastically complex; but they are not really different from the problems of making any super-technical invention available to everyone. They are concerned with two things: size and cheapness. If you have ever seen a modern computer—a whole roomful of complicated equipment, with banks of magnetic or paper tape readers hesitantly disgorging their information—you will be wondering how anybody can ever expect to compress it all down to living-room furniture scale. Well, we already have part of the answer to that.

MEMORY BANK

A large part of what you see of a modern computer is its *memory*: the part that contains all the information it needs to draw on to do its work. The rest—the actual calculating circuits—is relatively small; and already up-to-date micro-integration techniques have developed a calculating circuit that fits into a small portable box. In a few years, the equipment will get even smaller.

But the breakthrough really came when scientists devised a technique of 'Time-sharing', enabling several computers working on quite different problems to share *one* memory: and this, it is hoped, is the core of To-morrow's domestic computer.

Every town will have its own memory store, which the domestic computers in the houses of that town will have instant access to: for more difficult work there will be larger regional memory stores ser-ving several counties. There will undoubtedly also be a gigantic National Memory containing every fact known to man. That takes care

Already cal-culating cir-cuits can be fitted into a box as small as this

of the size problem—now what about cost?

At the moment a computer capable of doing what the scientists have in mind costs more than most men earn in a lifetime. But with **centralized** memories, and mass-production tech-niques of the future, it will not be the cost of the actual unit that will be the main problem. It will be the installation of the complex nation-wide network of connections be-tween the computers, rather like to-day's telephone cables but needing to carry vastly more information than a telephone cable could ever hope to transmit.

A MIRACLE

The answer may be another miracle of this century—the wave-guide.

This is a rectangular metal tube which carries thousands of times more information than a cable at close to the speed of light. Experts say we may soon have to go over to waveguides for our telephone system anyway, so why not make the network just a little bigger to leave room for the domestic com-puter?

EAGLE
and BOYS' WORLD

3 December 1966 Vol. 17 No. 49

EVERY WEDNESDAY 7d

DID IT EVER HAPPEN?

Everyone loves a yarn, but of course we can't trust them. Here's one, for instance. And we ask you to guess: Did It Ever Happen?

Niagara is the world's mightiest waterfall. But the world's highest is the Angel Falls, which plunges 3,212 feet down a canyon in Venezuela. And until a few decades ago it was the site of the world's strangest and most savage custom.

Wrongdoers of the Cacawowo tribe who argued their innocence were made to shoot the waterfall in a canoe with two blazing torches. If they were killed or the torches were dowsed, they were held to be guilty. If they survived the ordeal and their torches still burned, they were held to be innocent.

Well, did it ever happen like that? For the answer, turn to page 3.

EAGLE
ANNUAL 1966

What World Cup? *Eagle* had a refreshingly hype-free build-up to the tournament.

It is worth highlighting that the artist of this advert, Leo Baxendale, is best known as the creator of the Bash Street Kids.

Boy! get

PALITOY REGD

ACTION man

best-equipped movable fighting man you ever commanded!

20 movable parts His head turns, his arms move, elbows, wrists, knees, and ankles all bend. You can place him in hundreds of action positions — firing a rifle, hurling a grenade, charging with fixed bayonet.

Almost a foot tall ACTION MAN is the world's most realistic model fighting man — big enough for you to kit him out for action on all fronts.

Authentic battle gear Only ACTION MAN has such a huge arsenal of weapons and equipment — machine-guns, rifles, grenades, packs, field telephones, first aid kits, tents, flamethrowers, frogman outfits — everything the modern fighting man needs right down to his knife, fork, and spoon! Every item a perfect scaled-down version of the real thing. And it all fits!

★ **Get one free!** Collect the stars from ACTION MAN packs and get another ACTION MAN for nothing! Details in the ACTION MAN equipment manual (see coupon).

32/6 complete with work suit, cap, boots, identity tag, equipment and training manuals. Equipment sets from 4/11. Three versions — ACTION SOLDIER, ACTION SAILOR, ACTION PILOT. And over 100 separate items of superbly detailed equipment.

FREE equipment manual illustrating the entire range of ACTION MAN figures and equipment in full colour. Post this coupon (unsealed envelope 3d stamp) to Action Man Command, Cascelloid, Coalville, Leicester.

NAME...........................

ADDRESS.......................

....

COUNTY.........................

BLOCK LETTERS PLEASE

What do you want out of life?

Plenty of excitement?

PLUS a worthwhile career, with companionship, plenty of sport a travel, security and good pay? . . . then the Army is right for y And you can start young with the Army—if you're between 15 and and leaving school this year, the Army Junior Entry Scheme co be the beginning of the career you've been looking for. You can jo

AS A JUNIOR LEADER, with the chance of becoming one of the high-ranking N.C.O's of the future. And you'll get all the excitement you could wish for. The Army needs leaders, and this course is specially designed to train them.

AS A JUNIOR TRADESMAN and learn a worthwhile skill in just one year. The Army will train you to become a radio operator, a driver, or a medical assistant — these are some of the interesting trades to choose from.

AS A JUNIOR INFANTRYMAN

joining your Brigade Depot stra away, continuing your education getting infantry training designed develop leadership qualities. In addi there are opportunities to learn to the drums, pipes and bugles.

OR

If you are fascinated by technical th and want a career in Electronics, R or aircraft and vehicle maintenance example, there is an Army APPR TICE COURSE which will give y technical qualification in just t years.

Start young with the Army

Send off this coupon now!

---- **YES, I WANT TO KNOW MORE!** ----

TO: ARMY CAREERS MP6(A), LANSDOWNE HOUSE, LONDON W.I.
Please send me full details of Army Junior Entry.

NAME ....

ADDRESS .... TOWN...................

COUNTY................................... DATE OF BIRTH...........

(You must be resident in the UK)

B.761001 **APPLY NOW FOR ENTRY IN SEPTEMBER**

WORLD CUP STORY by EX-PRO

PART FOUR

THE scene is set for the greatest sporting spectacle ever to be staged in England, the eighth World Cup football Championships.

Fourteen nations who have won their way through 127 qualifying and matches in 53 different countries, plus Brazil (the holder) and England (the hosts) go on parade for the Opening Ceremony at Wembley on July 11.

On that date England kick-off against Uruguay, apparently the toughest nut to crack in her London group which also includes France and Mexico.

Centred in the Midlands, at Aston Villa and Sheffield Wednesday grounds, are West Germany, Spain, Switzerland and Argentina. Germany were the last European team to win the Cup, but Argentina won the 'Little World Cup' tournament in 1964 and are reckoned to have an almost impenetrable defence.

Lancashire welcome the champions, Brazil, together with Hungary, Portugal and Bulgaria at Manchester United and Everton. I'd say that the match of the tournament will be at Everton on July 15 when Hungary and Brazil meet in a world tie for the first time since their notorious 'Battle of Berne' 12 years ago, one of the roughest football matches ever played.

Sunderland and Middlesbrough in the North-East have drawn an attractive quartet in Russia, Italy and little North Korea, mystery team of 1966.

QUARTER FINALS

Russia, quarter finalists in 1962 and beaten once by Wales on their way to the present Finals, have sounded and studied Brazilian methods and – it's said – worked out scientific means of beating them. But to meet Brazil, they must first qualify for the quarter finals. Each team plays all the others in its group once – two points for a win, one for a draw. The top two teams in each group go on to the last eight. Should points and goal average be identical in any case, qualifiers will be decided on the toss of a coin.

Quarter finals will be played on July 23 at Wembley, Sunderland, Everton and Sheffield Wednesday grounds. If England reach this far, her most likely opponents could be Argentina or West Germany. England would then face the possibility of a semi-final against mighty Brazil.

The semi-finals are to take place on July 25 at Everton and July 26 at Wembley.

Nearly 2½ million tickets have been printed for the 32 World Cup matches, and a sell-out plus TV fees could bring in £2 million. Every match will be televised, to an audience of an estimated 400 million viewers. What will all these people see?

Brazil aim to make the Cup their own by winning a third time, then to put up a Winston Churchill Trophy for the next World Finals in Mexico in 1970. England reckon they have their best-ever chance as host country, and probably it is a better chance than their hard-to-please supporters would credit.

Argentina is a country they must both fear. And if there is to be an out-and-out surprise victory, keep a careful eye on France. They are very fast, strong – and I think underrated. England are due to meet France at Wembley on July 20.

This is bound to be a defensive-minded World Cup with the goals coming from sudden breakaways. The stakes are very high, so on occasions I fear the play could get pretty rough. But you will see fantastic techniques from the acrobatic ball jugglers from South America, and skilful and thoughtful interpassing from the European artists. You can look forward to

sensations, thrills and drama, and a feast of football such as you've never seen before and may never see on such a scale in this country again.

★ ★ ★

THE COUNTRIES TAKING PART

ARGENTINA
Colours: Light blue and white vertical stripes, black shorts, grey socks.
Qualified: Winners Group 13 v. Paraguay, Bolivia.
Founded: 1893. Clubs: 1,972.
Language: Spanish.
Living Quarters: Albany Hotel, Birmingham.
Training: Police Training Centre, Birmingham.

BRAZIL
Colours: Yellow, green collar and cuffs, blue shorts with white stripe, green and yellow socks.
Qualified: Automatically, as holders.
Founded: 1914. Clubs: 4,950.
Language: Portuguese.
Living Quarters: The Lymm Hotel, Lymm, Cheshire.
Training: Bolton Wanderers Ground.

BULGARIA
Colours: All white.
Qualified: Winners Group 1 v. Belgium, Israel.
Founded: 1924. Teams: 8,920.
Language: Southern Slavaic.
Living Quarters: Mollington Banastre, nr. Chester.
Training: Chester F.C.

CHILE
Colours: Red jersey, blue shorts, white socks.
Qualified: Winners Group 12 v. Columbia, Ecuador.
Founded: 1895. Clubs: 1,505.
Language: Spanish.
Living Quarters: Five Bridges Hotel, Gateshead.
Training: Gateshead and Newcastle upon Tyne.

ENGLAND
Colours: White shirts, blue shorts, white socks.
Qualified: Automatically, as hosts.
Founded: 1862. Clubs: 31,000.
Living Quarters: Hendon Hall Hotel, Middlesex.
Training: Roehampton and Wingate F.C.

FRANCE
Colours: Blue jersey, white shorts, red socks.
Qualified: Winners Group 3 v. Yugoslavia, Luxembourg, Norway.
Founded: 1919. Clubs: 8,795.
Living Quarters: Homestead Court, Welwyn Garden City.
Training: Welwyn Sports Stadium.

★ ★ ★

HUNGARY
Colours: Wine-red jersey, white shorts, green socks.
Qualified: Winners Group 6 v. East Germany, Austria.
Founded: 1901. Clubs: 19.
Language: Magyar.
Living Quarters: The Palace Hotel, Birkdale, Lancs.
Training: Guinness Export Club, Thornton and Southport.

ITALY
Colours: Blue jersey, white shorts, blue socks with white top.
Qualified: Winners Group 8 v. Scotland, Finland and Poland.
Founded: 1898. Clubs: 1,179.
Living Quarters: Houghall Agricultural College, Durham.
Training: College grounds.

MEXICO
Colours: Green jersey, white shorts, green socks.
Qualified: Winners Group 15 v. Costa Rica, Jamaica.
Founded: 1927. Clubs: 359.
Language: Spanish.
Living Quarters: Alexandra National Hotel, Finsbury Park.
Training: Arsenal and Crystal Palace.

NORTH KOREA
Colours: Red or dark blue jersey, white shorts, red and white or dark blue and white socks.
Qualified: Winners Group 16 v. Australia (15 African countries and South Korea withdrew, South Africa were suspended).
Founded: 1958. Clubs: 7,000.
Language: Korean.
Living Quarters: To be arranged.

PORTUGAL
Colours: White jersey, blue shorts, blue socks with white top.
Qualified: Winners Group 4 v. Turkey, Czechoslavakia, Rumania.
Founded: 1914. Clubs: 423.
Living Quarters: Stanneylands Hotel, Wilmslow, Cheshire.
Training: Styal and Altrincham.

U.S.S.R.
Colours: Red jersey, white shorts, red socks.
Qualified: Winners Group 7 v. Wales, Denmark, Greece.
Founded: 1919. Teams: 80,000.
Living Quarters: Grey College, Durham.
Training: Durham University.

SPAIN
Colours: Red jersey, blue shorts, black socks with red and yellow border.
Qualified: Winners Group 9 v. Eire (Syria withdrew).
Founded: 1905. Clubs: 2,107.
Living Quarters: Penns Hall Hotel, Walmsley, Birmingham.
Training: Delta Metal Co., Erdington.

SWITZERLAND
Colours: Red jersey, white shorts, white socks with red rings at top.
Qualified: Winners Group 5 v. N. Ireland, Netherlands, Albania.
Founded: 1895. Clubs: 916.
Language: French, German, Italian.
Living Quarters: Hallam Towers Hotel, Sheffield.
Training: Sheffield F.C. and University.

URUGUAY
Colours: Sky blue jersey, black shorts, black socks with blue border.
Qualified: Winners Group 11 v. Peru, Venezuela.
Founded: 1900. Clubs: 600.
Language: Spanish.
Living Quarters: The Saxon Inn, Harlow New Town, Essex.
Training: Harlow Sports Centre.

WEST GERMANY
Colours: White jersey with black collar trim, black shorts, black socks with white top.
Qualified: Winners Group 2 v. Sweden, Cyprus.
Founded: 1900. Clubs: 14,380.
Living Quarters: Peveril of the Peak, Thorpe, near Ashbourne, Derbyshire.
Training: Ashbourne and Derby County F.C.

WHO WILL WIN?

Jim Armfield (No. 2) watches closely as Jackie Charlton and Dragan Dzajic go up for the ball in the match against Yugoslavia, part of England's preparations for the World Cup series.

WORLD CUP PIN-UPS NUMBER 19
NORBERT STILES
(Manchester United and England)

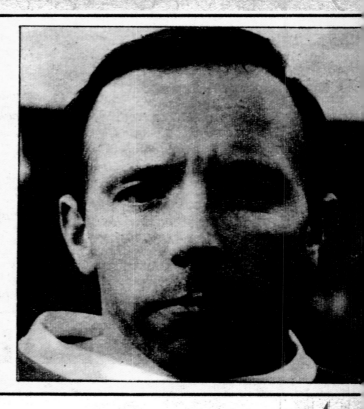

Nobby has been at Old Trafford since he was a boy, and once it seemed he was destined always to be the reliable understudy, and never the star. Then, a couple of years ago, he won a regular place at wing-half in the Manchester United side, and, in April 1965, his first England cap. He now looks a fixture in both teams, a player of tremendous energy, determination and bite who has at last earned recognition as a player of world class.

Whether his role is in attack or defence, Nobby never knows when he is beaten – just the type other players like to have in their side.

(This completes our series of WORLD CUP PIN-UPS. Starting next week, we shall be introducing you to The Champions from all fields of sport.)

WORLD CUP PIN-UPS

No. 6 EUSEBIO

The phrase Pin-Ups was liberally used in the 1960s. This is also, apparently, the last time Mr Stiles was referred to as Norbert.

WORLD CUP PIN-UPS
No. 8 GIANNI RIVERA (Italy)

AN under-23 International star at 16 – and still only 22 – Gianni Rivera is the Golden Boy of Italian soccer. His fans look to this slim, artistic inside-forward both to create and score goals to put Italy on the road to World Cup success.

If Italy could win the 1966 Finals, then they would become entitled to keep the Jules Rimet Cup because, like Brazil and Uruguay, they have won it twice before. But they have been given a stiff task in Group 4 against Russia, Chile, and North Korea (the mystery team of the competition) at Sunderland and Middlesbrough grounds.

Rivera was transferred from Alessandria, his local club, to Milan, Jimmy Greaves's old club, in 1960, and a transfer fee of £60,000 changed hands. The same year he was in Italy's Olympic team. Two years later, he gained his first full cap and was selected for the World Cup Finals in Chile.

Gianni's greatest performance in this country to date was at Wembley, in 1963, when he helped Milan to win the European Cup Final against Benfica. He has highly-developed positional sense and brilliant ball control. Opponents are liable to be fooled by his slight appearance and deceptively casual approach; too late, they realize that they have been playing with dynamite.

WORLD CUP PIN-UPS
No. 6 EUSEBIO (PORTUGAL)

IN qualifying for the World Cup Finals for the first time, Portugal owe a great deal to the inspiration of this stocky, dark-skinned inside-forward known as the 'Black Panther' and the 'Pelé of Europe'.

Born in Mozambique in January, 1942, Eusebio da Silva Ferreira (to give him his full name) played football barefooted as a boy. Benfica, of Lisbon, snapped him up in 1961 and he promptly won his international place which he has kept ever since. He played for Portugal against England in the 1961 World Cup qualifying match at Wembley, and has been seen over here many times with Benfica. He was selected for the Rest of the World team which opposed England in 1963.

Eusebio plays his football 'by ear', acting as the mood takes him, and specializes in scoring spectacular goals with overhead kicks, volleys and drives from long distance. In whatever competition he plays, he has a habit of topping the goal-scoring charts.

Eusebio 5 feet 7½ inches tall, weighing 11 stones 8 pounds, is at present serving as a Corporal in the Portuguese army. On returning to 'civvie street' next July, his first job will be to inspire Portugal in their tough Group 3 matches at Everton and Manchester against Brazil, Hungary and Bulgaria.

WHO IS IT?

Can you guess who this famous sportsman is? He'll be giving you a 'Star Tip' next week.

WORLD CUP PIN-UPS
No. 15
MANOEL GARRINCHA
(BRAZIL)

NO star shone brighter in Brazil's 1958 and 1962 World Cup triumphs than this lightning-fast, bag-of-tricks right-winger with the curiously-shaped legs.

Few know that, but for a successful operation for deformed legs as a boy, he could never have played football.

Last January, Garrincha was transferred from Botafogo of Rio to Corinthians of São Paulo. He is subject to considerable ups and downs of form, but at his best still rates among the world's greatest wingers, as England's Ray Wilson will readily testify.

EAGLE
and BOYS' WORLD

21 January 1967 Vol. 18 No. 3   EVERY WEDNESDAY **7d**

DID IT EVER HAPPEN?

Here is the latest in our Fact or Fiction series: did this incredible race ever take place? Read on and decide for yourself if it is true.

The most improbable race of all time took place only a year or two ago at Cortina d'Ampezzo, the famous Italian bobsleigh ice-track. Instead of the usual sleds hurtling down the icy run against the clock, nineteen Ford Cortina motor cars took over. And there was only a single casualty!

The casualty? Jim Clark, ex-world champion racing car driver. He slipped a disc while playfully throwing a snowball at a press photographer!

What do you think? Did it ever happen? The answer is on page 3.

Lead the THUNDERBIRDS

Get this Scott Tracy outfit
(worth £2 5s. 0d.) for only 19/11

when you buy any Cadbury's Cake

BE the most important member of International Rescue in this Scott Tracy outfit, complete with cap, belt and bandolier. Made of long-wearing, washable fabric, it comes in two sizes for rugged boys aged 5 to 10.

To get this outfit for less than a pound – a terrific bargain – just do this. Cut out the 'Guarantee of Satisfaction' panel from the side of your Cadbury's Cake box. Then post it, along with a cheque or postal order for 19/11, to the address on the coupon.

Offer closes 30th November 1966. Please allow three weeks for delivery.

Cadbury's
Chocolate Cake
Covered with real chocolate

THUNDERBIRDS Playsuit Offer

Quick, get the scissors!

WOULD YOU BELIEVE IT . . .?

No, these aren't young Indian braves – they're six pupils of a school in Hamburg. They bet their teacher that they would have a complete haircut and, with a box of lemonade to tempt them, went along to the barber. But because they thought being an ordinary 'baldy' was too boring, they got the barber to give them a real 'Iroquois brush'. They won their bet!

Clarence is a pretty smart cockatoo – he can actually ride a bike across a tight-rope. He performs this fantastic balancing act at his home in the Miami Parrot Jungle.

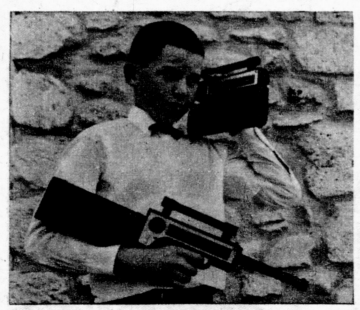

What will Santa think of next? He certainly can't have anything more unusual up his sleeve – or in his bag – than this 'James Bond' transistor radio. By pressing a button it becomes a machine-gun! It will be on sale in Paris this Christmas. Quick – let's join the Common Market!

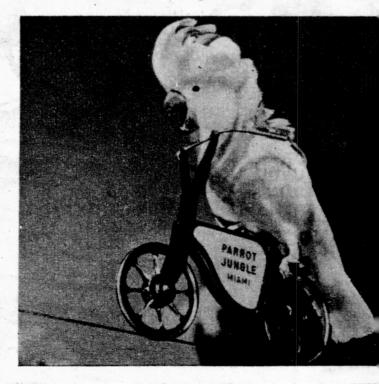

sporting pin-ups

Ian Storey-Moore

CUP-TIE of the season for my money was Nottingham Forest's thrilling 3-2 defeat of Everton, the holders, in the Sixth Round, *writes EX-PRO.*

The star of that match, and many others this year, was young Ian Storey-Moore, Forest's left-winger with the knack of scoring match-winning goals. Against Everton he got all three – his first big-time hat-trick, and best-ever performance.

"Ian seems to have grown up in the last few months, and begun to believe in himself," John Carey, his manager, told me. "He has already been honoured by England Under-23 and could have a great future ahead of him."

"I love banging in the goals, and I've had the luck to get quite a few recently," said Ian. "Forest are a great side, and I've learnt a lot since I joined them as a sixteen-year-old junior. Our trainer, Tommy Cavanagh, demands a tremendous amount of hard work from us, but this has certainly paid dividends in my case."

Born in Ipswich on 17th January, 1945, the son of an architect, Ian moved to Scunthorpe at an early age and became captain and centre-half of Scunthorpe Boys team. On leaving school he tried to join Blackpool, but was told he was too small to make the grade. Forest had different ideas. "He's got the skill and the speed, we can give him extra height and weight through weight training," they said, and proceeded to prove their point. Now Ian stands 5 ft. 9 ins. with the build of a middleweight boxer and lightning reflexes to match.

Keep your eyes on this likable lad – he's destined for top honours in my crystal ball.

Ian Storey-Moore's winning goal in the Sixth Round F.A. Cup-tie against Everton.

With scores level at 2-2, and only two minutes left to play, Ian burst into the Everton goal area and shot. The ball struck the goalkeeper's legs and rebounded into the air. Ian leapt forward and headed the ball against the crossbar. Again the ball rebounded, again Ian headed it, and this time it went into the net, followed by Ian himself, who had completed the first hat-trick of his first-class career when goals mattered most.

It's fun to be a twentieth-century pirate!

LIFE ON RADIO CAROLINE

Caroline's tender Essex Girl comes alongside

RADIO CITY. Radio 390. Radio Caroline. Radio London. Radio Scotland. Radio Yorkshire. Each month sees new plans announced for more and more 'pirate' radio ships anchored around Britain – all feeding pop music to millions of transistor radios.

What is life like on board these outlawed ships? EAGLE visited one of the first, Radio Caroline North, floating three and a half miles out in Ramsey Bay, Isle of Man. It began broadcasting in mid-1964.

The MV (Merchant Vessel) *Caroline* doesn't fly the Jolly Roger's skull and crossbones. Instead, a red light winks from the tip of its mast. And the only plank you may have to walk is a gangway from the ship's bridge to the bows during your tour round the decks.

But to get here, first you take the ship's tender (*Essex Girl*) from a Ramsey quay, where the Customs officials check your passport and camera. Then you chug out towards international shipping waters, and the 763-ton bulk of the pirate ship . . .

The boats bang together 30 minutes later. Pirates look down grinning, and throw down a big rope ladder. There are jokes as we climb aboard, and sacks of fan mail are hauled on to the decks. One huge envelope for DJ Mike Ahern had almost filled the tender's cabin.

Pop music sounds from a speaker. "199, Caroline?" I ask. "How did you guess," says Ray Teret, 18, an EAGLE reader, and self-claimed 'ugliest DJ in Britain'. "We're mad keen on pop music here. You've got to be – we listen to other stations, too, of course, but Caroline's tops."

There is much to see. Towering overhead is the cobweb of the ship's antenna – a folding dipole with the mast making one leg and a sausage aerial the other, 168 ft. high.

THE STUDIO

Below decks, the captain and sailors (total 10 – all Dutch) show me the 1,000 h.p. Diesel capable of driving the MV *Caroline* at 14 knots through a single screw. It does this in a storm when the ship circles one heavy-duty anchor. In mild conditions, the vessel stays put on two anchors.

Next we see the generators – two Mercedes-Benz units humming quietly

and linked to their two transmitters, capable of a joint output of 20 kilowatts.

"The real powerhouse is upstairs, man," says DJ Mike Ahern with a grin. "The studio!" He is the third DJ on board, the other three – Tom Lodge, Jerry Leighton and Jim Murphy – being on the week's holiday which the DJs take after every fortnight on board.

We go into a room sound-proofed with white panels looking like pegboard. Inside is a U-shaped desk below a hanging microphone.

At the desk sits DJ Bob Stewart, hard at work. He has a large record turntable at each elbow, and is surrounded by the latest chart-entries in racks. The record sleeves are marked either FF (Fab Fifty) or HH (Hot Hundred). He has a large mug of coffee on the switch panel in front.

"Once the ship rolled badly and the coffee went all over the place," says Mike. "SSSShhhh," says Bob, pointing to a sign – "On Air" – which has suddenly lit up. The record that was playing had stopped, and Bob talks closely into the mike, announcing the next disc – the Manfreds.

The 168-ft. high mast that feeds out pop music to millions of transistor radios

ON THE TURNTABLE

He switches it on, then presses another button which cuts noise in the studio off the air. He slips a Yardbirds disc on to the other turntable – ready for playing next – and says: "This system is fab. We used to signal cues through a window to a panel operator in the sound room. Now we handle everything here – a sound control, discs and commercials.

"We can play what we like, but commercials are limited to six minutes an hour. We think what to say while each disc plays. It's all impromptu. In fact, if you would sit in that chair over there you can introduce the next disc . . ."

And the studio equipment? There are two transcription turntables, ampex machines, spot masters, mixers, and an ultra-accurate clock for time checks. Weather forecasts are brought down from the bridge on bits of paper.

"We have arguments on what the best records are, and everyone wants to play the new ones," says Mike Ahern. "But we get on well, and the time shoots past. There's always fishing, reading, sunbathing and work like answering fan mail. We get stacks of it, and answer all the sensible ones."

I asked Ray Teret his advice for EAGLE readers who want to become DJs. "I began at 11," he said. "I was a keen conjurer, then started compering records in the youth club. That's the best start. Your friends are your hardest critics, and you learn a lot this way."

DJ Mike Ahern in the common room

DJ Bob Stewart working at the studio desk

Bob Stewart relaxes between recording sessions

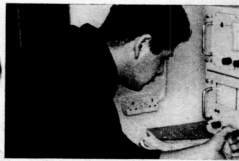

The radio operator adjusts controls on the bridge of MV *Caroline*

TIC-TAC
TACTICS

HAVE you ever looked in at the television to watch the horse races? Or been to a meeting yourself? Then you have probably been mystified by the number of men who wave their hands about in a frantic manner. At first glance, they seem to be crazy; their flashing hands touch head, nose, ears and shoulders with lightning speed.

But the men are far from daft; they are the secret signallers of the race course – the tic-tac men.

The tic-tac system was perfected in Australia during the 1880s, by 'Fingers' Donovan. The bookmakers liked it, but the runners, whose jobs were threatened, did not. And one angry runner shot off several of Donovan's nimble fingers!

The system found its way to England in the 1890s. The signals have remained a closely-guarded secret, usually passed on from father to son. But EAGLE has managed to discover a few of the meanings behind the mysterious signals. Below, one of our staff artists demonstrates.

When the fingers of the right hand are placed on top of the head, it signifies the number 'one'.

Both hands held in front of the chest and moved forward one over the other in a rapid circular movement, means 'odds-on'.

When the two index fingers are extended in front of the chest and moved up and down, this means 'even money'.

Clenched fists, placed one on top of the other in front of the chest, signifies '50' – therefore, this twice done is '100'.

Right hand 'thumbs up' sign, means 'the favourite'.

Right hand placed on left shoulder means '7 to 4'.

NEWS FROM THE ZOOS

There's nothing like a nice snooze in the sunshine – especially when the temperature is in the upper seventies. It certainly seemed a good idea to the Russian polar bears Amos and Mosa at London Zoo.

Mitzi the lynx eagerly awaits her turn to be fed as Jacky the jackal gets his lunch first. The two little balls of fur were disowned by their mothers at Chester Zoo – so one of the keepers turned 'Dad'.

This South American woolly monkey at Whipsnade Zoo would have made a perfect model for Rodin's statue of 'The Thinker'!

Here's another chap who found the heat wave too much for him. This London Zoo penguin was absolutely parched, and when he spotted that tap gushing water he could hardly get there fast enough. Now he's a real cool chick!

THE FLYING SAUCERS OF

"Do you believe in flying saucers?" That question has been debated for years – and still nobody knows the truth of the matter. Books have bee written about them, science fiction writers have flown us to Mars in them, authorities say they don't exist – and people go on seeing them. Pe haps, one day, a spaceship from outer space really will land on Earth and put an end to all speculation. Until then, well, there's no harm wondering about this strange mystery of the skies . . .

WHEN it comes to inventions, the Dan Dare team of writers and artists have always been way ahead of the field. Many of the 'impossible' machines, craft and weapons which have appeared in EAGLE in the past have later become realities.

In his new book – 'Piece for a Jigsaw' – Leonard Cramp says: "Regardless of the magnitude of the ship's acceleration, the crew would experience the gravitational environment of their home planet, while alternative 'g' arrangements could be made for any different beings they were transporting. It is interesting to note that these and other similar inclusions have been made by the authors of the famous Dan Dare series !"

... FOR AM I NOT XEL, THE ONE WHO IS OBEYED !

◄ Anything Xel can do, we can do better ! So say the Americans – who built this saucer-shaped craft recently

like plume behind it. It was moving quit slowly. What struck me most was that made no noise."

When the roll of film was handed her colleague, Mr Charles Gibbs-Smit the aviation historian, he said: "I hav seen scores of saucer photos, but th is the first in which I can guarantee th integrity of everybody concerned.

"The object could not have been meteorite or fireball. These things don travel horizontally. I don't see what els it could have been but some kind interplanetary flying machine." T account for the silence of the strang object, Mr Gibbs-Smith said that th 'saucer' might have been powered b some kind of anti-gravity motor n

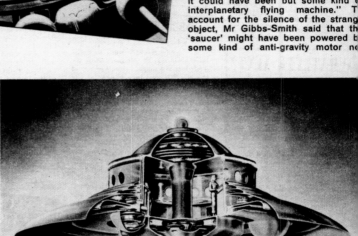

Artist's impression of the workings of a saucer. Who knows we might feature an accurate cutaway drawing in the future

'Piece for a Jig-Saw' is a book about flying saucers. Many books on flying saucers have appeared in recent years, and Leonard Cramp, a qualified engineer, brings the research right up to date by examining

Mr Cramp's machine exists only in theory, but two other scientists, one in Australia and one in America, have recently designed flying machines on the classical saucer pattern. Both hope to prove that the disc shape is a practical one for travelling the sky.

A model saucer built by the Austra-

model could be mass-produced for about £1,000.

The existence of flying saucers – Unidentified Flying Objects, as they are technically called – has been tantalizing us for nearly 20 years and still nobody knows the truth about them. Hundreds of U.F.O.s. have been seen. One of the latest 'authentic' sightings has been reported by two young women who saw an object while motoring in Ireland – and photographed it!

One of the women, Miss Jacqueline Wingfield, an official of the Victoria and Albert Museum, said: "It was like a large silver bullet, with a bright flame-

understood by scientists.

What flying saucers really ar where they come from, and who man them remains one of the greates mysteries of modern times.

Except, that is, to EAGLE reader Thanks to Major Grant and 'Boffi Bailey, the U.F.O. agents, you kno more than most people about Unident fied Flying Objects and the Zetans wh brought them to earth. Once agai EAGLE is way ahead of the field.

* 'Piece for a Jig-Saw' is publishe at 12s. 6d. by Somerton Publisher Ltd., Newport Road, West Cowe Isle of Wight.

This strange object was photographed in Ireland. "It was like a large silver bullet, with a bright flame-like plume behind it . . ."

the various sightings on a purely technical basis. He gives his reasons why, for example, saucers should hover and stop instantly; why they are silent; and why they move through the atmosphere at high velocity without heating up.

The author also advances a theory of how spaceships could be propelled by means other than the rocket. He discusses the possibility of completely converting mass into energy, thereby creating gravitational fields.

He also reveals that in such a vehicle man could travel to the moon and back in under an hour – without suffering any accelerating or decelerating forces whatsoever.

lian, who wishes to remain anonymous, has recently been successfully tested in Canberra. The actual machine, he says, will fly with the aid of jet motors which will make the outer rim of the saucer rotate at high speed. The problem of keeping the cabin, situated in the 'hub' of the craft, from revolving also, has been solved with 'neutralizing motors' says the inventor. But he is keeping the details secret.

Professor Paul Moller, of California University, who is building the other flying saucer, is equally cautious about revealing details of his craft. All he will say is that it has been designed to take off vertically and fly at 100 m.p.h. on four engines. Both men think of their saucers as family flying cars of the future. Professor Moller calculates that his

This flying saucer and the friendly Zetan spaceman on the right are well known followers of U.F.O. Agent

TODAY AND TOMORROW

THIS new design for a helicopter combined with a conventional aircraft gives the impression of a real flying saucer. To be built for the U.S. Army, it is called the Hughes Hot-cycle Rotor Research Aircraft. The 'hot-cycle' part of the name comes from the rotor blade 'tip-jet' propulsion by full use of gas-turbine engine exhaust, diverted through helicopter rotors. This is distinct from the 'cold cycle' tip-jet propulsion using compressed air, as used on some helicopters.

The hot-cycle aircraft takes off and lands as a normal helicopter. At about 100 m.p.h. the hot-cycle gas is diverted from the rotor blades by means of valves, and the gas-turbine engine at the tail gives direct forward propulsion. The rotor blades are brought to rest with one blade facing forward. The large circular structure, which gives the appearance of a saucer, acts as a lifting hub to the rotor blades. When they are stopped the streamlined hub acts as an aerofoil for fixed wing, forward flight.

As a result of this, the aircraft has high efficiency, both as a helicopter and as a conventional fixed-wing aircraft.

DIMENSIONS . . .
Diameter of Rotor: 47 ft.
Fuselage length : 73 ft.
Height from ground : 20 ft.

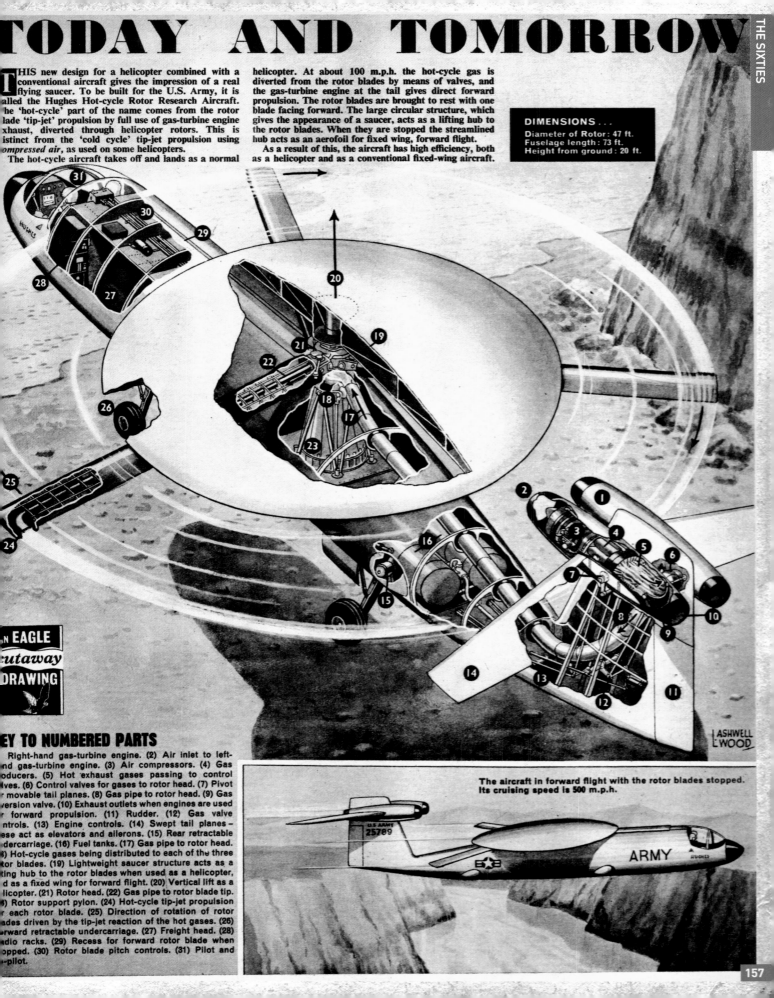

EAGLE
cutaway
DRAWING

ASHWELL WOOD

KEY TO NUMBERED PARTS

(1) Right-hand gas-turbine engine. (2) Air inlet to left-hand gas-turbine engine. (3) Air compressors. (4) Gas producers. (5) Hot exhaust gases passing to control valves. (6) Control valves for gases to rotor head. (7) Pivot for movable tail planes. (8) Gas pipe to rotor head. (9) Gas diversion valve. (10) Exhaust outlets when engines are used for forward propulsion. (11) Rudder. (12) Gas valve controls. (13) Engine controls. (14) Swept tail planes – these act as elevators and ailerons. (15) Rear retractable undercarriage. (16) Fuel tanks. (17) Gas pipe to rotor head. (18) Hot-cycle gases being distributed to each of the three rotor blades. (19) Lightweight saucer structure acts as a lifting hub to the rotor blades when used as a helicopter, and as a fixed wing for forward flight. (20) Vertical lift as a helicopter. (21) Rotor head. (22) Gas pipe to rotor blade tip. (23) Rotor support pylon. (24) Hot-cycle tip-jet propulsion for each rotor blade. (25) Direction of rotation of rotor blades driven by the tip-jet reaction of the hot gases. (26) Forward retractable undercarriage. (27) Freight head. (28) Radio racks. (29) Recess for forward rotor blade when stopped. (30) Rotor blade pitch controls. (31) Pilot and co-pilot.

The aircraft in forward flight with the rotor blades stopped. Its cruising speed is 500 m.p.h.

U.S. ARMY 25789
ARMY

space diary

SCANNER OF THE SKIES

IF you are anywhere near the New Forest or Christchurch in Hampshire for your holidays, you might see the white dome shown in the photograph. No, it is not a giant beehive, nor is it from outer space, but it certainly has a great deal to do with space.

This inflatable dome, 60 ft. high and 60 ft. wide, is made of a double layer of nylon. It contains the first of three British earth stations to be used under the Anglo/American Initial Defence Communications Satellite Project. This will provide a military communications system using satellites, which will allow telephone as well as telegraphic messages to be sent across the world. The designers and builders, Marconi, will carry on gathering data for more advanced radar.

The second photograph shows what it looks like inside the structure. The transmitter and part of the control and communications equipment can be seen.

DID IT EVER HAPPEN? No. There is not and neve was such a creature as the Aprilla.

SPACE DIARY

THEY SMELL OUT DANGER

HAVE you ever noticed the smell which greets you when you get into a new car? Or have you ever been inside an aircraft? There is something about the smell of the interiors of the new car and aircraft that is unlike any other. It is the materials that go into their manufacture that make this smell.

Space-craft such as Gemini have the same sort of smell, but unlike that of the aircraft and car, it causes at least sickness, and on a long journey, say to Mars and back, death by poisoning. The fact was discovered when astronauts were sealed up in a 'space chamber' to give a 30-day test to a new series of systems and equipment. After five days, the subjects were all violently sick and the test cancelled.

FINE PARTICLES

Space smog had been discovered!

Unlike the interior of a car or aircraft, the interior of a space-craft does not get air blowing through occasionally to clear the smell which, after all, is made up of small particles of the material from which it comes.

More than 600 different materials will go into the production of the *Manned Orbital Laboratory*, for instance, and each of these will be continually releasing small particles. Unless the atmosphere inside is completely changed every day, an enormous concentration of particles mixed with oxygen will become poison gas.

To help find a cure for this trouble, U.S. bioastronautic scientists have recruited some beagles into the U.S. Air Force. They live in a sealed chamber, occasionally breathing oxygen that has passed over space capsule construction materials.

Any new or improved material is tested in this manner. If a beagle looks sick he is immediately removed and a vet soon has him feeling fine again, but at the same time is able to learn a lot about what made him ill.

AIR FORCE PAY

All the beagles receive Air Force pay, which is banked for their old-age care, and are well looked after. One even receives corporal's pay because he has been in the Force longer than the others. Their hunter's noses are helping to solve a very important problem in the U.S. space programme.

To defuse an unexploded bomb that might blow up in your face at any second is an alarming spect. But to the steel-nerved heroes the Bomb Disposal Squads it's all in day's work, deadly work which they kle with cool courage and fantastic ll.

Almost every week, workmen, mers and other members of the blic unearth or discover bombs, lls, grenades and mines, either pped by the Germans during the r or left by the Allied forces on old ining areas. When found, these still-nal missiles must be disarmed mediately and carried to a safe place. his task is done by special Bomb sposal Squads from all three services: Royal Engineers deal with all bombs pped by German aircraft; the R.A.F. h British bombs and missiles; the yal Army Ordnance Corps is responsi-for shells, mortar bombs and other es of ammunition; the Royal Navy ndles bombs under the water.

The Royal Engineers tackled 12 big mbs last year. One of them was found workmen on a London building site. squad raced to the spot like firemen h a police motor cycle escort.

Bomb doctor' Captain David Owens lt down beside the giant 500-lb. rman missile and examined it with a cial stethoscope. Then, gambling his e on his nerve and skill, he began to erate. He drilled delicately into the mb's fuse cavity, sucked out the air and mped in oil to dissolve the dangerous rate crystals. Next came the ticklish of withdrawing the fuse.

But the corroded 25-year-old fuse denly snapped in two! Faced with a sis, Owens ordered the bomb to be efully loaded on to a truck and, packed

like an egg between sandbags, it was rushed to the Horsham depot where the base plate was unscrewed and the explosive 'steamed out'. Another dicey job had been superbly done.

A boy playing on a heap of earth at Aldershot found a number of strange-looking partly-buried objects; he did the right thing and notified the police. The boy had had a narrow escape. The objects were war-time 'sticky bombs' filled with the most sensitive explosive of all – nitro-glycerine.

Bomb Squad experts soon arrived.

BOMB SQUAD!

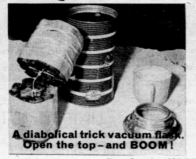

A diabolical trick vacuum flask. Open the top – and BOOM !

A bomb - disposal expert defuses a powerful bomb hidden in a school satchel

Major William Musson and Warrant Officer Sidney Brazier studied the condition of the deadly charges and found them to be in a highly dangerous state: some were cracked and others leaking. They knew that the slightest vibration would detonate them.

Working with extreme care and not daring to use a trowel, the two gallant men set about uncovering the sensitive bombs with thin wooden probes and small paint brushes. After a nerve-racking session they managed to deal with the whole batch of 50. Both were awarded the George Medal.

On active service abroad, the British Army maintains B.D. 'Flying Squads' to deal with time bombs and other dia-bolical contraptions planted by political terrorists.

In Malacca, Malaysia, last year,

Captain Drummond Hall and C.S.M. Brian Reed spent three and a half spine-chilling hours dismantling a new type of 'suitcase' bomb, fully realizing that the merest slip of the hand or slightest jar would spell doom.

It was impossible to tell whether the 'death-trap' worked on a time bomb principle or contained anti-handling devices. In case the bomb exploded and killed them, Captain Hall arranged for a full photographic record of the dis-mantling to be made. This was to ensure a full record of the knowledge obtained to that point.

But the skill of the two men beat the bomb. Working in bad light, they managed to make it safe. The George Medal went to both of them.

RACE AGAINST A TIME-BOMB

Major John Elliott also worked in adverse conditions when, in June last year, terrorists blew up part of an officers' mess in Aden. Searching amid the ruins by torchlight, he found three more time bombs. Faced with the ticking containers and not knowing when they were due to go off, he worked feverishly to dismantle them and, despite the cramping nervous tension which suddenly attacked his nimble fingers, he won his race against time.

Throughout 1965, Major Elliott risked his life daily in Aden to investigate 189 incidents involving 309 explosive objects. In March this year (1966) he was awarded the George Medal for his sustained feat of courage.

And now a word of warning. If you come across any strange metal objects – don't touch! Leave them well alone, mark the location with a stick or stone and then report quickly to the police. The Bomb Disposal Squad will soon be at the spot to deal with the menace.

Photos: By courtesy of SOLDIER, the British Army Magazine

INVENTORS' CORNER

The old grey matter has certainly been exercised recently, and these three brainy inventors have won a POUND each.

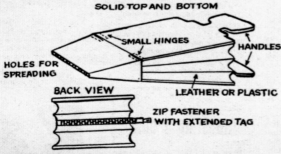

SOLID TOP AND BOTTOM
SMALL HINGES
HANDLES
HOLES FOR SPREADING
BACK VIEW
LEATHER OR PLASTIC
ZIP FASTENER WITH EXTENDED TAG

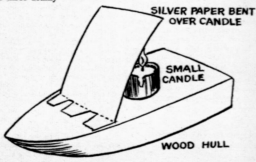

SILVER PAPER BENT OVER CANDLE
SMALL CANDLE
WOOD HULL

BUTTER SPREADER

Fourteen-year-old H. Sidlow, of Bolton, thought it was time that something was invented to spread butter, instead of using the old-fashioned knife. So he has invented a butter spreader of his own. He claims it would make spreading butter much quicker and easier. It is re-filled by opening a zip at the back.

CANDLE-POWERED BOAT

John Monk of Littleover, Derby, has sent in this design for propelling boats.

The hot air rising from the candle is pushed backwards by the silver paper and this pushes the boat forward.

MAGNETIC GOLF

David Cripps, of Canterbury, has devised this interesting game of Magnetic Golf.

Take a piece of cardboard about 18 inches square and mark out on it a 'course' of nine holes. Each hole has a tee and a green with a hole in it big enough for the steel ball to pass through. The 'rough' may be made by glueing small pieces of coarse cloth, velvet, sandpaper, etc., to the board. 'Lost ball' areas are cut-out slots between which the ball must pass. Undulations on the course are made by sticking on paper ridges. If you want to, you can invent other obstacles for yourself. Tees and greens are numbered from one to nine. Each 'hole' can be as long as you like, and holes can cross each other. Here is a suggested layout:

To play, hold the course in your left hand and the magnet underneath it in your right. Starting with the ball on the first tee, you have to steer it down the course until you 'hole out' in the first hole. Each time the ball touches the line on either side of the track, it counts as one stroke. If you can drive it from the tee to the hole without getting stuck or touching either

line, you have holed out in one. Two players take it in turns to play each hole, the winner being the one with the fewest strokes. The winner of the most holes wins the match. A 'lost ball' loses the hole.

The repulsion ray affected anything metal . . .

AAAAH!

HAVE A TABLE ON ME, FRIEND!

MIGHT I SUGGEST WE LEAVE—FASTER THAN FAST!

The engine suddenly spluttered . . .

A few moments later . . .

I'VE NEWS FOR YOU—THIS CAR BELONGS TO THE POLICE COMMISSIONER.

NOW I'VE NEWS FOR *YOU*—WE'RE OUT OF PETROL.! HOW DO YOU FANCY FIVE YEARS INSIDE THE BASTILLE?

OH, NO-O! NO WONDER THE 'PACK'S' ON OUR TAIL!

I HAD THE SAME THOUGHT!

LOOK OUT! WHAT THE BLAZES . . .?

WHAT MORE UNLUCKY THAN 'CRASHING' THE COMMISSIONER'S CAR!

THE CIRCUS WANDERERS

Football was big news in the mid and late 1960s and *Eagle* was eager to make hay. With plenty of features on real football and footballers there was still deemed room for an addition. Previously there had been a very strait-laced attempt at football in strip form in Home of the Wanderers. The perceived gap left by them was filled for better or for worse by Circus Wanderers. It does not take much imagination to guess the rest.

GAY GHOULS OF TELEVISION

The Munsters make the audience scream with laughter rather than with terror

In spite of the comedy, old Herman Munster strikes a pretty horrific figure

NUMBER forty-three, Mockingbird Lane, looks like a typical American home – except that there are always fearsome black storm clouds hanging over it, even when the rest of the road is bathed in sunshine.

Herman, its owner, looks like a typical American householder – except that he's seven feet tall, has two bolts protruding from either side of his neck, sunken eyes and an ancient sabre scar across his forehead. And he spends his time digging deep holes in the back yard.

Lily, his wife, is quite beautiful, as attractive as the day she died – which was slightly more than a century ago.

While Herman's father, who also lives there, fires lightning bolts from his fingers, works among fuming beakers and boiling cauldrons in a dungeon in the house making poisonous food, and keeps trying to turn the postman into a frog.

The three are, of course, members of the Munster family, the gay ghouls of the TV series, The Munsters.

The Munster household also includes Eddie, the 10-year-old son of Herman and Lily. He's only a bit of a monster.

Lily's niece, Marilyn, completes the family. But she's a non-monster, strictly normal and, therefore, the outcast of the family.

Where did the idea for The Munsters come from? There's no secret about that. The makers say openly that they are "the descendants of those infamous motion picture personalities, Frankenstein's Monster, his bride, and Count Dracula."

As Herman, Fred Gwynne wears make-up based on that worn by Boris Karloff in the original Frankenstein picture in 1930.

Horror Tale

Though it is hard to believe, the Frankenstein Monster was the creation of a girl, Mary Shelley, wife of the poet Percy Bysshe Shelley, and she was just 19 years old when she created it.

That was in 1816. She and Shelley, Byron the poet and John Polidori, their doctor, were on holiday in Switzerland. It was a wet summer and, kept indoors by rain, they read ghost stories. Then Byron suggested they should each write a horror tale.

The three men produced nothing to rival Mary's story, though she had difficulty with it at first . . . until one night in a dream she saw a corpse rise up and walk. And she began the story of Frankenstein.

He was a Swiss scientist who got the idea of making a man, a living being who, being mechanical, would be immortal. For parts he used bits of bodies collected in churchyards and he brought his creation to life with an electric spark.

But the man he had built was a monster.

(He never had a name other than 'the Monster'.) Huge and hideous and without a soul, he turned against the man who made him, murdered Frankenstein's best friend, brought about the death of Frankenstein's sister and pursued the scientist across the world.

In his efforts to shake off the remorseless, pursuing monster, Frankenstein headed for the North Pole but the monster caught up with him there in an ice-bound sea. And Frankenstein died.

It was a gloomy story but it made history as the first horror tale involving science. And it was so well written it has become a classic of English literature.

Count Dracula

Grandpa Munster (played by Al Lewis) is based on a story by a different writer, Bram Stoker. Bram (short for Abraham) was an Irishman who studied law and science before becoming a journalist and then became business manager of Sir Henry Irving, the great Victorian actor.

It was during this time, in 1897, that he wrote Dracula, which has been called the most bloodcurdling horror story in the English language. With hypnotists, wolves, blood, vampires and stakes through hearts, it is all of that.

It opens at Transylvania (which means Hungary), the castle home of Count Dracula. The Count has wolf-like teeth, burning eyes and hairy hands and is one of what Stoker called 'the Un-Dead'. In other words, the Count was dead but he wouldn't lie down for long. He was a vampire.

He travelled in a coffin filled with earth, rising from it to attack people and suck their blood. This prolonged his own life but the people he attacked became Un-Dead as well and they went in search of fresh victims to prey on.

Dracula came to England and there attacked the young wife of a solicitor, Jonathan Harker. And there was a chase across Europe before Jonathan and his friends finally nailed the Count – through the heart.

Dracula was first filmed in English in 1931 – a year after Frankenstein. It starred Bela Lugosi, a Hungarian actor who died in 1956. From then on he and Boris Karloff were to be identified always with horror.

Dracula has also had its film sequels . . . Son of Dracula, House of Dracula, Brides of Dracula, Kiss of the Vampire, and so on.

Both Frankenstein and Dracula were re-made in Britain ten years ago with Christopher Lee in the starring parts. But recently the trend has been more and more to turn the thrills into laughs, the chills into chuckles, and The Munsters, described as 'mad, mad, mad, mad, mad', is the biggest spoof on Mary Shelley's and Bram Stoker's terrifying creations that there has ever been, or is likely to be.

The terrible Count has risen from his coffin many [tim]es since the turn of the century – striking terror into film-goers the world over

King of the heart-stoppers, Boris Karloff portrayed the first monster of them all – Frankenstein's hideous creation – giving rise to a whole series of sequels

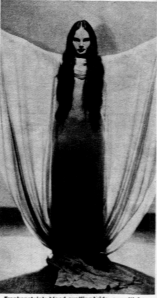

Frankenstein's blood-curdling bride – a wraith from the world of celluloid who was the 'un-dead' ancestor of Herman Munster's wife, Lily

"Hey, Lou – we're surrounded!" Bud Abbott and Lou Costello shiver with fright as they meet Frankenstein's monster and the Wolf Man

DAN DARE in "GIVE ME THE MOON!"

● SPORTS SPECTACULAR ●

STAR TIP
SO YOU WANT TO BE A SOCCER STAR

From ALAN BALL (of England)

Believe you are better than the next man – and you will be, says Alan Ball. But that does not prevent him from practising ball control at every opportunity

Kicking with Two Feet. This is simply a matter of mind over matter. It just never dawned on me that I couldn't kick equally well with either foot, so if you *think* you are, say, a right-footed player, go out and kick the ball with your *left* foot – and keep kicking with your left.

Heading. Either you are gifted in this skill, or you are not – but you can always improve through practice. It's as simple as that. And remember, even if you are a little chap like me, you can still score if you jump high enough.

Dribbling. Nobody can tell me that you can learn to dribble a ball by going round a few sticks placed at intervals in the ground. Sticks are predictable, people are not. If I want to improve, I know that I must have the challenge of a man to beat every time. So when you practise your dribbling, do so with an opponent who is trying to stop you.

Throw-ins. If you are receiving a throw, try and make space for yourself. A lot of players are content to stand still and simply kick the ball back to the thrower. They don't get any medals from me.

Fouls. Fouling is nearly always a matter of bad timing. No professional player ever goes into a tackle with the deliberate intention of crippling an opponent. Always pick the time to tackle, then go in hard but fairly.

Penalty. It just never enters my head that I might miss a penalty. Before taking the kick, I know for certain that it will end up in the back of the net.

Summing It All Up. To be a soccer star, you must believe that you are better than the next man.

WIN A
FOOTBALL – FREE!

With the football season getting into its stride, EAGLE switches from cricket bats to footballs as prizes in its weekly, free sports competitions. And the balls are well worth having for they are the super ECLIPSE footballs, made by Slazengers – who supplied the balls for the World Cup games.

To win this week's Eclipse football, here is all you have to do.

Study our action picture taken at a Tottenham Hotspurs v. West Bromwich Albion match. Besides the actual ball, our artist has painted in five more balls. Which ball is the actual one?

Next, study the list of centre-forwards below. Each participated in the World Cup matches, but which four played in the SEMI-FINALS?

Albert, Banishevskiy, R. Charlton, Cortes, Onega, Pak Doo Ik, Seeler, Torres

At the top of a postcard, write the NUMBER of what you judge to be the actual ball in our picture. Next, neatly write the names of the four World Cup centre-forwards who played in the Semi-Finals.

Remember – neatness will count! The winner will be the reader who not only gives the correct answers but who is also judged to have submitted the best-written and neatest entry – with ages being taken into consideration.

Add your age and your name and address, in block letters, and post your card (3d. postage) to: FOOTBALL COMPETITION, EAGLE, 96 LONG ACRE, LONDON, W.C.99. Entries must arrive by not later than WEDNESDAY, 24th AUGUST, 1966.

Only one entry per reader is allowed. Entry is free. The competition is open to all readers in the U.K. and Eire other than children of employees of the proprietors of EAGLE.

The Editor's decision is final in all matters relating to the contest, and no correspondence will be entered into. The result will be published in EAGLE.

THE film fan was watching his first League soccer match. As the players trooped back on to the field after half-time, he remarked to his companion: "It's far more exciting than I expected, but I wouldn't want to sit through the whole show again. Isn't this where we came in?"

Next Saturday we welcome back King Soccer (domestic version) while last season's exciting, closing stages are still fresh in the mind, and no more than a World Cup away.

Do soccer fans want to sit through it all again? You bet they do! The World Cup was a great spectacle, a once-in-a-lifetime experience. But it had very little to do with our local team, and its Saturday afternoon skirmishes with deadly League rivals. And what is soccer without the Irish, Welsh and Scots?

Your regular supporter can't get enough of his favourite sport, and now that the World Cup is all neatly tied-up for a few more years he can get down to the real thing – such as, will this be another gear year for the Whackers? (Surely you don't need reminding that Liverpool hold the League title, and Everton the Cup?)

Certainly they can expect a fierce challenge from their Lancastrian neighbours – Burnley, and the two Manchester clubs. Manchester City seem confident that they can more than hold their own at the top, as do Southampton, also newly-promoted, in their case for the first time in their eighty-year-old history.

Success in domestic competition means entry into European competition, and that's where financial success lies today. No wonder that the Midlands and North-Eastern clubs are anxious to get

WHOOSH! THAT WAS SOCCER'S CLOSE-SEASON, THAT WAS

BY EX-PRO

in on the honours act! I think we ma see a bold bid from clubs like Birming ham, Wolves, Newcastle United ar Sunderland to achieve 'super-clu class in the next few years.

The eventual formation of a Sup League is surely inevitable. Already it evolving naturally, for in the last s years we have seen nine clubs domina the major competitions in Britain. The are Spurs, Liverpool, Manchester Unite West Ham United, Everton, Lee United and Burnley in England; Range and Celtic in Scotland. And success clubs like these attract the star playe like magnets, so shifting the prese *élite* from their perch will be no ea task.

Of course, there are those who ca little for the giants of the game, who pleasure comes from following throu thick and thin the struggles of su underprivileged minnows as Stockpo Lincoln, Wrexham and Rochdale. Go luck to them! Such is the charm League football. We've seen it all befo but we'll enjoy it again and again . . .

MEET THE CHAMPIONS
No. 5
BASIL D'OLIVEIRA

(WORCESTERSHIRE AND ENGLAND)

WE'VE taken a real whacking this summer from those worthy World Champions from the West Indies, and more than one England player's reputation has been bruised in the process. What's more, Sobers could have still more punishment to dish out when the 5th Test starts at the Oval on 18th August!

However, it's not all been bad. Adversity has bred new English heroes like Colin Milburn, that 17-stone Billy Bunter of the batting crease, who will not allow the most furious fast bowling to divert him from his favourite occupation – hitting sixes. And like plucky, and talented, 21-year-old Derek Underwood.

But perhaps the most affectionate of our greetings has been the 'Hullo, Dolly' reserved for that likable and brilliant Test newcomer, Basil D'Oliveira.

Five years ago, Dolly was one of 25,000 coloured cricketers in South Africa forbidden by law to play with, or against, the Whites. Recognizing that he had considerable natural ability, friends persuaded him to come to England and try his luck with Middleton in the Lancashire League. Success didn't come overnight – he'd never played on turf before – but eventually he won it by perseverance. He became a British citizen, qualified for Worcestershire, and

last season helped his county, both wi bat and ball, to win the Championsh

Dolly couldn't believe his luck la May when he was chosen as 12th m for England at Trent Bridge. Then ca his Test début at Lord's. "I don't ca what happens to me now," he said. "I met the Queen, I've played in a T match at Lord's." He couldn't belie that so much glory could happen to coloured man from Capetown. In fa he's still living in a dream. But there h been nothing dreamlike in D'Oliveir performances for England this summ He has made substantial contributio to our batting, bowling and fieldi strength, and is clearly destined to we an England cap for several years come.

SECRETS BEHIND THE WORLD CUP 'VICTORY' STAMPS

World Cup 1966
HARRISON AND SONS LTD.

IT'S now many weeks since the memorable 'Battle of Trafalgar Square', on 18th August, when stamp collectors and dealers fought at the Post Office counters to snap up the 4d. World Cup stamps, over-printed 'ENGLAND WINNERS'. But among stamp collectors the excitement still prevails, because this stamp has become

were neither famous nor professionals.

The G.P.O. engaged two young men, who play football as a hobby, to pose for photographs from which the artist, David Gentleman, designed the now famous stamp.

Their names are Barrington Smith and David Wridway. They kicked a football for hours at the Leytonstone Recreation Ground in London, E.15, while a press photographer, Peter Boyce, made scores of snaps with his cinema camera. The artist then designed several stamps, showing them in various positions, but finally only one was selected for the stamp picture, which we know so well. We show you some of the other designs, which

'rarity' and is difficult to get even at a price many times its face value.

If you were lucky to secure a First Day Cover of this stamp with the special postmark, then you got a winner. In not so many years it will probably be worth a few pounds.

But apart from the sensation which shook the philatelic world, there are other secrets behind the World Cup stamps. Many of you might have been wondering whether the players shown on these stamps are 'real' footballers. Indeed, many people believed they recognized on the 4d. stamp such famous players as Bobby Charlton, Jimmy Greaves or Bobby Moore. They could not quite agree who was who, but they were all wrong. The two players were 'real' enough, but they

were actually printed as stamp 'proofs' but never released to the public.

Finally, we show you a funny cartoon, published by an Italian stamp magazine. It shows a World Cup stamp 'as it might have been', depicting one of the sorry scenes when play deteriorated into fight. The artist, rather irreverently, suggested that the Queen should have been depicted as a referee, blowing the whistle at a particularly bad foul.

World Cup 1966   6d

THEY WERE PREPARED

Comedian Frankie Howerd is an ex-Scout. He belonged to a group in Eltham, Kent, first as a Cub and later as a Scout.

Recently he returned to his old Scouting area – to open a fête run by local Cubs to mark their Jubilee Year. The ex-Scout was a great attraction, and the fête raised £600.

KEN DODD joined the Group attached to the Oak Hill Methodist Church in Liverpool as a Cub and later became a Scout.

He is still a great believer in Scouting, and during the last Bob-a-Job Week – the annual money-raising effort – he arranged for a party of Scouts from Knotty Ash to clean his car.

"I enjoyed myself enormously when I was a Scout," says Ken.

WILFRED PICKLES, the well-known radio personality, spent 10 years in the Scouts. He belonged to a group in his home town of Halifax.

Says Wilfred of his Scout days: "I enjoyed every minute of it."

World Cup Winners. As we have seen, *Eagle* had a fair bit of build-up to the World Cup but due to the advanced printing times there was no coverage of the actual tournament. Almost three months after Bobby Moore lifted the trophy finally the comic acknowledges it.

NIPPY LITTLE
'MONKEY BIKE'

The 'Monkey Bike' being stowed in the boot of a Ford *Zodiac*

AN EAGLE
cutaway
DRAWING

L.ASHWELL WOOD

This little 50 c.c. motorized two-wheeler, the Honda 'Monkey ...', is an ideal runabout for avoiding traffic jams and parking meters. The name implies that you can 'monkey' around on it anywhere.

It differs from most other motorized two-wheelers and scooters in that it has a 4-stroke engine instead of the usual 2-stroke engine.

The overhead-valve engine delivers 4½ horsepower and the bike can cruise around all day at up to 35 m.p.h. and can cover 175 miles on only one gallon of petrol. An automatic clutch and three-speed gearbox makes gear changing simplicity itself.

Weighing just over 1 cwt., the Honda 'Monkey Bike' can be stowed in the boot of any fair-sized car.

KEY TO NUMBERED PARTS:

(1) Twist-grip carburettor throttle control; (2) Front brake lever; (3) Speedometer; (4) Steering head; Electric horn; (6) Front brake cable; (7) Internal expanding-type front brake; (8) Speedometer drive; Rigid front forks – springing is taken up by the balloon tyres; (10) Exhaust pipe; (11) Sparking plug; Piston – 40 mm. diameter, 39 mm. stroke; (13) Generator; (14) Split flywheel; (15) Automatic clutch; and camshaft drive to overhead valves. The engine primary drive to gearbox is also on this side; head inlet valve; (17) Downdraught carburettor; (18) Petrol tank – main frame through centre; frame; (20) Petrol tap; (21) Coil ignition lock; (22) Three-speed gearbox; (23) Secondary chain drive; wheel; (24) Second- and top-gear change pedal; (25) First-gear change pedal; Exhaust; silencer from engine exhaust pipe on other side; (27) Final drive sprocket; (28) Exhaust outlet.

TOMMY SIMPSON

TOMMY SIMPSON, first Briton to beat the Europeans at their own game of Cycle Racing, thinks that this could be his 'best-ever' season.

He got off to a great start in March by winning the marathon 8-day Paris-Nice race. This month (May) he is competing in the Montreal six-day event. Then comes the big one, and possible realization of his greatest remaining ambition – to lead a British team to victory in the classic, 2,800-mile Tour de France, the biggest cycling event in the world.

No Briton has ever won the mighty Tour since it started in 1903. But no Briton had ever been professional world cycling champion until Simpson captured that prize at San Sebastian in 1965.

At the age of 16 Tommy was winning junior events for his Harworth, Notts., cycling club, which is near Doncaster, Yorks. At 18 he won an Olympic bronze as a member of Britain's 4,000-metres team at Melbourne, and two years later an Empire silver medal for the individual pursuit event. At the age of 21 he gave up his job as an engineering draughtsman to live in France and compete as a full-time professional star.

Continental experts think Simpson capable of ending the reign of Jacques Anquetil, five times winner of the Tour de France, and establishing himself as the Tour's Number One ace. Last season saw his only set-back, but the Englishman's disappointing form was due to a serious injury suffered while ski-ing. Now he's back in the peak of condition, so it's 'look out, Anquetil'!

Tommy Simpson has one great remaining ambition – to lead a British team to victory in the Tour de France

Tommy Simpson died during the 1967 Tour de France. This article appeared just two months before the fatal day when exhaustion and the alleged effects of performance-enhancing drugs proved too much for his body to take. He was only 29 when he died.

super colour pictures of your favourite players

THE WONDERFUL WORLD OF SOCCER STARS

COLLECT AND SWOP

Just two of the hundreds of pictures you can collect – all in full colour

7 photographs for only 6d. And there's a great colourful album (13in. x 9in.) to keep them in. It's got details of all the players' careers.

Collect the whole series – be one of the first to complete an album. When you get any duplicates, swop them with your friends. And don't forget the password: "It's a Wonderful World"

On sale at newsagents and toyshops in England and Wales only

REMEMBER THE PASSWORD

IT'S A WONDERFUL WORLD

ANOTHER GREAT CHANCE TO WIN A BICYCLE! Page 19

EAGLE
and BOYS' WORLD

12 August 1967 Vol. 18 No. 32   EVERY WEDNESDAY **7d**

Mike Lane's New
Adventure
Page 6

New Scout
Badges
Page 17

Australia 10c. New Zealand 1/- (10c)
South Africa 8c.   Rhodesia 1/-
East Africa 1.00.   West Africa 10d.

We continue this great new series with the story of a dynamic fighter whose amazing career as Heavyweight Champion of the World has never been equalled – a career that was to place him among those immortals who became

LEGENDS IN THEIR LIFETIME

JOE LOUIS
Turn to Page 4

DAN DARE

AND as their spaceship hurtled towards Earth, another of Dan Dare's adventures came to an end. What was waiting for them on their return? They did not know. But Digby was right when he said it would be something exciting.

A fortnight after they had landed, Dan was sent for by the Prime Minister – and appointed CONTROLLER OF THE SPACEFLEET. And a week later at a presentation ceremony attended by former companions who had shared many of his perilous space adventures, Dan was warmly congratulated by his ex-chief, Sir Hubert Guest . . .

THE incredible adventures of Dan Dare have made his name famous throughout the world – indeed throughout the Universe. Seldom can one man have packed so much excitement into so short a time. But as he gets to grips with his new job, his adventures must come to a temporary halt.

One of the tasks which will keep him deskbound is the request by World Space Control that he should put on record the story of his amazing career. It is intended that the completed manual shall be presented to every Space Cadet as he begins his training.

We, too, have been looking back at some of his exploits, and we have decided to give today's Space Cadets a preview of the manual's contents.

Beginning next week, we shall be recalling some of Dan's greatest adventures. It's a series you can't afford to miss!

DAN DARE

DAN DARE'S amazing adventures as a space pilot have temporarily come to a halt, for the Prime Minister has just paid a fitting tribute to his outstanding work on behalf of humanity by appointing him Controller of the Spacefleet.

But just as he proved an inspiration to Space Cadets when on active service, so Dan will carry on that good work by putting on record the story of his astonishing career as a guide to the space pilots of the future.

We interrupted Dan in the act of writing his memoirs and asked him what would be an appropriate adventure to begin with. He thought for a moment, and then recalled one that had started, innocently enough, at the Astral Training College. It was to lead him to a life-or-death struggle with his arch-enemy, the Mekon.

And so we are privileged to present to our readers the incredible affair of . . .

Prisoners of Space

LUCKY STEVE VALIANT! YOU'RE A 'CERT' TO WIN THE EARTH GOVERNMENT AWARD FOR THE ACE CADET AT TOMORROW'S PASSING OUT.

I WISH I FELT AS SURE AS YOU DO, TONY.

WHICH OF YOU BLIGHTERS PINCHED MY SPATIAL GAZETEER?

AT THE ASTRAL TRAINING COLLEGE ATTACHED TO SPACE H.Q., THREE SENIOR CADETS — STEVE VALIANT, TONY ALBRIGHT AND MARK STRAIGHT — ARE PREPARING FOR THE NEXT DAY'S PASSING OUT PARADE.

IT'S TIME YOU TRADED THAT SIEVE FOR A *REAL* HEAD, MARK! YOU LOANED YOUR GAZETEER TO YOUNG SPRY — GENIUS OF THE JUNIOR SCHOOL — LAST WEEK.

'FLAMER' SPRY'S BUILDING A MODEL OF COLONEL DARE'S NEW 'PERFORMING FLEA' — THAT HUSH-HUSH JOB THEY'VE JUST TAKEN OFF THE SECRET LIST.

THE BOFFINS SAY DAN DARE WILL BE ABLE TO DO A SOLO PATROL OF THE ENTIRE *SPACE-STATION* PERIMETER — RIGHT OUT TO VENUS AND BACK — IN THAT CRATE.

THAT KID PROMISED TO RETURN MY BOOK NEXT DAY. *FAG!*

HEY, TUBBY POTTS! CUT ACROSS TO JUNIOR SCHOOL AND TELL SPRY IF HE'S NOT HERE IN TWO TICKS WITH MY BOOK, I'LL HAVE HIS RED SCALP FOR A BOOT-BRUSH.

STRAIGHT AWAY, STRAIGHT!

AS THE BOYS PREPARE FOR THE ANNUAL CEREMONY, SIR HUBERT GUEST AND COLONEL DAN DARE DISCUSS A MATTER OF GRAVE IMPORTANCE AT SPACE H.Q. . . .

PEGASUS, OF THE TRANSPORT FLEET, WAS DUE IN FROM VENUS AT 17·03 HOURS YESTERDAY. SOMEWHERE HERE, IN AREA X, OUR COMMUNICATIONS ROOM LOST CONTACT. EMERGENCY PATROLS WENT OUT IMMEDIATELY, BUT FOUND ABSOLUTELY *NOTHING*. BRIEFLY, THE *PEGASUS* HAS VANISHED IN SPACE!

WHICH MAKES FIVE SHIPS LOST ON THE RUN IN AS MANY WEEKS. IT REMINDS ME OF THE OLD DAYS WHEN WE FIRST TRIED TO REACH VENUS . . .

. . . THE *PEGASUS* TYPE WAS SPECIALLY BUILT FOR THE VENUS TRADE. THERE'S NOTHING WRONG WITH THE DESIGN OR CONSTRUCTION — I TESTED THE FIRST ONE OFF THE ASSEMBLY LINE MYSELF. COULD IT BE SABOTAGE, SIR HUBERT?

OUT OF THE QUESTION, DARE — EVERYONE CONNECTED WITH THE OPERATION HAS BEEN THOROUGHLY VETTED. WE'RE UP AGAINST A NEW AND UNKNOWN FACTOR!

OR A *HIDDEN ENEMY*, SIR?

FRONTIERS OF SCIENCE

THIS WEEK

FALL-OUT

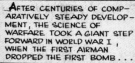

AFTER CENTURIES OF COMPARATIVELY STEADY DEVELOPMENT, THE SCIENCE OF WARFARE TOOK A GIANT STEP FORWARD IN WORLD WAR I, WHEN THE FIRST AIRMAN DROPPED THE FIRST BOMB...

THE STRATEGISTS SOON REALISED THE IMMENSE VALUE OF THIS NEW WEAPON AGAINST CIVILIAN POPULATIONS...

"TERROR-BOMBING" REACHED ITS PEAK DURING WORLD WAR II — FIRST WITH THE DESTRUCTION OF EUROPEAN CITIES BY BLAST AND FIRE...

...AND FINALLY BY THE ATOMIC BOMBING OF JAPAN — AN EVENT WHICH INTRODUCED INTO THE VOCABULARY OF MAN A NEW AND FRIGHTENING WORD— *FALLOUT!*

THE FIRST A-BOMB WORKED BY "FISSION" — THE SPLITTING OF NUCLEI OF URANIUM 235 IN A "CHAIN REACTION"...

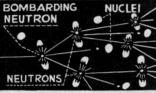

BOMBARDING NEUTRON — NUCLEI — NEUTRONS

...IN WHICH, LIKE A MATCH DROPPED INTO A BOX OF FIREWORKS, NEUTRONS FREED BY ONE FISSION CAUSED FISSION IN OTHER NUCLEI NEARBY.

A-BOMB POWER IS MEASURED IN "KILOTONS" (THOUSANDS OF TONS OF T.N.T.). THE FISSION BOMB IS OVERSHADOWED TODAY BY THE "FUSION" BOMB, IN WHICH A FISSION EXPLOSION IS USED TO FORCE TOGETHER NUCLEI OF "HEAVY HYDROGEN" OR DEUTERIUM — THE "H-BOMB"!

HYDROGEN NUCLEUS = 1 PROTON
DEUTERIUM = 1 PROTON, 1 NEUTRON

FUSION OF *DEUTERIUM* GIVES — HELIUM 3 — OR — TRITIUM — ENERGY

HELIUM 3 AND *TRITIUM* FORMED ABOUT 50-50

THIS FUSION RELEASES VAST AMOUNTS OF ENERGY — AND H-BOMBS ARE MEASURED IN "MEGATONS", OR *MILLIONS OF TONS OF T.N.T.!*

FINALLY, IT HAS BEEN FOUND THAT A FANTASTIC "SUPERBOMB" CAN BE MADE (THEORETICALLY, OF *ANY* SIZE) BY THE "3-F" PRINCIPLE (FISSION-FUSION-FISSION)

THE SUPERBOMB, ALTHOUGH HORRIFYING TO CONTEMPLATE, IS A MARVEL OF SCIENTIFIC INGENUITY...

THE SUPERBOMB IS REALLY THREE BOMBS, ONE INSIDE THE OTHER — IN THE CENTRE URANIUM 235, WHICH SUSTAINS A CHAIN REACTION, BUT IS EXPENSIVE; NEXT A MIXTURE OF DEUTERIUM AND LITHIUM, OR "LITHIUM DEUTERIDE", AND FINALLY AN OUTSIDE JACKET OF URANIUM 238, WHICH IS CHEAP AND PLENTIFUL — BUT WHICH WILL NOT SUSTAIN A CHAIN REACTION.

U 235 — LITHIUM DEUTERIDE — U 238

FISSION IN U 235

U 238

FUSION IN LITHIUM DEUTERIDE

WHEN THE INNER U235 "TRIGGER" IS FIRED, IT STARTS A FUSION REACTION IN THE SURROUNDING LITHIUM DEUTERIDE. THIS FUSION RELEASES A GIGANTIC BLAST AND HEAT WAVE...

...AND ALSO A SWARM OF *FAST NEUTRONS*, SUFFICIENT TO CAUSE *FISSION IN THE NORMALLY RELUCTANT U238 NUCLEI IN THE OUTER JACKET!* THE RESULT IS A STUPENDOUS EXPLOSION, SUCH AS THE RUSSIANS HAVE ACHIEVED.

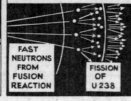

FAST NEUTRONS FROM FUSION REACTION — FISSION OF U 238

BUT WHILE THE PURE FUSION EXPLOSION, OR H-BOMB, IS "CLEAN", RELEASING LITTLE HARMFUL RADIOACTIVE MATERIAL, THE OUTER FISSION JACKET OF U238 PRODUCES LARGE QUANTITIES OF DEADLY MATERIAL IN THE FORM OF *FALLOUT.*

A SUPERBOMB EXPLODED ANYWHERE NEAR THE EARTH'S SURFACE NOT ONLY FORCES RADIOACTIVE DUST FROM ITS CRATER INTO THE ATMOSPHERE BUT ALSO RELEASES *DEADLY PRODUCTS OF FISSION*, INCLUDING *STRONTIUM 90* AND *CAESIUM 137*.

RADIOACTIVE PRODUCTS

DUST — DUST

A 50 MEGATON SUPERBOMB USING A 50:50 RATIO OF FUSION TO FISSION ENERGY — AN "ECONOMICAL" RATIO — WOULD RELEASE MORE THAN 2,500 POUNDS OF *RADIOACTIVE MATERIAL INTO THE UPPER ATMOSPHERE*...

STRATOSPHERE — TROPOSPHERE — WIND — RAIN — FALLOUT 3-6 MONTHS — LOCAL FALLOUT

SOME FALL-OUT COMES DOWN LOCALLY WITHIN A FEW DAYS... MORE IS WASHED TO EARTH WITHIN MONTHS BY RAIN AND SNOW... BUT AN UNKNOWN PERCENTAGE IS FORCED INTO THE STRATOSPHERE, WHERE THERE IS NO RAIN, AND CONTINUES TO FLOAT AROUND THE EARTH FOR YEARS — SPREADING EVERYWHERE AND SETTLING SLOWLY.

THE SOVIET EXPLOSIONS OF 1961 ADDED AS MUCH FALLOUT TO THE ATMOSPHERE AS ALL PREVIOUS TESTS COMBINED — AND MOST OF THIS WILL FALL IN THE NORTHERN HEMISPHERE WITHIN TWELVE MONTHS OF THE EXPLOSIONS....

PATH OF FALLOUT — U.S.S.R. — NORTH POLE — CANADA — EUROPE — U.S.A.

*

NEXT WEEK

THE ATOM HARNESSED

*

A SUPERBOMB DESTROYS BY BLAST, HEAT, "GAMMA RAYS", AND NEUTRONS AND LONG-TERM RADIOACTIVITY THROUGH FALLOUT.

HEATWAVE — GAMMA RAYS — BLAST WAVE

GAMMA RAYS AND NEUTRONS CAN INJURE LIVING CELLS, AND NEED AT LEAST A FOOT OF CONCRETE TO BLOCK THEM OFF...

STRONTIUM 90 AND CAESIUM 137 FOLLOW A ROUNDABOUT ROUTE INTO THE BODY...

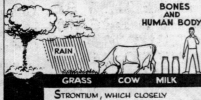

BONES AND HUMAN BODY — RAIN — GRASS — COW — MILK

15-5

STRONTIUM, WHICH CLOSELY RESEMBLES CALCIUM, IS ATTRACTED TO THE BONES, AND CAUSES CANCER AND LEUKEMIA. CAESIUM, WHICH RESEMBLES POTASSIUM, CAUSES GENETIC DAMAGE AND CAN PRODUCE MALFORMED CHILDREN.

SO FAR THE LEVEL OF RADIATION FROM FALLOUT IS MUCH LESS THAN NATURAL RADIATION (RADIOACTIVE ROCKS, RAYS FROM SPACE) OR FROM MEDICAL RADIATION (THE USE OF X-RAYS)...

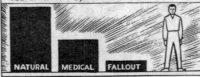

NATURAL — MEDICAL — FALLOUT

BUT THE REAL CONCERN TODAY IS THAT *NO ONE REALLY KNOWS* WHAT THE "PERMISSIBLE LEVEL" OF RADIATION IS OVER THE LONG PERIODS DURING WHICH "FALLOUT" WILL CONTINUE TO SETTLE FROM THE STRATOSPHERE.

IS YOUR NAME   GORDON?

The first Gordon in Britain was a Frenchman who came over with William the Conqueror in 1066. He spelled his name Gourdin, which is French for cudgel. He wielded his cudgel so well at Hastings that William the Conqueror gave him an estate in England. In the twelfth century, one of Gourdin's descendants settled in Aberdeenshire, Scotland, where he founded the Clan Gordon to which all Gordons now belong.

One of the most famous of all white hunters in Africa was George Gordon-Cumming. He slaughtered hundreds of lions and elephants, but in 1845 he nearly met his match at the claws of a lioness. He was taking aim at a charging elephant when the lioness, which had stalked up behind him, sprang for his back. Fortunately, one of his African servants saw the danger and shot the lioness while she was in mid-air. The noise of the shot frightened the elephant, which promptly made off.

Jake Gordon's only claim to fame is that he played snooker. But it was snooker with a difference. To win a bet of 50 dollars, he potted with his cue a black snooker ball for ten miles along a country road in South Dakota, U.S.A. And just to make things more difficult for himself, he wore an old army respirator. Jake performed his fantastic feat in 1963 and took six hours to complete the course.

During the Second World War, Britain and the Free French were fighting to prevent Syria falling into the Nazi net. On the night of 10th July, 1941, a company of Australian infantry was advancing on a strongly fortified position at Jezzine when it came under heavy machine-gun fire and was pinned down. One of the Australians, Private James Gordon, then crept forward over an area swept by machine-guns. Within a few yards of the enemy position, he jumped up and charged the machine-gun post single-handed, killing the machine-gun crew with the bayonet. This completely demoralized the enemy and the post surrendered. Private Gordon's gallantry won him a well-merited Victoria Cross.

Patrick Gordon was a Scottish soldier of fortune who always joined the side that captured him in battle. In 1655 he enlisted in the Swedish Army, was captured by the Poles and then joined their army. Then in 1661, the Poles were defeated by the Russians and Patrick Gordon sold his sword to Russia. This was the most profitable change he made. He was never captured again and eventually became a Russian General. In fact, he owed his promotion to using his regiment of Cossacks to defeat a revolt of Peter the Great's household troops.

In 1780, a number of Protestants in Britain, led by Lord George Gordon, wanted Parliament to bring in a law denying religious freedom to Roman Catholics. Headed by Lord George Gordon, rioters attacked the Bank of England but were defeated by a battalion of Grenadier Guards. Over 400 rioters were killed and wounded and Lord George Gordon was captured. He escaped to the Continent but was brought back and died in prison.

General Gordon was sent to the Sudan in 1884 to put down a rebellion of the tribesmen. Gordon was besieged at Khartoum and sent a despatch to London asking for more troops. The Government decided the situation didn't warrant it and waited some months before acting. At last a relief force was sent out and arrived at Khartoum on 28th January, 1885 – two days after the Sudanese had captured the fortification and killed Gordon. The siege had lasted for 317 days.

GORDON BENNET MOUNT

Mount near Albert Nyanza, Africa. It was discovered by Sir Henry Stanley in 1875.

GORDONSTOUN SCHOOL

Public school in Morayshire, Scotland. It was founded in 1934, and among its many distinguished pupils were the Duke of Edinburgh and Prince Charles.

GORDON BOYS' SCHOOL

Boys' school nr. Woking, England, founded in 1885 as a national memorial to General Gordon.

ADVANCE '67 ▶ THE *NEW* CUB SCOUT AND SCOUT Proficiency Badges

Compiled by David Harwood

INTEREST

Bell Ringer · Artist · Camp-Cook · Athlete · Collector · Horseman · Librarian · Model Maker · Musician · Naturalist · Photographer · Smallholder · Swimmer

SERVICE

Ambulance · Camp Warden · Conservator · Fireman · Guide · Interpreter · Jobman · Lifesaver* · Pilot · Quartermaster · Secretary

In ADVANCE '67 in the last few months you've read about and seen many of the things which are being done to implement the new Progress Scheme. This week, *Scouts' World* is pleased to present ALL the new Proficiency Badge designs for Cub Scouts and Scouts. Just like the detailed requirements for the badges, they're exciting and modern in concept. You'll be proud to wear them on your uniform!

As a general guide:

INTEREST BADGES are primarily intended for Scouts in the 12-13 age group.

PURSUIT BADGES are more for the 13-15-year-olds and their requirements are of a practical nature.

SERVICE BADGES are passed at a higher standard and are recommended for the older Scout, and include the practical application of service and NOT just theory.

Instructor Proficiency Badges

INSTRUCTOR BADGES are of at least as high a standard as the SERVICE BADGES and are for the Scout who is interested in specializing in a particular field to channel his interest towards service to the Movement.

The basic requirements for any Instructor Badge are:
– hold the PURSUIT BADGE of the particular skill (or if no Pursuit Badge, the INTEREST BADGE)
– have a good working knowledge of the basic principles of the particular skill
– attend a course giving training in technical skills and training methods
– put into practice what he has learnt over a regular period (of at least three months) by helping with the training of young Scouts.

A Scout will normally hold an Instructor Badge in ONE subject only and NEVER in more than TWO.

Note: Instructor Badges may be gained in those on this page which are marked with an asterisk (*).

CUB SCOUT PROFICIENCY BADGES

In the new Cub Scout scheme, there are two groups of Proficiency Badges: ...e-stage ... indicating three progressive levels of achievement. The ...ge design remains the same at all stages, but the background colour is ...rent. 1st stage – GREEN; 2nd stage – YELLOW; 3rd stage – RED. ...le-stage all have a RED background.

...Cyclist and Swimmer Badges can be gained any time after Investiture; ... further badges (or stages of badges) may be gained while working for ... of the Bronze, Silver and Gold Arrow Badges.

...ee-stage badges

Artist · Athlete · Handyman

Naturalist · Scientist · Swimmer

...le-stage badges

Book Reader · Cyclist · Explorer

First Aider · Fisherman · Linguist

Map Reader · Photographer

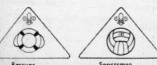

Rescuer · Sportsman · Troubadour

HOBOS' SECRET SIGNS

FOR a long time the hobos, or tramps, of America have had a set of secret signs by which they could warn each other of danger, or possible good fortune.

If a hobo was well treated at a farm, he would carve or chalk a mark on a nearby stone or tree to tell any other hobo, who was looking for a night's sleep in a barn, that the folk of the farm were friendly people. Many of the old hobos couldn't read or write, but they understood the meanings of these simple signs.

Here are just a few of them:

 DANGER

 A RELIGIOUS FAMILY

 THESE PEOPLE WILL FALL FOR A HARD-LUCK STORY

 SAFE TO CAMP HERE

 KEEP AWAY

 VERY NICE PEOPLE

 BULL'S-EYE. GOOD LUCK, OR GOOD FOOD, TO BE FOUND AT THIS HOUSE

KIND-HEARTED LADY

DON'T MAKE A NOISE

 DON'T DESPAIR. GOOD FRIENDS ARE NEARBY

 POLICE PATROL THIS AREA

 BEWARE OF THE LAW

 THIS FARMER IS VERY WEALTHY

 BEWARE OF THE DOG

 IF YOU TRESPASS ON THIS LAND YOU WILL BE PUT IN PRISON

THIS SPOT IS DANGEROUS FOR CAMPING

 HALT

 BEWARE OF THE MAN WITH A GUN

 DOCTOR NOT FAR AWAY

 WATCH OUT FOR THE GAMEKEEPER WITH A STICK

TOP TEAMS
NOTTINGHAM FOREST
THE CENTURIONS WITH FIZZ AND FIRE—
NOT TO MENTION POW! SOCK! AND ZING!

Forest's new sparkle has brought a new hunger for goals

"FIZZ it about!" That is manager John Carey's formula for Forest's football future. He likes to see the ball flow from man to man until it ends up in the opponents' goal-net. It is a policy that fits in very well with Forest's long tradition for fluent football and good manners on the field, but which needs another ingredient – fiery determination (?) – to put Nottingham Forest in the position they have been seeking in vain for over 100 years: top of the First Division.

Halfway through the present season, the team – once considered steady at home but a 'pushover' on opponents' grounds – suddenly acquired bite. Youngsters on the Mini-Kop behind the Trent End goal were quick to recognize and cheer this new sparkle, while crowds at away matches ceased the mocking chant of 'EAS-Y'.

What set Forest alight, according to skipper Terry Hennessey, was that humiliating 4—0 defeat to the Champions, Liverpool, at Anfield last Guy Fawkes Day. Liverpool taught them a lesson in do-or-die determination and gave Nottingham Forest a new hate-to-lose complex.

Could it be that this elderly club, steeped in 'the game's the thing' tradition, has eventually got the

Joe Baker – the Forest spearhead

message that success is all that counts; that 'good losers' are suckers? In 100 years, Forest have won the F.A. Cup twice, but never finished higher than fourth in the First Division.

To 'Gentleman' John Carey, of course, the means to the desired end will always be significant. In 17 years with Manchester United, as a player in every position on the field including goal, he won every honour in the game without ever sacrificing his high ideals of fine football and fair play.

When Manchester United trailed 2—1 to Blackpool in the 1948 Cup Final, a colleague asked Carey at half-time: "What do we do now, skipper?"

"We keep on playing as well as we did in the first half," replied John. "Keep playing good football and the goals MUST come."

And come they did, carrying Manchester United to a 4—2 victory in the best footballing Final ever seen at Wembley.

But as Nottingham Forest manager, does John Carey have the talent at his command?

With Lincolnshire-born Peter Grummit, an England Under-23 international, between the posts, and a six-foot defence which includes Bob McKinlay, recommended to the club by his uncle (a former Forest wing-half) six years ago and still going strong, they don't give many goals away.

Terry Hennessey, the tall, elegant Welsh

international star, completes a back row of four but moves up to midfield to exploit his attacking flair whenever the position allows.

Ex-Arsenal star John Barnwell and local boy Henry Newton have proved themselves enterprising and tireless linkmen, while up front there is a goal-hungry quartet in Ian Storey-Moore, twin spearheads Joe Baker and Frank Wignall (both of whom have led England's attack), and Barry Lyons, the £40,000 newcomer from Rotherham.

If the name Ian Storey-Moore is not too familiar to everyone now, it soon will be. This versatile young forward made his début for Forest against his home-town club, Ipswich, in 1963; since when he has made himself a rare reputation for scoring match-winning goals.

Former players do not hesitate to recommend Forest as a good club. David Stainwright's father and uncle both played for Forest as amateurs during the War. They have good reserve strength, much of it comprised of local talent.

Forest's history is full of 'firsts'. They were the first club to adopt the formation of five forwards, three halves and two full-backs (1884), first and only club to play against teams from all four home countries in the F.A. Cup, first to play in a match in which the referee used a whistle (1878).

S. W. Widdowson, a Forest player, first introduced shinguards (1874). Frank and Fred Forman were the first pair of brothers to play in all England's home internationals in 1899 (a record recently equalled by the Charlton brothers). Forest were one of the first clubs to play under floodlights (1889) and to tour in South America.

They have been first in Division Two twice, and in Division Three once. But in Division One – never!

Can Carey's fizz, plus the fire they found after Firework Day, put Forest first? It may take a season or two, but there's no doubt this new-look team has got POW, SOCK and ZING in abundance.

Skipper Terry Hennessey – Welsh star with attacking flair

EAGLE Adventure Holidays, 1967

THE aim of these holidays is to give young people a greater knowledge, love and enjoyment of their country. They will be staying at Youth Hostels which range from old-world cottages to historic castles, from large town houses to country mansions. There are nearly three hundred in England and Wales and all provide simple accommodation, plenty of appetizing food and a friendly welcome. Each hostel is looked after by wardens, usually a married couple.

The leaders are chosen with great care and are experienced hostellers. Their job

is to ensure that each party enjoys every minute of its holiday. Whether members come on their own, as many readers do, or with a friend, the leader will see that they miss none of the fun. Parents can be assured that their children will be looked after in the best possible way.

What is a holiday like? If a walking or cycling tour is chosen, the week will be spent touring between Youth Hostels. During the holiday, there is usually at least one rest day, when, using the same hostel, the surrounding district is more thoroughly explored. If a specialized

holiday is chosen, such as fishing, bird watching or skin diving, you can be sure each is designed to give maximum enjoyment.

Usually, a party consists of seven on a cycling tour, eleven on a walking tour and between ten and twenty on other activities. An average day's cycling is about thirty-five miles – for walking about ten miles – and are well within the capabilities of a beginner. The walking and cycling holidays cost, with a few exceptions, £8 0s. 0d. Prices of other activities vary, but they are all inexpensive and give

maximum value for money, and include full meals, accommodation, special visits to places of interest and the services of a first-class leader.

For fuller details of these holidays, write today for our exciting Brochure designed to meet the tastes of boys and girls between 11 and 15 years of age. Send to EAGLE Holiday Brochure, Y.H.A., Trevelyan House, 8 St Stephen's Hill, St Albans, Herts. Please enclose a stamped, self-addressed gummed label for your reply.

CAVALCADE OF CARS

PEUGEOT 404KF

SPECIFICATIONS
88 b.h.p. at 5,500 r.p.m.;
4 cylinders; 1,618 c.c.;
Kugelfischer fuel injection;
4 forward speeds or automatic transmission;
Drum brakes all round, servo assisted;
Independent suspension all round;
Top speed: 97.8 m.p.h.

Peugeot have come a long way since their first three-wheeled steam carriage with coke-tired boiler.

Their latest model has all the up-to-date assets such as automatic transmission or manual 4-speed synchromesh transmission; fuel injection, which takes the place of the carburettor and is likely to be the form of fuel delivery on all cars within about five years; and power brakes.

To add luxury and comfort, the car has reclining seats, door-to-door carpeting, a sliding roof and a special fresh-air ventilation system which provides a smooth flow of air exactly where required — it is adjustable for volume and direction.

PEUGEOT

Copy Cats

Dear Editor,

I should like to inform you that I have noticed several entries in Merry-go-round that are certainly not original. I know this point has been stressed several times but it does not seem to have made any impression.

I do not want to say that these people should not get their money, but I do not think that it is very fair using other people's ideas.

Graeme Findlay, Dundee, Scotland.

Agreed! – Ed.

EAGLE

and BOYS' WORLD

16 September 1967 Vol. 18 No. 37

EVERY WEDNESDAY **7d**

Australia 10c. New Zealand 1/-
South Africa 8c. Rhodesia
East Africa 1.00. West Africa

Hazard in Peril Page

More Great Socc Secrets Page

LEGENDS IN THEIR LIFETIME

Three circling killer sharks moved in for the kill . . . but just as the two men seemed to be at their mercy, one of the underwater swimmers intercepted the leading shark head-on and smashed it on the snout with his camera! This was just one of the extraordinary events in the career of one of the world's most legendary figures.

COMMANDER COUSTEAU

Turn to page 4.

EAGLE
and BOYS' WORLD

28 January 1967 Vol. 18 No. 4

EVERY WEDNESDAY 7d

DID IT EVER HAPPEN?

This story could be true—or it could be made up. Read on and then decide for yourself if it is true or false.

It was foggy as Jean Breuil drove along the motorway a few miles from Paris. Suddenly, out of the gloom, Jean sighted a huge truck crossing the road just ahead of him.

There was no time to brake and no chance to swerve either behind or in front. Jean did the only thing possible — he accelerated and drove his car between the wheels and underneath the truck.

The roof of the car was ripped off, and then the car was through. Jean was unhurt and the luckiest man in France that day.

Did it ever happen? The answer is on page 3.

THE GUINEA-PIG

Professor Dee, scientific controller of the secret government research centre on Dartmoor, was conducting experiments into colour-reflex-conditioning. His method: drugs and psychological brainwashing. His subject: the human guinea-pig, Mike Lane.

HEY KIDS!
3,300 SMASHING PRIZES

TO BE WON!
If you're under 15, you can enter
THIS SUPER KIT KAT
MOTHERS AND CHILDREN'S COMPETITION!

You paint a picture!   Your Mum writes a caption to it!

100 1st Prizes in each group! (50 for you! 50 for your Mums!)
1,000 Consolation Prizes in each age group! (500 for you! 500 for your Mums!)

CHILDREN 5-7 YEARS	CHILDREN 8-11 YEARS	CHILDREN 12-15 YEARS	MOTHERS' PRIZES
1st PRIZE	**1st PRIZE**	**1st PRIZE**	If your child wins a first prize you win a Kodak 'Instamatic' Camera (with film and flash cubes).
For boys Scalextric "50" Car Racing Set with Power unit. **For girls** "Chatty Cathy" Doll by Rosebud (says 18 sentences). **Consolation Prize** Reeves "61 A" Paint Box.	**For boys** Exactima Boy's Watch. **For girls** Ingersoll Girl's Watch (both gold plated with jewelled movements). **Consolation Prize** "GO" Board Game by Waddington.	PHILIPS "Popmaster Prince" transistor radio with case and batteries. **Consolation Prize** Black Parker "45" Convertible Pen.	'Instamatic' is the regd. trade mark of Kodak Ltd. If your child wins a consolation prize you win a Gift Box of Rowntree Chocolates and Confectionery.

 IT'S EASY

HOW TO ENTER

All you have to do is paint a picture of your family (having a picnic, driving in the car, sitting in the garden – anything you like) in paints or crayons, using a piece of paper not smaller than 10" x 8" and not larger than 20" x 15".
Then, when you've done this, get your mother to write a caption to your picture. She must start the caption with the words: "OUR FAMILY LIKE KIT KAT FOR BREAKS BECAUSE..." and finish it, adding *not more* than 10 words.
Make sure she writes a really good original caption to your painting, because prizes will be awarded to the best painting *and* caption, taken as one (i.e. if your painting is super, but the words underneath have nothing to do with it, you are unlikely to win a prize).
P.S. You can get your father or guardian to write the caption too, if you like.
When your painting, and the words to it, are finished, just fill in this entry form in BLOCK CAPITALS, stick it to the back of the painting, and send it, *together with 2 four-finger or 4 two-finger Kit Kat wrappers* to: **Rowntree & Co. Ltd., Kit Kat Children's Painting Competition, 18-20 St. Andrew St., London, E.C.4.**

ABRIDGED RULES

1. All pictures should be sent together with shopkeepers' leaflets or coupons cut from advertisements and 2 four-finger or 4 two-finger Kit Kat wrappers, to Rowntree & Co. Ltd., Kit Kat Children's Painting Competition, 18-20 St. Andrew Street, London, E.C.4.
2. All entries must arrive not later than the first post on 28th October, 1967.
3. All entries will be judged for originality and skill. The decision of the judges will be final and no correspondence can be entered into.
4. Any entries which are illegible, altered or which arrive late will be disqualified. Rowntree & Co. Ltd. cannot be responsible for entries lost, mislaid, damaged or delayed in the post or otherwise.
5. Anyone resident in the U.K. or Channel Islands is eligible to enter, except employees of Rowntree & Co. Ltd. (and their families), their advertising agents and anyone who is connected with the organisation of the competition.
6. Full rules are set out on shopkeepers' leaflets and copies are available from Rowntree & Co. Ltd., The Cocoa Works, York, England.

ENTRY FORM
Cut this entry form out and firmly attach it to the back of the painting, together with your caption.
Closing date 28th October, 1967.

Kit Kat

Child's Name..................
Mother's Name ....
Full Address ....
Child's date of birth...........(day)........(month)..........(year)
Signature of parent/guardian ....
(I certify that this painting is the unaided and original work of my child)
Remember to enclose the Kit Kat wrappers. E.1.

STANDING ROOM ONLY

BY LYALL WATSON, Ph.D; B.Sc., Hons, FZS.

To provide enough food for the vast population of the future, enormous mirrors could be placed in space to enable the sun to shine on the dark places of the Earth

IF you were to invite all your friends and relations to a party—it may be a little crowded, but it would certainly be possible to pack them all into an average-sized house. Even if you were to invite all the people that you know by name or even by sight—including the butcher, the bus-conductor and the man who walks his dog in the park, as well as every single person at your school—there still wouldn't be more than one or two thousand. And all these could be squeezed into an ordinary church hall.

Each of us comes into contact with a very small part of the human race and finds it difficult to appreciate just how many people there are in the world. At the moment there are over three-thousand million. That is, enough to fill two million church halls or, if they were laid end to end, enough to stretch from here to the moon and back, half a dozen times.

That's an awful lot of people, and there are more on the way. Two babies are born every second, 172,800 every day, which is the same as adding the entire population of Great Britain to the world, each year.

At the moment, all the people in the world could be packed heel-to-toe on to the Isle of Wight—so space is not yet a problem. But what about food? Already 15 per cent of the population are starving. What is going to happen in the year 2000 when there are twice as many people? Or in 2200 A.D. when there are one hundred times as many?

The answer is that it might not be nearly as bad as some people make out. We'll probably find a way to manage. Right now there is quite enough food being grown to feed everyone in the world—people are starving simply because nations cannot get along with each other and ensure that the available food is evenly distributed. Every year, millions of people die of malnutrition in Asia, and every year millions of surplus tons of food are destroyed in Europe and America.

If there was world-wide co-operation, and by then we hope there will be, food would not be a problem. Even with existing foodstuffs and our present, rather inefficient, farming methods—it should be possible to feed about 50,000 million mouths by 2100 A.D.

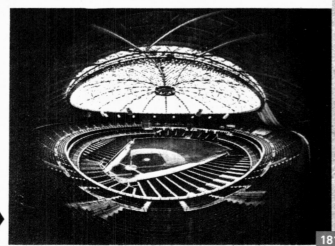

Whole cities of the future may be roofed over for farming purposes, in the manner of the enormous baseball stadium in Houston, Texas. ➤

PLANNING FOR THE POPULATION EXPLOSION

A.D. 1967	3,000,000,000	CARRY ON AS USUAL	Stage 1
A.D. 2000	6,000,000,000	KILL WILD LIFE	
A.D. 2100	50,000,000,000	ROOF OVER CITIES	Stage 2
A.D. 2200	400,000,000,000	GIVE UP MEAT	
A.D. 2300	3,000,000,000,000	KILL SEA LIFE	Stage 3
A.D. 2400	25,000,000,000,000	GROW ONLY ALGAE	
A.D. 2500	200,000,000,000,000	MIRRORS IN SPACE	Stage 4
A.D. 2600	1,500,000,000,000,000	ARTIFICIAL SYNTHESIS OF ALL FOOD	Stage 5
A.D. 2700	12,000,000,000,000,000		
A.D. 2800	100,000,000,000,000,000		
A.D. 2900	400,000,000,000,000,000	SEALING OFF THE EARTH'S ATMOSPHERE	Stage 6
A.D. 2967	1,000,000,00 0,000,000,000		

Then what? Well, then we will have to change our methods.

If all land wild-life were to be eliminated and roofs built over all the cities and roads so that the entire land surface of the world could be turned over to farming, we might be able to support double that number of people. And, if we all gave up eating meat and learned instead how to harvest the sea efficiently, then it should be possible to double the world population twice more. Bringing it up to 400,000 million by the year 2200 A.D.

Then we would have to concentrate on the sea. The area of ice-free sea is about three times that of land, and living in the sea are small green plants called algae which are much more efficient than any land plants. They can produce three times as much basic protein food as wheat or rice plants. With these being collected from all the oceans of the world, we could support three times as many people. We could then double our numbers a further three times if all the wild life in the sea, too, was removed and replaced with the planktonic algae. By this stage we will have doubled the earth's population ten times and have 3 million million people in 2300 A.D.

This would mean that every person would have about 150 square yards — about half the area of a tennis court. But even if two people with adjacent plots decided that they would like to play tennis, this would be impossible because no activity other than food production would be allowed on the surface of the land or the sea. Every single spot exposed to the sun would be devoted to algae busy turning the sun's energy into food.

More food could be produced if there were more sun — if half the earth were not in darkness for half of each day, or if the polar regions were not deprived of the sun for half of every year. Continuous daylight all over the world could be arranged by putting a number of enormous mirrors into orbit to reflect the sun's light on to the dark areas. The total area of the mirrors would need to be five time as large as Africa and the weight would be incredible.

The effect of lighting the world continuously would be to bring the whole earth to tropical temperature, melting the polar ice caps and allowing us to double the population yet again, bringing it by this time, 2400 A.D. to about 25 million million.

By producing food artificially in laboratories it should be possible to make the world of 2600 A.D. support more than 100 million people.

The whole world would by now be at equatorial temperatures and could be temporarily kept from going even higher by using the oceans as a heat sink. In other words, getting rid of the excess heat by pushing it into the sea. It would not be very long, however, before the oceans began to boil and evaporate. But, by this time, the seas would already have been roofed over to provide space for housing and, if the atmosphere were also sealed off hermetically to give us an air-conditioned planet, we could arrange to radiate heat from our solid outer skin directly into space.

Even with this extraordinary technological feat, though, we would never be able to in-

crease the population further than 120 perso per square yard. This is the absolute limit. An assuming that we go on multiplying at c present rate, we are going to reach this lin — of one million million million people — soon as 3000 A.D.

These two pictures show how the world's pop lation will densify, when the middle of the 20 century (above) is compared with the year 200 (below).

● Next Week : A PEEK INTO THE YEAR 2,00

IT'S NEW!

KEEPING SPACEMEN COOL

Here we see a spacecraft passing through the atmosphere on its return to earth. Friction with the atmosphere has created such heat that it has become a glowing mass; yet the crew inside do not feel any great heat because the outer shell, or shield, prevents the heat from getting through.

To find out just how much heat a spacecraft could stand without the crew being roasted alive, scientists at the Avro Corporation in America, built a spacecraft and then passed it through an electric furnace at a temperature of 11,000 degrees. At the same time they took this photograph to show the effects of the searing heat. Curiously enough, the heat shield is not of metal but of a special heat-resisting plastic. It is probable that the plastic heat-shields will be used to give 100 per cent protection to the Apollo spacemen who will make the journey to the moon and back.

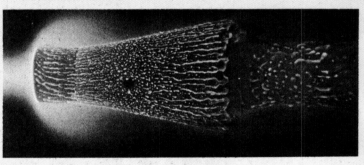

BALLOONS FOR AIRLINERS

Balloons for airline passengers is the latest idea to protect people from injury in crashes. The safety belts now used only reduce the risk of injury. Each passenger would have his own balloon which normally would be deflated and stored below or behind his seat. They would be connected by tubing to an air compressor controlled by a switch in the aircraft's cockpit. In the event of the pilot anticipating a bad landing or a crash, the passengers would be told to wrap the balloons around them. The pilot would then pull down the compressor switch, inflating the balloons, thus pinning the passengers in their seats and preventing them from being thrown forward.

* * *

A SPOONFUL OF POWER

If a visitor from another planet landed on the earth and was told that the small objects photographed in the spoon were power plants he might well think that he had come to a world of midgets, for these tiny objects are transistor power packs now being developed for use in spacecraft. They are also used in the high-speed computers that work out in seconds mathematical problems that would take humans years to complete.

* * *

LEGENDS IN THEIR LIFETIME

DIXIE DEAN

KING OF THE HEADERS

THE motor cycle roared round the bend of the road with its rider and pillion passenger hunched into the rushing wind. At the same time, a car sped into the bend from the other direction—and a head-on crash was inevitable.

The big, dark-haired young man riding the motor cycle reacted instantly. He calmly swept his passenger off the machine into a grassy ditch and safety, and faced the oncoming car alone . . .

He tried to swerve, but the motor cycle hit the car with a crunch of metal, and the rider hurtled through the air into black oblivion.

The football world was shocked at the tragic news of the injuries suffered by the young motor cyclist. For he was Bill 'Dixie' Dean, star of Everton and the soccer idol of Merseyside. His multiple injuries included a fractured skull and the doctors said that he would never play again. The fateful joy ride had cut short a football career that had brilliant promise.

But they reckoned without Bill Dean's toughness and fighting spirit. Football was his life and he refused to give it up. As soon as he left hospital he insisted on riding a motor cycle to test his nerve. Then he tested his damaged head—which had proved a formidable goal scorer, starting first with a soft bladder, then a harder one, then a light football, until he was satisfied that he could still 'nod 'em in' with his old dynamic force.

Dixie Dean returned to top league soccer to become a living legend, one of the immortals of football, and the greatest header of a ball the game has ever seen.

Dixie Dean, captain of Everton, leads out his team against West Ham United in the 1933 Cup Semi-final

A powerful six-footer with dark curly hair, Dean was blessed with everything that makes a great football star. He was built like a heavyweight boxer, could sprint like a champion, and had an uncanny sense of knowing what the other fellow was going to do. He could jump higher than any of his opponents and his incredible ability to aim a ball in any direction with a flick of his cannonball head, made him the scourge of goalkeepers.

Before Dixie Dean nobody knew what heading a ball could be. Here's a story to prove it.

GOLDEN BARGAIN

During a game against Burnley, he was standing 15 yards away from the rival goal, with his back towards it. The sun was shining bright and, as the ball came fast upfield, he noticed out of the corner of his eye the goalkeeper's shadow coming closer. It was clear to Dean that the 'keeper was coming out—so, without turning round, he jumped high for the flying ball and backheaded it over the 'keeper and into the net. No wonder they called him 'King of the Headers'.

William Ralph Dean was born in Birkenhead in 1907. He played first with Tranmere Rovers and, after scoring 29 goals for them, he attracted the notice of Everton, whom he joined in 1925 at the age of 17.

And what a golden bargain Everton got when they signed up the promising teenager for a mere £3,000.

In the 13 years he played for the club, as centre-forward and captain, he scored 349 goals, won every honour and broke all soccer records. And it was mainly the magic of Dean which enabled Everton to beat Manchester City 3-0 in the 1932-3 Cup Final, in which Dixie slammed home one of the goals.

He was known as Everton's 'goal machine' and he established two remarkable records. He scored the greatest number of goals in the Football League—379, a record which stood until 1963; and the highest number for one season in the First Division—60, which is still unbeaten.

He scored his record-making 60th goal during the 1927-8 season, in which he cracked home a total of 82 goals, three of them in Cup-ties. And scoring that 60th goal was the most exciting moment of his career.

It was Everton's last League game of the season. So it was do-or-die for Dixie if he wanted that record. His team was facing a strong Arsenal side. Marked by centre-half Herbie Roberts, who stuck to Dean like a shadow, Dixie managed to bang home two goals in the first eight minutes—and with just one goal to go for the record (George Camsell had scored 59 the previous season), the crowd roared encouragement. Could 'Dynamite Dixie' get that tantalizing 60?

But, try as he might, he could not slam home another ball. Several times he scraped the bar, trying desperately for the elusive clincher. And each time he missed the crowd groaned, echoing his own frustration.

Then, with only three short minutes to go, with Everton losing 3-2, a team-mate took a corner kick and belted the ball at Dixie—who shot high like a rocket and smashed it into the net with his fabulous head. The crowd went crazy with excitement, rushed on to the field and chaired their amazing idol off the pitch.

Dixie's phenomenal ability to nod in a ball was a nightmare to goalkeepers. The story is often told of the time when Dixie was walking down a street and passed Elisha Scott on the opposite side of the road. Scott was goalkeeper for Liverpool and had been a victim of Dean's goal-scoring head on many occasions. Dixie nodded his curly head in recognition—and Scott automatically dived full-length in the street to save the 'header'.

FAMOUS NICKNAME

Bill Dean got his famous nickname from an unknown fan who, early in the star's career, called out in a game: "Give the ball to 'Dixie'." Bill never liked the name, but it was a catchy one and the sports writers made the most of it.

Dixie finally left Everton for a short stay with Notts County and, after scoring three goals for the club, retired from the game in 1938.

It was a moment of great nostalgia when, in 1964, nearly 4,000 soccer fans, young and old, saw the legendary Dixie Dean, then 57, kick off the benefit game between Scotland and England. The crowd clapped him all the way on and off the field of memories.

It was a fine tribute to the unforgettable 'King of the Header'. Yes, the name of Dixie Dean still has a lot of magic.

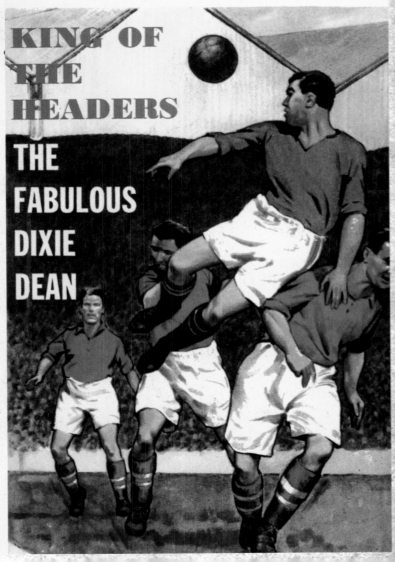

KING OF THE HEADERS

THE FABULOUS DIXIE DEAN

EAGLE

The modern paper for the modern boy

20 January, 1968. Vol. 19, No. 3
EVERY WEDNESDAY

7d

Australia 10c. New Zealand 1/- (10c). South Africa 10c. Rhodesia 1/-. East Africa 1.00. West Africa 10d.

VOYAGE TO VENUS

Russia's space-probe bang on target after historic 4-month journey

A few months ago, on October 18, the Russian space-probe Venus-4 made history by achieving a soft landing on the planet, sending messages back to Earth as it slowly parachuted through the thick Venusian atmosphere. These pictures have just reached us from Russia and show some of the preparations for this historic flight.

And now, if you turn to page 8, you can read about another historic space flight, planned by the U.S.A. to the Moon.

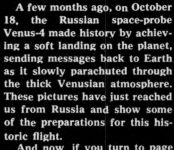

1 Mounting the instruments for the landing apparatus.

2 Adding a protective coating to the space station.

3 Preparations for the testing of the landing apparatus.

4 Testing the systems of Venus-4.

5 Mounting the various units of the space station.

6 One of the final stages of flight preparation.

7 The scientific apparatus that was parachuted on to the surface of the planet.

8 Showing how the capsule containing the scientific instruments was parachuted on to Venus.

9 The pennant with the state emblem of the U.S.S.R. landed on the planet by Venus-4.

PORTABLE HOSPITAL

A complete operating room in an outsize packing case—that is what this portable hospital really is. It is used by the United States Army in remote areas and by other medical units working in isolated places far from town or city hospitals. The portable hospital is made from a large packing case or shipping container with double skin insulation all round. An inflatable shelter that goes with it is used as an extra hospital ward.

The whole unit can be moved at any time and is easily transported on a lorry—the one shown here can go over land or move on water like a boat. Inside, the portable hospital is equipped with everything needed for an emergency operation—anaesthetic and blood transfusion units, full medical supplies, special lighting and air-conditioning. Another important factor is the disposal after use of all surgical gowns, sheets, etc., by burning—thus reducing the risk of infection. Research is going on with a view to disposal of an entire operating room made from plastics—even including the inside atmosphere.

AN EAGLE cutaway DRAWING

ASHWELL WOOD

Disposal by Burning
Surgical gowns, sheets, pillow cases, stretcher sheets made of plastic fibres are all disposed of after use, also hypodermic needles. This cuts the risk of spreading disease and infection.

The portable hospital on its way to another area. This particular lorry can cross water as well as ground.

KEY TO NUMBERED PARTS

(1) Entrance door to hospital ward. (2) Inflatable and portable ward attached to the operating room. (3) Portable bed for an extra patient. (4) Entrance door to operating room. (5) Air-conditioning unit. (6) Medical supply cupboards. (7) Anaesthetic table. (8) Anaesthetist (an-es-thee-tist) — the person who applies the anaesthetic to the patient. (9) Anaesthetic appliances. An anaesthetic is a drug which causes deadening of the senses of the patient, enabling the surgeon to operate without causing pain or distress. (10) Blood transfusion unit. (11) Assistant surgeon. (12) Blood count and drip. (13) Operating surgeon. (14) Electrical supply plug. (15) Special lighting. (16) Hospital Sister in charge of instruments. (17) Instrument trays and medical supplies. (18) Sterilizing trays. (19) Instrument table. (20) Legs for jacking up the portable case. (21) Insulated lining. (22) Air-conditioning unit. (23) Electrical supply cables. (24) Transporter lorry supplying electrical power.

are hardly any brass instruments at all.

The man on the first stamp plays a kind of ukulele, but in contrast to the Hawaiian four-string instrument it has only two strings and is played with a bow, like a violin.

Ironing board

The woman with the instrument which looks like an ironing board — called 'kaya-keum' — strums the many strings with her fingers. So does the other woman, who plays a 'vol-keum', which is rather similar to a banjo. The harp is much more familiar, and we can certainly approve of and understand the player with the flute.

Music From The Far East

The music lovers among you — even those who can only blow a few bars on the recorder — will be interested to see some very strange musical instruments depicted on a set of postage stamps issued by the Republic of North Korea.

Oriental music is, of course, very different from our own. Many of us who hear it for the first time find the high-pitched sounds of Chinese music, for example, rather strange. One reason for this is that the people of the Far East use very different musical instruments from those we know.

The Chinese civilization is very ancient. They had poets and writers, scientists and excellent craftsmen 5,000 years ago, when the people in Europe still lived in caves and were savage hunters.

Stringed instruments

They also invented many things — printing, paper-making and also gunpowder — long before we knew anything about them. They even had musical instruments and, it seems, they stuck to them for thousands of years. Hence they appear quaintly old-fashioned. Nearly all these are stringed instruments, although the flute is also widely used. But there

SCOUTS' WORLD
COMPILED BY
DAVID HARWOOD

Fire Type	Fuels	Fire Extinguishers	Notes	Other Methods
1 FREE BURNING	Wood, paper furniture carpets curtains etc.	Water/Gas Expelled Soda Acid Carbon-dioxide		Fire blanket Water Sand or earth
2 LIQUID	Petrol oil, paraffin fat etc.	Foam Dry Powder	NEVER use water	Fire blanket
3 ELECTRIC	Electrical	Dry Powder Carbon-dioxide Carbon-Tetra-chloride (CTC)	NEVER use water	Dry Fire blanket Dry sand or earth

EMERGENCY EQUIPMENT
Fire Extinguishers

A Reminder

Last week we told you that FUEL, OXYGEN and HEAT must all be present before there can be fire, and that a fire may be extinguished by starving it of fuel, smothering it, or by cooling.

Types of Fire

As far as fire fighting is concerned, there are three main types of fire, depending on the cause or sort of fuel which is burning.
(1) wood, paper, etc.
(2) liquid
(3) electricity

It is VERY IMPORTANT that you should know which type of fire you are dealing with BEFORE DOING ANYTHING because its type will determine HOW it should be put out. If you use the wrong method, you could make matters very much worse.

Fire Extinguishers

As you can imagine, you must not only be able to identify the type of fire, but you must also be able to identify the various types of extinguishers, so that you use the correct one. Extinguishers are used on small fires before they get out of control.

WHAT TO USE

The photograph left shows:

A The fire blanket—this is asbestos covered material and is very effective in putting out any type of small fire. It can also be used to deal with a person whose clothes are on fire.

B Carbon Dioxide—use on Type 1 and 3 fires, e.g., free-burning material, car engine, electric plugs, etc.

C Foam—use especially on Type 2 fires. Direct the foam on to the edges of the fire. The foam spreads rapidly over the surface of the burning liquid, smothering the flames.

D Carbon Tetrachloride (CTC)—use on Type 3 fires. This extinguisher produces gases which smother the fire but which are highly dangerous to breathe. So, having used the extinguisher, leave the room quickly and close the door. When used on a burning car engine, close the bonnet after use.

E Soda Acid—for Type 1 fires only. As it's rather heavy, put it on the ground near the fire and direct the jet from the nozzle on to the fire.

F Water/Gas Expelled—for Type 1 fires only. This Leading Fireman is demonstrating how to hold this extinguisher. As the jet will last for only a minute or so, you should not 'set it off' until you actually go into action. It can be used only in relatively small fires.

LEARN THE DRILL

HAVE A GOOD LOOK AT A FIRE EXTINGUISHER EACH TIME YOU SEE ONE. READ AND LEARN THE INSTRUCTIONS. NEXT TIME YOU MAY HAVE TO USE IT.

Special Note: Only tackle a fire yourself if it is small and you can put it out quickly. Always make sure the fire brigade has been called. The fire brigade's advice to you is: 'When in doubt, turn us out!'

I always say that the one certain method og getting a decent bowl of porridge in the morning is the hay box.

FEBRUARY 1968
Thursday
22

This is the joint birthday of both B-P and his wife Lady Baden-Powell who is World Chief Guide. On February 24, Scouts and Guides will attend a special Founder's Day Service in Westminster Abbey at which a representative from each Movement will lay a wreath beside the Memorial Stone to B-P.

Future Airport In London's Centre

The ever-increasing delays in travelling between existing airports and city centres, like London and Paris, causes a barrier to fast air travel — even if the passenger goes by 600 m.p.h. jet! The answer is vertical take-off and landing (VTOL) airliners which will bring passengers to the city centres. The possibility of an airport site for these VTOL airliners, at Nine Elms on the South bank of the River Thames in the heart of London, has been studied by Hawker Siddeley Aviation. It would be used for inter-city travel, the major airports being utilized for the long-distance supersonic and airbus jets. The big problem for the city centre airport is defeating engine noise; this has brought about a design study for 'quiet' turbofan lift aircraft with wing-mounted lift pods used only during take-off and landing. Separate jet engines will take over for forward power. We show an impression of such a central airport as it might appear in the future with rail and bus services close at hand for reaching offices and hotels in London. The airport would have two separate take-off and landing pads with exhaust noise suppressors and five loading bays.

Proposed design for a 90-seat short-haul transport with wing-mounted lift pods for vertical take-off and landing. (A) Light-weight jet engines for lift. (B) Engine-driven turbofans which give lift and reduce engine noise by lowering the speed of the exhaust gases. (C) Lift ducts can be closed in forward flight. (D) Separate jet engines for forward power.

AN EAGLE *cutaway* DRAWING

KEY TO NUMBERED PARTS

(1) Aircraft movement and plotting room. (2) Vertical take-off and landing control tower. (3) Public viewing gallery. (4) Floodlights. (5) Radar scanners. (6) Overbridge from airport offices and communications. (7) Car and coach park. (8) Lift for aircraft refuellers and ground equipment. (9) Take-off exhaust outlets. (10) Exhaust noise suppressors. (11) Take-off pad over the River Thames. (12) Passenger lift raised. (13) Passenger lounge and restaurant. (14) Separate drive in and entrances for passengers and baggage. (15) Main concourse and access to lifts. (16) Rear passenger entry to aircraft. (17) Airport apron with five loading bays. (18) Passenger lifts. (19) Customs and booking office. (20) Existing railway sidings at Nine Elms converted to passenger services to Victoria and Waterloo Stations. (21) Vertical landing pad with exhaust noise suppressers. (22) Victoria railway bridge. (23) Aircraft after vertical take-off transferring to forward flight over the river.

L'ASHWELL L'WOOD

EAGLE

The modern paper for the modern boy

23 September 1967. Vol.12. No 38
EVERY WEDNESDAY

7d

Australia 10c. New Zealand 1/- (10c) South Africa 8c. Rhodesia 1/- East Africa 1.00. West Africa 10d.

"Take me to your Leader"

says . . .

see page 14

MODERN WONDERS OF THE WORLD

TOWER IN THE CLOUDS see page 6

For a moment the worker on Moscow's 1,700-foot-high television tower had unhooked his safety belt from the life line. Then his foot slipped and he started hurtling to the ground half a mile below.

MICKY MERLIN

HA! HA! HA!

see page 2

Also inside . . .

* BRITAIN'S NEW QUEEN LINER
* RETURN OF JENNINGS
* THE SOLAR DEATH RAY

CHATTER BOX

HE'S been and done it! HE'S actually cut his first L.P.! If you haven't cottoned on yet — we're talking about our good ol' faithful **EAGLE** art editor, who just happens to be a jazz band leader in his spare time. For those of you who haven't already heard, he's Brian Green, whose brand-spanking-new long player, containing twelve soul-swinging numbers, is in the shops from September 6th.

This Fontana record, priced at 28s., is the new duo, stereo **OR** mono sound, to suit **ALL** record-players. Remember, it's ' BRIAN GREEN'S DIS-PLAY ' — and we up here can assure you — it's quite a show. We've heard nothing else all week!

★ ★ ★

While we're on the record kick, Kink Dave Davis's latest single ' Lincoln County ' — originally due for release in mid-July — has finally reached the disc dens; just a few days ago to be precise. Why the mysterious delay, you Krazy Kink followers might be asking yourselves. Could be that they didn't want to cut across the group's joint effort 'Days' — and don't tell me you haven't heard of that, yet? Whatever the answer, the record was worth waiting for. It's . . . k . . . kkk . . . Kinky!

★ ★ ★

Odham's ' Aircraft of the World ' will carry you up into the clouds. This multi-illustrated saga of the future. At 16s., it's a snip!
flight begins with man's first feeble efforts to become air-bound, soars through the ' jet-set ' era and leaves you boggling wondrously on planes of the future. At 16s., it's a snip!

SCOUTS' WORLD
COMPILED BY
DAVID HARWOOD

BEHIND THE SCENES OF THE
WAYFINDERS HOME

I expect that you've all seen the advertisement in EAGLE for Wayfinders shoes and have noticed they contain the words: "They're the only shoes approved by The Scout Association for Scouts and Cub Scouts . . ." So a little while ago I set off for the British Bata Shoe Company's factory at East Tilbury, Essex, to see exactly how your shoes are made . . .

With the Company's Marketing Manager, I went to the Leather Footwear Factory's second floor, only part of which is devoted to producing Wayfinders. The two principal parts to the shoes are the leather upper and the sole. The sections of the upper are cut on a lower floor in the main cutting room, and the sole moulds (or blanks as they are called) are manufactured in the adjacent Rubber Factory.

Now let's go along the actual production line and see how these two main components—and dozens of other minor ones—are put together . . .

HOW HITLER WAS OBLITERATED — ON STAMPS

IN May we shall remember the end of Hitler's Nazi rule in Germany and the end of the war in Europe. On 1st May, 1945, Adolf Hitler shot his wife and committed suicide in the underground 'bunker' of the Reich Chancellery in Berlin, while Russian troops were converging on the city. Four days later a mission of German generals and admirals arrived at Field Marshal Montgomery's headquarters to offer the surrender of all German armies in the Reich, Holland and Denmark, and on 7th May General Eisenhower, as Supreme Allied Commander, accepted the complete capitulation of Germany. The war in Europe had come to an end, after nearly six years of terrible slaughter and air bombardment, which laid many cities in ruins. The war against the Japanese in Asia continued until August.

Like so many historic events, war and peace had been pictured on postage stamps. This year, several countries which were occupied by the Nazis during the war will issue special stamps commemorating their liberation in 1945. But probably the most interesting stamps of this kind are those issued during the days following the collapse of the Nazi rule, when Germany was being occupied by British, American, French and Russian troops. For twelve years, since 1933 when he grabbed power, the vast majority of Germans hailed Hitler as their great 'Führer' and approved of (or at least did not protest at) the atrocities committed by Hitler's secret police – the mass murder of Jews, the deportation of Resistance members in the occupied countries, slave labour and concentration camps. But as soon as Hitler was dead, in many towns and villages all postage stamps which bore his portrait were defaced, overprinted or destroyed. Some of these stamps were very crudely obliterated by using burnt cork, others were overprinted with Churchill's famous V-sign; a few (like the one shown on our fourth illustration) bore Russian letters, apparently to please the Soviet occupation forces.

These stamps, on which the Germans were trying to hide the ugly face of their former 'Führer', are now rare and eagerly sought after by collectors.

1. The various cut pieces of leather upper are stitched together by skilled seamstresses, using strong nylon and Terylene threads.

2. The shoe receives its first shaping as it is pulled over a wooden last and connected to the insole, and is then put on a steel last. The heel and the 'blank' sole (i.e., it hasn't got its animal tracks) are placed carefully in the right position, ready for insertion into the mould.

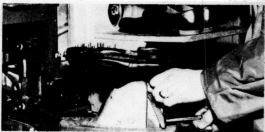

3. The mould is a remarkable machine, which is really a moulder, vulcanization boiler and fixer all rolled into one. In a matter of seconds, at high temperature and pressure, the rubber is vulcanized, the sole welded to the upper, and the reliefs of the animal tracks and points of the compass embossed. Here you can see it coming out of the mould.

4. A view of the moulded animal tracks which show in relief so that they make track marks.

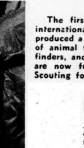

5. Making the secret compartment into which a small compass will be inserted.

6. The rubber soles are then expertly cleaned, the leather buffed and polished, laces inserted, etc. Before the shoe or boot is passed to the packing bench, critical eyes are focused on the 'end product' and a minute fault means rejection. Only footwear which is a perfect example of craftsmanship reaches you, the customer!

The first pair of Wayfinders was made in August, 1965, and became an international 'hit' with boys and, more recently, with girls when Wayfinders produced a shoe for them. The girls' version has Zodiac signs on the soles instead of animal tracks. Today, Bata factories in 20 countries make or market Wayfinders, and the list is growing. More and more Scout Associations in other lands are now following Britain's example and are adopting Wayfinders as official Scouting footwear.

FIRST AID HINT — Friction Blisters

ALL blisters are caused by heat of one sort or another – sometimes by friction, sometimes by either:

Direct dry heat (e.g., fire, hot metal, etc.): these are called BURNS

or

Direct wet heat (e.g., boiling water or other hot liquid): these are called SCALDS.

The treatment of FRICTION BLISTERS is different from BURNS and SCALDS.

When two things are rubbed together, the resultant friction produces heat. (You can try this for yourself by rubbing the palms of your hands together.) When a fair amount of heat is produced by friction against your skin, a blister is liable to form unless your skin is hard enough to 'resist' the heat. A badly-fitting shoe or boot, your hand slipping up and down the haft of an axe or chafing on the handle of an oar are all potential blister-makers.

If a friction blister forms, wash it in cold water and dab (NOT RUB) it dry. Then prick each side of the blister with a *sterile* needle and press out the

fluid. Prevent further friction and possible infection by covering with a sterile dressing and secure either with a strip of adhesive plaster if the blister is small, or with a bandage.

N.B. – DO *NOT* OPEN BURN OR SCALD BLISTERS.

ROADS ON STILTS

A teeming city wrapped in ribbons of highways—that's an apt description of Los Angeles. The highway interchange or crossover shown here is the most complex and the busiest in the world. Some 368,000 vehicles roll across the four-layer structure every weekday! Traffic jams and accidents have been reduced to a minimum by making fast and slow speed lanes. Interchange roads connect the four main highways, under and over, without any cross roads, thus maintaining a continuous flow of traffic. This flow can be followed by the arrows on the drawing. This Los Angeles interchange is only one of many fine examples of highway engineering in concrete and steel. The American project for an Interstate Highway System is already under way and 27,000 miles of the planned 41,000 miles have been built. These huge figures by British standards but then, as our mini-map shows, the U.S. [is a] huge country!

AN EAGLE *cutaway* DRAWING

ASHWELL WOOD

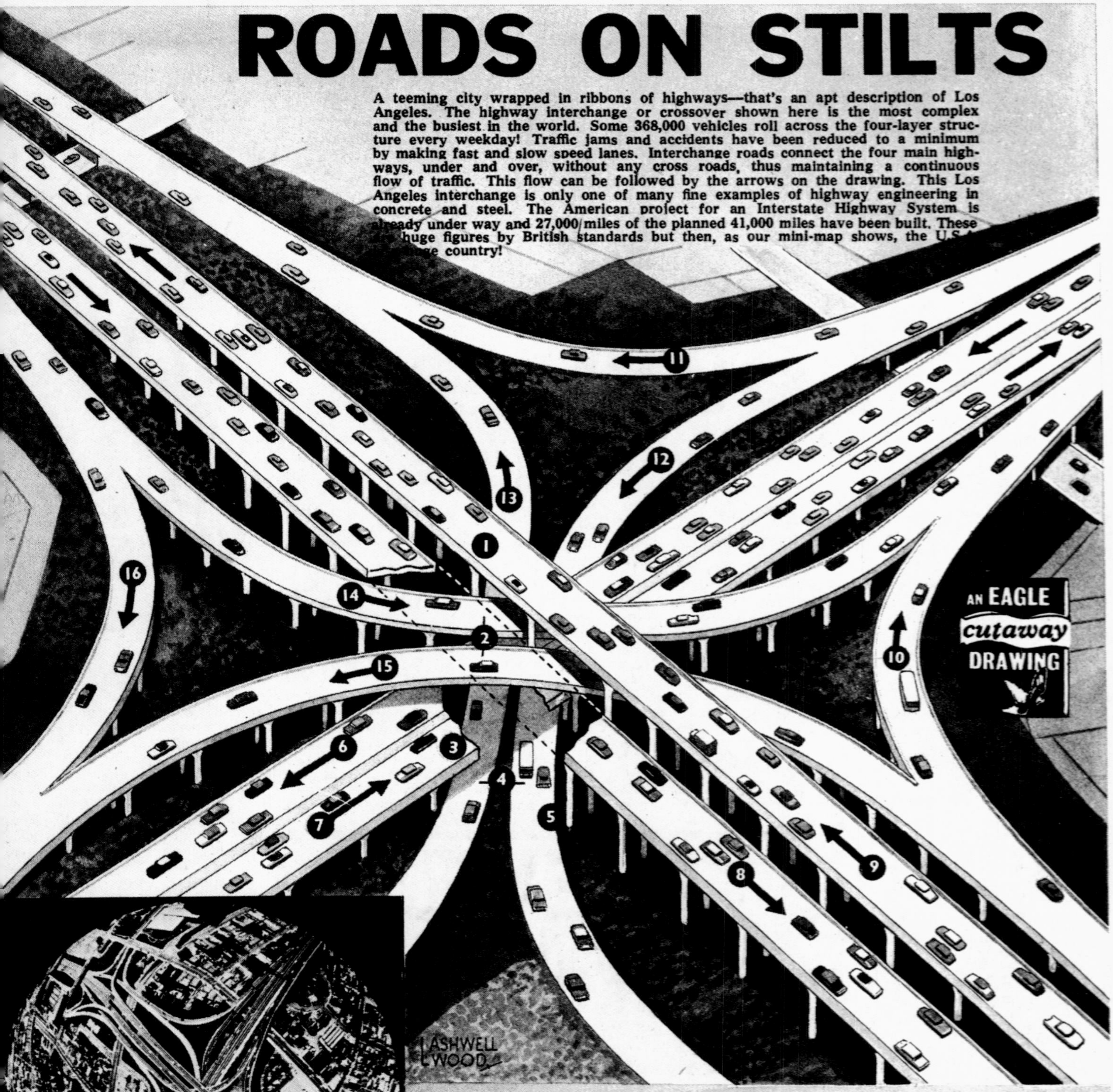

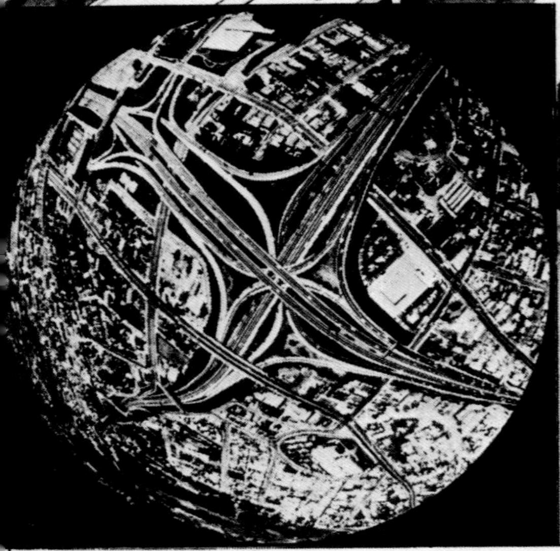

(1) Top layer main highways of the four layer central structure. (2) Second layer interchange roads. (3) Third layer main highways. (4) Bottom layer: ground level interchange roads. (5) Steel support columns on stilts. (6) 3-lane main highway—West. (7) 3-lane main highway—East. (8) 3-lane main highway—South. (9) 3-lane main highway—North. (10) Interchange road—North to East highway. All interchange roads are 2-lane. (11) Interchange road—West to North highway. (12) Interchange road—West to South highway. (13) Interchange road—East to North highway. (14) Interchange road—South to East highway. (15) Interchange road—North to West highway. (16) Interchange road—South to West highway.

Left. An amazing photograph of the Los Angeles highway interchange, taking in much of the city as well. It was made with a camera with wide-angle lens, on the end of a pole lowered from a helicopter.

One of the main American Interstate Highways will, when completed, connect New York with San Francisco. The present completed stretch runs from New York to Omaha. The tremendous distances involved can be gathered by the size of Great Britain to the same scale.

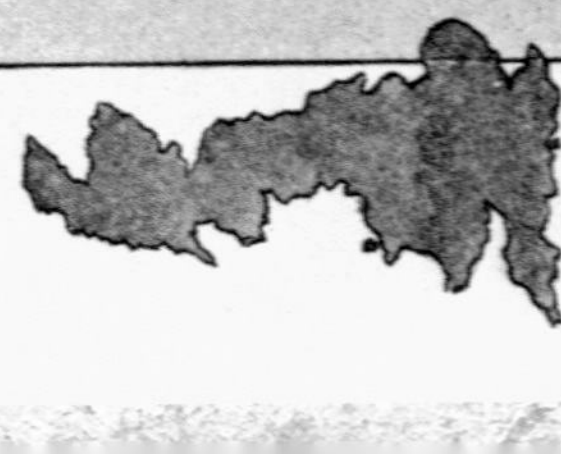

EAGLE BECOMES LION

So much of the content of *Eagle* over its two decades related to space travel and alien planets that it would be possible to put together a handy guide to the advances in the post-war period just from its pages. Thus it is achingly sad that as the launch of Apollo 11 approached the end of *Eagle* was signalled. It leaves a hole in the comic's archives and creates an unscratchable itch. Like Don Bradman, the Australian master batter, retiring with a test average of 99.9, it just doesn't seem fair.

Other Eagle-related publications of interest this Christmas

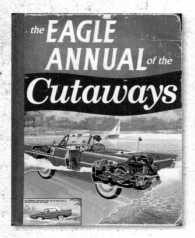

THE FIRST EVER
Dan Dare audio CD

available on AUDIO

DANIEL TATARSKY has edited the *Eagle* annuals of the 1950s and the cutaways. He is also the author of the *Flick to Kick: an Illustrated History of Subbuteo*.

First published in hardback in Great Britain in 2009 by
Orion Books
an imprint of the Orion Publishing Group Ltd
Orion House, 5 Upper St Martin's Lane,
London WC2H 9EA
An Hachette Livre UK Company

A CIP catalogue record for this book is available from the British Library.

Designed by Richard Norgate
Printed in China by C&C Joint Printing Co., (Shanghai) Ltd.

The Orion Publishing Group's policy is to use papers that are natural, renewable and recyclable and made from wood grown in sustainable forests. The logging and manufacturing processes are expected to conform to the environmental regulations of the country of origin.

Every effort has been made to fulfil requirements with regard to reproducing copyright material. The author and publisher will be glad to rectify any omissions at the earliest opportunity.

www.orionbooks.co.uk